Taste the FREEDOM

250⁺ WAYS TO A BETTER LIFESTYLE

ORIGINAL TITLE : TASTE THE FREEDOM
@COPYRIGHT 2013 - LABORATOIRES C.O.P. INC.
- ALL RIGHTS RESERVED
R/TM/MD/MC TRADE MARKS OF LABORATOIRES C.O.P. INC.

AUTHOR: DANIEL VERATI

EDITOR: DANIEL VERATI
COLLABORATOR: JONATHAN RUSSEL
RECIPES STANDARDISATION: DANIELLE TREMBLAY ET LISE LAFONTAINE

GRAPHIC DESIGN: ALEXE HOUTART // WWW.HOUTARTDESIGN.COM
PHOTOGRAPHY: SYLVAIN MARIER // WWW.SYLVAINMARIER.COM

PRINTING: ST-JOSEPH PRINTER
PRINTED IN CANADA

ISBN

MERCI

MY FIRST AND FOREMOST THANKS GO OUT TO OLIVIER BENLOULOU AND DR. TRAN TIEN CHANH FOR HAVING FAITH IN ME AND FOR GIVING ME THE OPPORTUNITY TO CREATE MY SECOND BOOK.

THANK YOU TO TONI KOUTSOMITOPOULOS FOR PERMITTING US TO USE ONE OF HIS RESTAURANTS KITCHENS FOR PICTURE TAKING AND THANKS TO WILLIAM HOUTART FOR HIS PRECIOUS ADVICE. THANKS TO DANIELLE TREMBLAY FOR REPRESENTING IP SO WELL, FOR HER INSIGHT AND FOR REVIEWING MY BOOK. I EXTEND MY THANKS TO JONATHAN RUSSEL AS WELL FOR HIS RECIPE SUGGESTIONS AND IDEAS THAT WERE OF PRECIOUS HELP.

ALEXE HOUTART, GRAPHIC DESIGNER, FOR HAVING SUCH PASSION FOR HER SPECIALTY. SYLVAIN MARIER, ARTIST PHOTOGRAPHER, FOR HIS CRAZY IDEAS THAT REPRESENTED MINE SO WELL.

LISE, MICHÈLE AND ALIZÉ MY HEART FILLED THANKS TO YOU, THE LOVES OF MY LIFE, FOR BELIEVING IN ME AND SUPPORTING ME THROUGHOUT ALL MY CRAZINESS.

• • •

Table of CONTENTS

AUTHOR'S PREFACE // CHEF VERATI ·································· 9

FOREWORD // OLIVIER BENLOULOU ···························· 13

BREAKFAST // OVER EASY FREEDOM ······················· 14

SOUP & SALAD // A DROP OF FREEDOM ················· 60

POULTRY // ROASTED FREEDOM ···························· 130

MEAT // GRILLED FREEDOM ······························· 216

FISH & SEAFOOD // OCEAN OF FREEDOM ··············· 308

FUN DAY // A LIFESTYLE ································· 398

CHEF VERATI

MERCI, TO MY FAMILY FOR MAKING THIS BOOK POSSIBLE. YOU ARE MY LIFE AND INSPIRATION! THOSE SATURDAY «CRÊPES» ARE SIMPLY DELIGHTFUL.
-CHEF VERATI

Author's PREFACE

I HAVE SPENT 25 YEARS OVERSEEING KITCHEN PERSONNEL ALL OVER THE WORLD. WITHIN ALL OF THESE YEARS: 2007 IS WHEN THINGS SUDDENLY AND PROFOUNDLY CHANGED. I WAS NEWLY DIAGNOSED WITH A HEART CONDITION. STANDING AT A MERE 5'8" AND TIPPING THE SCALE AT 293 LBS, I NEEDED LITTLE CONVINCING TO ACCEPT THAT I HAD SPENT THE PAST EIGHTEEN YEARS BEING OVERWEIGHT. IT WAS CLEAR THAT I COULD NO LONGER CONTINUE THIS LIFESTYLE IF I WANTED TO SEE MY CHILDREN GROW UP.

AT THE TIME WHERE I WAS DIAGNOSED, I WAS A TEACHER FOR LE CORDON BLEU - OTTAWA CULINARY ARTS INSTITUTE. MY CHILDHOOD AND CLOSEST FRIEND TODAY, OLIVIER BENLOULOU, WAS CHANGING PEOPLES LIVES AS THE CEO OF IDEAL PROTEIN. WITH NOTHING TO LOSE (EXCEPT FAT!!) I FOLLOWED MY FRIEND'S ADVICE AND STARTED THE IDEAL PROTEIN WEIGHT LOSS METHOD. I WAS RUNNING OUT OF TIME...

DESPITE CONTINUING TO TEACH FRENCH CUISINE, I FOLLOWED THE WEIGHT LOSS PROGRAM DILIGENTLY. THAT MEANT SPITTING OUT EVERYTHING I TASTED - TRADITIONAL FRENCH CUISINE IS NOT PART OF THIS PROGRAM! IN SOME CASES, THIS WAS UNBEARABLE... IN OTHERS, IT WAS ACTUALLY QUITE THE RELIEF! FIVE MONTHS LATER AND 100 LBS LIGHTER, I QUIT MY JOB AT LE CORDON BLEU OTTAWA, READY TO TAKE ON NEW AND EXCITING CHALLENGES AT IDEAL PROTEIN.

THERE IS NO DOUBT THAT THIS EXPERIENCE NOT ONLY CHANGED MY LIFE, IT'S THE REASON WHY I AM STILL ALIVE TODAY. IT IS BECAUSE OF THIS THAT I DECIDED TO PUT MY CULINARY EXPERTISE AND PASSION INTO SHARING ALL OF THE DELECTABLE CREATIONS THAT I HAD PERSONALLY PREPARED DURING THE COURSE OF THE DIET. TAKE A LOOK AT A FEW OF MY RECIPES. YOU WILL BE AMAZED! TO SIMPLIFY THINGS, ALL RECIPES YEILD 4 SERVINGS.

I WILL DEMONSTRATE THROUGHOUT MY BOOK THAT HEALTHY EATING DOES NOT HAVE TO BE BORING NOR DOES IT HAVE TO BE BLAND. A CLAIM MADE BY MANY! THIS IS NOT A TREND, IT'S A LIFESTYLE.

• • •

DANIEL VERATI
IDEAL PROTEIN CHEF

CHEF
VERATi.

THANK YOU OB FOR GIVING ME THE CHANCE
TO REALIZE A LIFELONG DREAM.
-CHEF VERATI

President FOREWORD

HERE WE ARE JUST A LITTLE OVER ONE YEAR AFTER CHEF VERATI'S FIRST IDEAL PROTEIN INSPIRED RECIPE BOOK WAS LAUNCHED. MY *IDEAL RECIPES* WALKED DIETERS THROUGH TASTY, CREATIVE AND COMPLIANT RECIPES FOR THE WEIGHT LOSS PHASES OF THE IDEAL PROTEIN WEIGHT LOSS METHOD.

THE TIMING OF CHEF VERATI'S NEW RECIPE BOOK COULD NOT BE BETTER AS IT IS A PERFECT COMPLIMENT TO THE MESSAGE THAT I AM SO DEDICATED TO: LONG TERM DIETER SUCCESS AND LIFESTYLE. TO ME, SUCCESS IS MORE THAN JUST THE IMMEDIATE THRILL OR SATISFACTION OF THE INITIAL WEIGHT LOSS, IT'S MOREOVER OUR DIETERS ABILITY TO SUSTAIN THEIR WEIGHT LOSS NOT JUST FOR A FEW WEEKS BUT FOR A LIFETIME, BY EMBRACING A NEW LIFESTYLE. MANY DIETS MAY HELP WITH WEIGHT LOSS BUT TO TRULY DEEM A PROGRAM A SUCCESS, WE MUST SEE LONG-TERM RESULTS, AND THERE IS NO QUESTION IN MY MIND THAT NOTHING ELSE CAN BE THE TRUE MARKER OF SUCCESS.

IDEAL PROTEIN'S GOAL IS TO PROVIDE DIETERS WITH THE PROPER TOOLS. THE TOOLS NEED TO KEEP THE DIETER STRUCTURED, COMMITTED AND REMOVE ANY GREY AREAS. WE NEED TO REMOVE THE "GUESS-WORK" AND MAKE SURE THE DIETER HAS A PLAN SO THAT THEY ARE NEVER CAUGHT OFF GUARD. WITH THIS, WE BELIEVE THE DIETER CAN HAVE A PAINLESS TRANSITION INTO THEIR NEW LIFESTYLE WITHOUT SACRIFICING. THIS BOOK IS ONE OF THE PINNACLE TOOLS TO INCORPORATE INTO OUR DIETERS NEW LIFESTYLE.

EACH RECIPE HAS BEEN DESIGNED SPECIFICALLY FOR OUR MAINTENANCE PHASE. THE UNDERLYING THEME IS FUN, QUICK AND EASY! IF COOKING IS NOT FUN, QUICK OR EASY, IT CAN BECOME A CHORE AND WE WANT DIETERS TO LOOK FORWARD TO PREPARING MEALS.

CHEF VERATI, PRESENTS WEEKS AND WEEKS OF ENDLESS CHOICES OF DELICIOUS MEALS. THAT ARE PREPARED IN A VARIETY OF FLAVORS, COLORS, AROMAS AND TEXTURES. THE SECRET, ABOVE ALL, OF GOOD NUTRITION LIES IN THE VARIETY OF WHAT YOU EAT.

SO, BE ADVENTUROUS, LET YOUR CURIOSITY GET THE BEST OF YOU AND ENJOY WITHOUT GUILT EACH AND EVERY MEAL.

THANK YOU ONCE AGAIN MY FRIEND, CHEF VERATI FOR INSPIRING US WITH YOUR CREATIVE PALLET!

• • •

OLIVIER BENLOULOU
PRESIDENT & CEO IDEAL PROTEIN

BREAKFAST

TIPS & TRICKS

WRITE TO **CHEFVERATI@IDEALPROTEIN.COM**
FIND US ON **CHEF VERATI'S FACEBOOK PAGE**
VISIT **LOWFATLOWCARB.COM**

COMBINE GROUPS

Best at breakfast time

THE CAKE FRENCH TOAST PUDDING ·················· 22

NORWEGIAN SOFT BOILED EGGS ····················· 23

ASPARAGUS & LEEK FRITTATA ····················· 24

CRUSTLESS BROCCOLI GRATED QUICHE ··············· 25

INDIVIDUAL EGG CUPS WITH CREAMED MUSHROOM SAUCE 27

STUFFED TOMATOES CARAMELIZED ONIONS ··········· 28

EGG PIZZA ROLL-UPS ···························· 28

VEGGIE & BRIE PUDDING ························· 29

SMOKED CHEESE OMELET WRAP ····················· 29

THE TEAM BREAKFAST BUDWIG CREAM ·············· 33

TACO BREAKFAST WITH HOT PEPPER SAUCE ········· 34

SCRAMBLED EGGS WITH SALSA ····················· 34

POACHED EGGS WITH HAM ························· 35

DROP AN EGG MAKE A VEGETABLE OMELET ··········· 37

POACHED EGGS CREOLE-STYLE ····················· 38

SCRAMBLED EGGS WITH TUNA ······················· 39

APPLE & BRIE OMELET WITH FRUIT SALAD ·········· 4

SOFT BOILED EGGS MEDITERRANEAN STYLE ·········· 4

HAM PIPERADE WITH POTATOES ···················· 4

POTATO & EGG OMELET WITH LEEKS ················ 43

STUFFED EGGS WITH TUNA SALAD ··················· 45

EAT LIKE A CHAMPION, WHAT A BREAKFAST ········· 46

CHICKEN FRITTATA WITH FRESH HERBS ············· 4

BANANA OATMEAL CRÊPES ························· 49

MUSHROOM & SPINACH FRITTATA ··················· 50

HAM & PEPPERS FRITTATA ························ 5

DAD'S SAVORY PANCAKES ························· 55

CLUB BREAKFAST WITH FRUIT SALAD ··············· 58

FRUIT SALAD // STRAWBERRIES + MANGO ·········· 59

THE CAKE
French Toast Pudding

1 **CUP** NON FAT VANILLA YOGURT

1 1/2 **CUPS** APPLE CIDER

2 APPLES, PEELED & SLICED

1 PEAR, PEELED & SLICED

1 1/2 **CUPS** PRUNES, DRIED & PITTED

1 CINNAMON STICK

1 **TEASPOON** LEMON ZEST, GRATED

2 **TABLESPOONS** LEMON JUICE

10 **SLICES** SANDWICH BREAD, CRUSTS TRIMMED

2 EGGS

2/3 **CUP** LOW FAT MILK

1 **TEASPOON** VANILLA EXTRACT

2 **TABLESPOONS** SUGAR

1/2 **TEASPOON** GROUND CINNAMON

READY TO COOK

1. PREHEAT OVEN TO 400ºF.

2. LINE A SIEVE WITH A CHEESECLOTH OR A COFFEE FILTER AND SET IT OVER A BOWL.

3. SPOON IN YOGURT, COVER AND LET DRAIN IN THE REFRIGERATOR FOR 30 MINUTES TO 1 HOUR.

4. COMBINE CIDER, APPLES, PEAR, PRUNES, CINNAMON STICK, LEMON ZEST AND LEMON JUICE IN A SAUCEPAN AND LET SIMMER, STIRRING OCCASIONALLY.

5. DISCARD CINNAMON STICK AND POUR THE FRUIT MIXTURE INTO AN 8 X 11 INCH OR SIMILAR 2 QUART BAKING DISH.

6. CUT BREAD SLICES IN HALF DIAGONALLY. WHISK EGGS AND VANILLA IN A MIXING BOWL.

7. SOAK THE BREAD IN THE EGG MIXTURE AND ARRANGE IN OVERLAPPING ROWS ON TOP OF THE FRUIT.

8. COMBINE SUGAR AND CINNAMON AND SPRINKLE OVER THE BREAD.

9. BAKE UNTIL THE TOP IS CRISP AND GOLDEN, 20 TO 25 MINUTES.

10. LET COOL SLIGHTLY BEFORE SERVING WITH DRAINED VANILLA YOGURT.

Serve with non fat vanilla yogurt. (serves: 8)

NORWEGIAN
Soft Boiled Eggs

8 EGGS

1 TABLESPOON VINEGAR

8 OUNCES SMOKED SALMON

2 CUPS FENNEL, FINELY SLICED

4 CUPS FINGERLING POTATOES, UNPEELED

2 SHALLOTS, FINELY CHOPPED

1/2 CUP GREEN ONIONS, FINELY SLICED

1 TEASPOON DIJON MUSTARD

1/4 CUP NON FAT PLAIN YOGURT

1 LEMON, ZESTED & JUICED

4 SLICES WHOLE WHEAT TOAST, TOASTED (*OPTIONAL*)

4 CUPS FRESH BERRIES (*OPTIONAL*)

SEA SALT & PEPPER TO TASTE

READY TO COOK

1. COOK POTATOES IN BOILING WATER UNTIL JUST TENDER.

2. DRAIN, COOL AND PEEL.

3. SLICE POTATOES, PLACE A WET PAPER TOWEL OVER TOP AND LEAVE AT ROOM TEMPERATURE.

4. BOIL EGGS IN WATER AND 1 TABLESPOON OF VINEGAR FOR 7 MINUTES.

5. REMOVE EGGS AND PLACE IN COLD WATER FOR 2-3 MINUTES.

6. PEEL AND CUT IN HALF.

7. PLACE THE FENNEL IN ICE WATER TO KEEP THEM CRISP.

8. WHISK TOGETHER DIJON MUSTARD, YOGURT, LEMON JUICE, LEMON ZEST, GREEN ONIONS, SHALLOTS, SEA SALT AND PEPPER.

9. MAKE A BED OF SMOKED SALMON ON THE BOTTOM OF EACH PLATE.

10. SPREAD 1/4 OF DRAINED FENNEL AND 4 EGG HALVES ON TOP OF THE SALMON.

11. PLACE SOME OF THE SLICED POTATOES AROUND THE PLATE.

12. DRIZZLE MUSTARD AND YOGURT SAUCE OVER TOP.

Serve with whole wheat toast and a cup of mixed berries.

ASPARAGUS & LEEK
Frittata

12 EGGS

2 CUPS MUSHROOMS, CHOPPED

1 CUP GREEN ONIONS, CHOPPED

1 CUP RED PEPPERS, CHOPPED

4 CUPS ASPARAGUS, CUT INTO 1 1/2" PIECES

1/4 CUP PARMESAN CHEESE

1/2 CUP FRESH BASIL, CHOPPED

1 TEASPOON OLIVE OIL

2 TABLESPOONS WATER

4 SLICES MULTI GRAIN BREAD, TOASTED (*OPTIONAL*)

4 CUPS FRUIT SALAD (*OPTIONAL*) (*SEE RECIPE PAGE 59*)

SEA SALT & PEPPER TO TASTE

READY TO COOK

1. IN A LARGE NON-STICK, OVEN-PROOF PAN, SAUTÉ MUSHROOMS IN OIL UNTIL TENDER.
2. ADD ASPARAGUS AND WATER.
3. COOK UNTIL ASPARAGUS ARE TENDER AND WATER IS COMPLETELY ABSORBED.
4. ADD RED PEPPERS, GREEN ONIONS, SEA SALT, PEPPER AND BASIL AND HEAT FOR 2-3 MINUTES.
5. WHISK EGGS AND POUR OVER VEGETABLES, STIRRING TO ENSURE EVEN DISTRIBUTION.
6. COOK OVER MEDIUM HEAT FOR 2 MINUTES.
7. SPRINKLE WITH PARMESAN CHEESE AND PLACE THE PAN IN THE OVEN.
8. BROIL FOR 4-6 MINUTES, WATCHING CAREFULLY AS THE TOP BROWNS.
9. REMOVE FROM THE OVEN AND ALLOW TO COOL FOR 5 MINUTES OR UNTIL THE EGGS SET COMPLETELY.

Slide onto a warm plate and serve with fruit salad and multi grain toasted bread.

CRUSTLESS BROCCOLI
Grated Quiche

8 EGGS

1 CUP MILK

1 CUP ONIONS, FINELY CHOPPED

1 CUP RED PEPPERS, FINELY CHOPPED

3 CUPS BROCCOLI, COARSELY CHOPPED

3 CUPS CAULIFLOWER, COARSELY CHOPPED

1 CUP CHEDDAR CHEESE, GRATED

1 TEASPOON OIL

1 TABLESPOON BUTTER

4 WHOLE WHEAT ENGLISH MUFFINS, CUT IN HALF & TOASTED (*OPTIONAL*)

4 CUPS FRESH FRUITS (*OPTIONAL*)

SEA SALT & PEPPER TO TASTE

READY TO COOK

1. IN A LARGE BOWL, BEAT EGGS WITH MILK, SEA SALT AND PEPPER AND SET ASIDE.

2. PUT BROCCOLI IN A PAN OF ALREADY BOILING WATER, BOIL 1 MINUTE AND DRAIN.

3. IN A FRYING PAN, COOK ONIONS UNTIL THEY BEGIN TO SOFTEN.

4. ADD RED PEPPERS AND DRAINED BROCCOLI AND COOK FOR ANOTHER 1-2 MINUTES. SET ASIDE TO COOL.

6. COOK CAULIFLOWER IN WATER UNTIL TENDER. DRAIN AND RESERVE 1/4 CUP OF THE LIQUID.

7. MASH CAULIFLOWER WHILE STILL HOT WITH BUTTER, SEA SALT AND PEPPER. SET ASIDE AND KEEP WARM.

8. ADD BROCCOLI MIXTURE TO EGG MIXTURE AND STIR BEFORE POURING INTO AN OVEN-PROOF, OIL-GREASED, CASSEROLE DISH.

9. BAKE AT 350°F FOR 25-30 MINUTES OR UNTIL EGGS ARE SET.

10. REMOVE FROM OVEN AND DROP CAULIFLOWER MIXTURE OVER THE TOP AND USING A SPOON MAKE PEAKS. DO NOT SPREAD OR YOU WILL DISTURB THE EGGS.

11. SPRINKLE CHEESE OVER TOP AND RETURN TO THE OVEN UNDER THE GRILL FOR ABOUT 5 MINUTES, WATCHING CAREFULLY UNTIL CHEESE IS MELTED AND CAULIFLOWER BEGINS TO BROWN..

Serve with whole wheat English muffins and fresh fruits.

VERATITRICK
TO SAVE TIME, PURÉE THE CAULIFLOWER IN A FOOD PROCESSOR.
IF NECESSARY, ADD SOME OF THE RESERVED LIQUID TO GET A "MASHED POTATO-LIKE" TEXTURE.

INDIVIDUAL EGG CUPS
with Creamed Mushroom Sauce

8 EGGS	1/2 CUP 35% COOKING CREAM
8 CUPS MUSHROOMS, SLICED	1 TABLESPOON HAZELNUT OIL
12 SMALL MUSHROOMS OR CHANTERELLES, SLICED	8 SMALL OVENPROOF CUPS
2 CUPS CHICKEN STOCK	4 SLICES WHOLE WHEAT BREAD, TOASTED (OPTIONAL)
1 TABLESPOON FLOUR	1 GRAPEFRUIT, CUT IN SLICES (OPTIONAL)
2 TABLESPOONS BUTTER	SEA SALT & PEPPER TO TASTE

READY TO COOK

1. MELT 1 TABLESPOON OF BUTTER IN A SAUCEPAN AND ADD MUSHROOMS, SEA SALT AND PEPPER.

2. SAUTÉ UNTIL MUSHROOMS BEGIN TO SOFTEN.

3. ADD FLOUR AND A LITTLE CHICKEN STOCK AND STIR UNTIL SMOOTH.

4. ADD REMAINING CHICKEN STOCK AND SIMMER FOR 10 MINUTES.

5. ADD CREAM.

6. PLACE MIXTURE IN A BLENDER OR FOOD PROCESSOR AND BLEND UNTIL SMOOTH.

7. POUR THE MIXTURE BACK INTO THE SAUCEPAN AND KEEP WARM.

8. PREHEAT OVEN TO 350°F.

9. BREAK EACH EGG INTO ONE OF THE CUPS, SEASON WITH SEA SALT AND PEPPER AND POUR A SMALL AMOUNT OF THE MUSHROOM SAUCE OVER EACH.

10. PLACE THE EGG CUPS ON A COOKIE SHEET IN THE OVEN AND BAKE FOR 7 MINUTES.

11. HEAT THE REMAINING TABLESPOON OF BUTTER IN THE SAUCEPAN AND COOK THE SMALL MUSHROOMS UNTIL JUST TENDER.

12. REMOVE EGG CUPS FROM THE OVEN, PLACE SOME OF THE MUSHROOMS ON TOP AND DRIZZLE A LITTLE HAZELNUT OIL OVER EACH.

SERVE WITH WHOLE WHEAT TOAST CUT IN TRIANGLES AND DECORATE WITH GRAPEFRUIT SLICES.

STUFFED TOMATOES
Caramelized Onions

8 EGGS, POACHED
4 COUNTRY STYLE SAUSAGES, SKIN REMOVED
1/2 TABLESPOON OLIVE OIL
6 CUPS ONIONS, CHOPPED
1 CUP CELERY, FINELY CHOPPED
1/2 CUP FRESH PARSLEY, FINELY CHOPPED
4 LARGE TOMATOES, WHOLE
4 TABLESPOONS PARMESAN CHEESE
SEA SALT & PEPPER TO TASTE

READY TO COOK ⬇⬇⬇

1. CUT OFF TOPS AND HOLLOW OUT TOMATOES, RESERVING CONTENT. 2. SAUTÉ CELERY AND SAUSAGE MEAT IN 1 TEASPOON OF OIL. 3. ADD PARSLEY, SEA SALT, PEPPER AND TOMATO CONTENT. 4. COOK UNTIL TOMATO CONTENT HAS REDUCED. 5. ADD PARMESAN CHEESE AND PUT FILLING INTO HOLLOWED OUT TOMATOES. 6. PLACE ON RACK AND BAKE AT 350º F FOR 20 MINUTES. 7. SAUTÉ ONIONS IN REMAINING OIL UNTIL THEY ARE SOFT AND CARAMELIZED. 8. DIVIDE ONIONS AMONG 4 PLATES AND SPREAD OUT TO FORM A BED FOR THE EGGS. 9. PLACE 1 POACHED EGG ON TOP OF EACH BED OF ONIONS.

Serve poached eggs alongside stuffed tomatoes.

EGG PIZZA
Roll-Ups

8 EGGS
3/4 CUP PIZZA SAUCE
1 TEASPOON DRIED BASIL
1 TEASPOON DRIED OREGANO
1/2 TABLESPOON OLIVE OIL
4 PITA BREADS
1 1/2 CUPS MOZZARELLA CHEESE, GRATED
1 CUP GREEN PEPPERS, CUT INTO 1/2" CUBES
1 CUP FRESH MUSHROOMS, SLICED
4 CUPS FRESH FRUIT SALAD (*OPTIONAL*) (*SEE RECIPE PAGE 59*)
SEA SALT & PEPPER TO TASTE

READY TO COOK ⬇⬇⬇

1. IN A BOWL, COMBINE EGGS, 1/4 CUP PIZZA SAUCE, SEA SALT, PEPPER, BASIL AND OREGANO. 2. BEAT WITH A FORK UNTIL EGGS ARE BLENDED. 3. HEAT OVER MEDIUM-HIGH HEAT AND ADD OLIVE OIL. 4. WHEN OIL IS WARM, POUR IN 1/4 CUP OF EGG MIXTURE. 5. AS EGGS BEGIN TO SET, LIFT EDGES TO ALLOW THE UNCOOKED LIQUID TO RUN UNDER THE OMELET. 6. WHEN EGGS ARE SET, SLIP SPATULA UNDER THE OMELET AND SLIDE IT OUT OF THE PAN. 7. REPEAT 4 TIMES 8. WITH REMAINING EGG MIXTURE AND SET ASIDE. 9. WITH A SMALL SHARP KNIFE, CUT ALL AROUND PITA BREADS AND SEPARATE IN TWO. 10. LIE THEM FLAT ON A WORK SURFACE. 11. PLACE AN OMELET ON EACH PITA ROUND. 12. SPREAD 1 TABLESPOON OF PIZZA SAUCE OVER EACH. 13. SPRINKLE WITH CHEESE. 14. ARRANGE A FEW PIECES OF GREEN PEPPERS AND MUSHROOM SLICES IN A ROW ON EACH PITA. 15. PLACE THE REMAINING PITA BREADS OVER THE PIZZAS AND ROLL UP TIGHTLY.

Serve with a fresh fruit salad.

VEGGIE & BRIE
Pudding

1/2 ONION, THINLY SLICED

1 LARGE RED BELL PEPPER, DICED

1 LARGE YUKON GOLD POTATO, PEELED & DICED

2 TABLESPOONS OLIVE OIL

4 OUNCES BRIE CHEESE, CUBED

6 OUNCES SOURDOUGH BREAD LOAF, CUBED

2 OUNCES PARMESAN CHEESE, SHREDDED

4 EGGS

1 1/2 CUPS FAT FREE MILK

1 TABLESPOON DIJON MUSTARD

4 CUPS FRESH FRUITS (*OPTIONAL*)

SEA SALT & PEPPER TO TASTE

READY TO COOK ⬇ ⬇ ⬇

1. SAUTÉ ONIONS, BELL PEPPERS AND DICED POTATOES IN OIL FOR 10-12 MINUTES OR UNTIL VEGETABLES ARE TENDER AND SET ASIDE. 2. MIX ALL THE INGREDIENTS TOGETHER AND POUR INTO A 13" X 9" LIGHTLY GREASED BAKING DISH. 3. COVER AND CHILL FOR AT LEAST 8 HOURS AND UP TO 24 HOURS. 4. BAKE AT 350°F FOR 45 TO 50 MINUTES OR UNTIL TOP IS LIGHTLY BROWNED AND SET IN CENTER.

Serve with fresh fruits.

SMOKED CHEESE
Omelet Wrap

8 EGGS

4 TABLESPOONS WATER

4 TABLESPOONS CHIPOTLE PUREE

2 TABLESPOONS OLIVE OIL

8 TABLESPOONS GREEN ONIONS

1 SMALL GREEN APPLE, DICED

2 CUPS SMOKED CHEDDAR OR SMOKED GOUDA, GRATED

12 ASPARAGUS, COOKED & DICED

4 WHOLE WHEAT TORTILLAS

4 CUPS FRESH FRUIT SALAD (*OPTIONAL*) (*SEE RECIPE PAGE 59*)

SEA SALT & PEPPER TO TASTE

READY TO COOK ⬇ ⬇ ⬇

1. BEAT EGGS LIGHTLY WITH WATER, SEA SALT, PEPPER AND CHIPOTLE PUREE. 2. HEAT OIL IN A NONSTICK SKILLET. 3. ADD DICED APPLE AND EGGS. 4. WHEN EGGS START TO SET, SPRINKLE GREEN ONIONS, CHEESE AND ASPARAGUS ON OMELET 5. COOK A MINUTE LONGER. 6. MICROWAVE TORTILLAS FOR ABOUT 10 SECONDS. 7. SEPARATE OMELET INTO 4 PORTIONS, SLIDE ONTO THE TORTILLAS.

Serve with a fresh fruit salad.

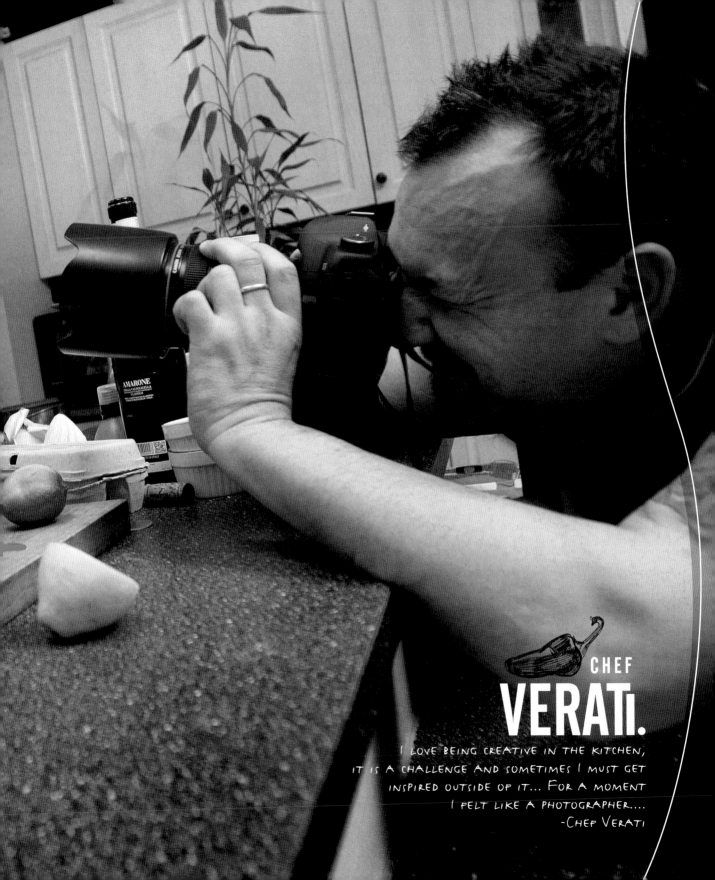

CHEF
VERATi.

I LOVE BEING CREATIVE IN THE KITCHEN,
IT IS A CHALLENGE AND SOMETIMES I MUST GET
INSPIRED OUTSIDE OF IT... FOR A MOMENT
I FELT LIKE A PHOTOGRAPHER....
-CHEF VERATi

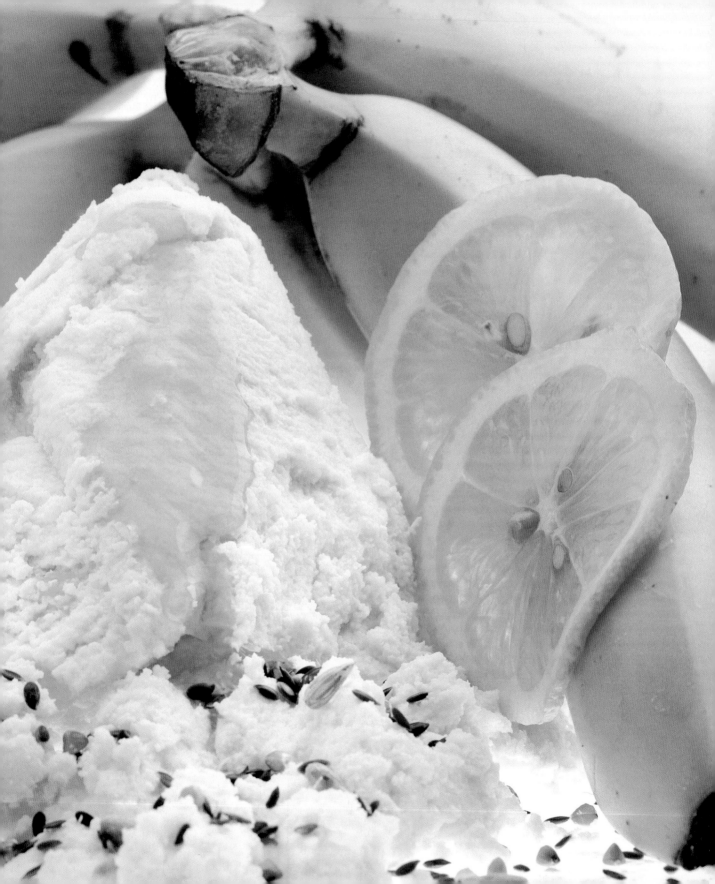

THE TEAM BREAKFAST
Budwig Cream

8 TEASPOONS FLAXSEED OIL

8 TABLESPOONS FRESH CHEESE OR GREEK YOGURT

4 BANANAS

2 LEMONS, JUICED

2 TABLESPOONS BUCKWHEAT, GROUNDED

1 TABLESPOON BROWN FLAX, GROUNDED

1 TABLESPOON SUNFLOWER SEEDS, GROUNDED

4 TABLESPOONS ALMONDS, GROUNDED

READY TO COOK

1 PUT FLAXSEED OIL, FRESH CHEESE AND LEMON JUICE INTO THE BLENDER AND MIX WELL.

2. ADD THE BANANAS, MIX ONE MORE TIME.

3. GRIND THE SEEDS IN A COFFEE GRINDER.

Serve in a bowl and add all the grains on top.

CHEF
VERATi.

EVERY PHOTO-SHOOT BEGAN WITH MY WIFE LISE
MAKING US A GREAT BUDWIG CREAM...
GREAT IDEAS, LAUGHS AND PHOTOS CAME
WHILE EATING THIS BREAKFAST.
-CHEF VERATI

TACO BREAKFAST
with Hot Pepper Sauce

SCRAMBLED EGGS
with Salsa

6 OUNCES CHORIZO SAUSAGES

8 CORN TORTILLAS, 6"

6 EGGS

1/4 CUP MILK

1 CUP SHREDDED MONTEREY JACK CHEESE

3 CUPS SPINACH

DASH OF HOT PEPPER SAUCE

1/2 CUP SALSA

4 CUPS FRESH BERRIES (*OPTIONAL*)

SEA SALT & PEPPER TO TASTE

COOKING SPRAY

1 CUP SALSA

12 EGGS

2 TABLESPOONS SKIM MILK

2 CUPS FRESH TOMATOES, CHOPPED

1 CUP GREEN ONIONS, CHOPPED

1 CUP RED PEPPERS, FINELY CHOPPED

1 CUP GREEN PEPPERS, FINELY CHOPPED

1 CUP PARSLEY, CHOPPED

1 TEASPOON GRAPE SEED OIL

4 CUPS POTATOES, DICED & BLANCHED (*SEE PAGE 129*)

SEA SALT & PEPPER TO TASTE

READY TO COOK ⬇ ⬇ ⬇

1. CRUMBLE SAUSAGES INTO A SKILLET OVER MEDIUM-HIGH HEAT. 2. COOK AND STIR UNTIL EVENLY BROWNED. 3. SET ASIDE. 4. IN A MEDIUM SIZE BOWL, WHISK TOGETHER EGGS, MILK, SEA SALT AND PEPPER. 5. HEAT A SECOND SKILLET OVER MEDIUM HEAT. 6. ADD A LITTLE COOKING SPRAY AND POUR IN EGG MIXTURE. 7. COOK AND STIR UNTIL ALMOST FIRM. 8. ADD SAUSAGES AND SPINACH. 9. CONTINUE COOKING AND STIRRING UNTIL FIRM. 10. HEAT A THIRD SKILLET OVER HIGH HEAT AND WARM EACH TORTILLA FOR ABOUT 45 SECONDS ON EACH SIDE. 11. SPRINKLE A LITTLE SHREDDED CHEESE ONTO THE TORTILLAS WHILE THEY ARE STILL HOT. 12. TOP WITH SOME SCRAMBLED EGGS AND ADD HOT PEPPER SAUCE AND SALSA.

READY TO COOK ⬇ ⬇ ⬇

1. IN A LARGE BOWL, WHISK EGGS WITH MILK, SEA SALT AND PEPPER AND SET ASIDE. 2. IN A FRYING PAN, OVER MEDIUM HEAT, ADD GRAPE SEED OIL AND SAUTÉ TOMATOES, RED AND GREEN PEPPERS, ONIONS AND POTATOES UNTIL HEATED THROUGH. 3. POUR EGGS INTO FRYING PAN AND COOK, STIRRING FREQUENTLY UNTIL EGGS ARE SET.

Serve tacos with a cup of mixed berries for a complete breakfast.

Serve scrambled eggs with a dash of parsley on top and salsa on the side.

POACHED
EGGS
with Ham

24 OUNCES HAM, SLICED

8 EGGS

1/4 TEASPOON VINEGAR

1 TEASPOON OIL

4 WHOLE WHEAT ENGLISH MUFFINS

4 CUPS FRESH FRUIT SALAD (*OPTIONAL*) (*SEE RECIPE PAGE 59*)

SEA SALT & PEPPER TO TASTE

VERATI**TIPS**
WHEN POACHING EGGS,
ADDING VINEGAR TO YOUR WATER KEEPS
THE EGG WHITES FROM SPREADING.

READY TO COOK ⬇ ⬇ ⬇

1. PLACE HAM SLICES IN A WARM OVEN WHILE YOU PREPARE THE EGGS. 2. HEAT WATER IN A FRYING PAN UNTIL IT STARTS TO BOIL. 3. REDUCE HEAT AND ADD VINEGAR. 4. BREAK EACH EGG INTO A SAUCER AND LOWER THEM INTO THE HOT WATER. 5. COOK UNTIL EGGS ARE WELL FORMED BUT STILL SOFT. 6. REMOVE EACH EGG WITH A SLOTTED SPOON AND PLACE ONE EGG ON EACH OF THE HAM SLICES AND ENGLISH MUFFIN HALVES. 7. ADD SEA SALT AND PEPPER.

Serve eggs with fresh fruit salad.

DROP AN EGG
Make a Vegetable Omelet

6 EGGS	2 CUPS CHERRY TOMATOES, HALVED
4 EGG WHITES	2 CUPS MUSHROOMS, SLICED
1 CUP GREEN ONIONS, CHOPPED	2 ENGLISH MUFFINS, CUT IN HALF & TOASTED
1 CUP YELLOW ONIONS, CHOPPED	1 TABLESPOON GRAPE SEED OIL
1 CUP GREEN BELL PEPPERS, CHOPPED	SEA SALT & PEPPER TO TASTE
1 CUP SWEET RED PEPPERS, CHOPPED	

READY TO COOK

1. HEAT OIL IN A LARGE PAN AND GENTLY SAUTÉ RED AND GREEN PEPPERS, YELLOW ONIONS AND MUSHROOMS UNTIL TENDER.
2. ADD CHERRY TOMATOES AND COOK ANOTHER 2-3 MINUTES.
3. BEAT EGG WHITES UNTIL FLUFFY, THEN ADD WHOLE EGGS AND MIX WELL.
4. POUR EGGS OVER VEGETABLE MIXTURE AND ADD SEA SALT AND PEPPER.
5. COVER AND COOK UNTIL EGGS ARE DONE.
6. DIVIDE OMELET INTO 4 PORTIONS AND PLACE EACH ONE ON TOP OF A TOASTED MUFFIN HALF.

SERVE OMELET WITH A DASH OF GREEN ONIONS ON TOP.

IT'S BREAKFAST TIME!
SIT DOWN TO ENJOY YOUR MEAL.

POACHED EGGS
Creole-Style

12 EGGS	**1 CUP** ARTICHOKES, BOTTLED
1 CUP GREEN ONIONS, CHOPPED	**1 TEASPOON** HOT PEPPER SAUCE
2 CLOVES GARLIC, FINELY CHOPPED	**1 TABLESPOON** GRAPE SEED OIL
1 CUP GREEN BELL PEPPERS, CHOPPED	**1 TABLESPOON** VINEGAR
1 CUP WHITE BEANS, CANNED	**4 SLICES** WHOLE WHEAT BREAD SLICES, TOASTED (*OPTIONAL*)
1 CUP GREEN OLIVES, PITTED	SEA SALT & PEPPER TO TASTE
3 CUPS SPINACH	

READY TO COOK

1. **HEAT** OIL IN A FRYING PAN AND SAUTÉ CHOPPED GARLIC UNTIL SOFT.

2. **ADD** WHITE BEANS, GREEN PEPPERS AND GREEN OLIVES, COOK UNTIL...SOFT.

3. **ADD** SPINACH AND ARTICHOKES AND COOK JUST UNTIL SPINACH IS WILTED.

4. **KEEP** WARM.

5. **BRING** A SHALLOW PAN OF WATER TO A BOIL.

6. **ADD** VINEGAR AND IMMEDIATELY TURN DOWN THE HEAT.

7. **GENTLY** POACH THE EGGS.

8. **DIVIDE** SPINACH MIXTURE AMONG 4 PLATES, SPREADING TO FORM A BED FOR THE EGGS.

9. **ADD** 3 POACHED EGGS TO EACH PLATE.

10. **SEASON** WITH SEA SALT, PEPPER AND HOT PEPPER SAUCE AND DISTRIBUTE SOME OLIVES AND GREEN ONIONS ON EACH PLATE.

Serve poached eggs with whole wheat toast.

SCRAMBLED EGGS
with Tuna

4 EGGS

1/4 CUP 35% COOKING CREAM

1/4 CUP CHEDDAR CHEESE, GRATED

2 TABLESPOONS GRAPE SEED OIL

2 CANS TUNA, CHOPPED

2 CUPS RED ONIONS, FINELY SLICED

2 CUPS RADISH, FINELY SLICED

2 TABLESPOONS LEMON JUICE

2 TABLESPOONS LIGHT MAYONNAISE

4 WHOLE WHEAT ENGLISH MUFFINS, CUT IN HALF & TOASTED *(OPTIONAL)*

4 CUPS FRESH FRUITS *(OPTIONAL)*

READY TO COOK

1. **COMBINE** RED ONIONS, RADISH AND TUNA.

2. **TOSS** WITH LEMON JUICE, MAYONNAISE AND 1 TABLESPOON OF GRAPE SEED OIL AND SET ASIDE.

3. **HEAT** REMAINING OIL IN A FRYING PAN.

4. **BEAT** EGGS WITH CREAM AND ADD TO THE PAN, STIRRING TO SCRAMBLE.

5. **WHEN** EGGS ARE ALMOST COOKED, ADD GRATED CHEESE.

6. **WHEN** CHEESE HAS MELTED, REMOVE FROM HEAT AND DISTRIBUTE EGGS AMONG 4 PLATES.

Serve scrambled eggs topped with tuna mixture alongside whole wheat english muffins and fresh fruits.

APPLE & BRIE
Omelet with Fruit Salad

8 EGGS

2 TABLESPOONS GRAPE SEED OIL

2 GALA APPLES, PEELED & THINLY DICED

8 OUNCES BRIE CHEESE, 1" CUBES

4 SLICES MULTI GRAIN BREAD, TOASTED (*OPTIONAL*)

4 CUPS FRUIT SALAD (*OPTIONAL*) (*SEE RECIPE PAGE 59*)

SEA SALT & PEPPER TO TASTE

READY TO COOK

1. HEAT A NONSTICK OVENPROOF SKILLET OVER MEDIUM HEAT.

2. ADD 1 TABLESPOON OF GRAPE SEED OIL IN SKILLET.

3. SAUTÉ APPLES FOR ABOUT 2 MINUTES OR UNTIL SLIGHTLY TRANSPARENT BUT NOT TOO SOFT.

4. REMOVE FROM PAN AND KEEP WARM.

5. BEAT EGGS.

6. HEAT SKILLET OVER MEDIUM-HIGH HEAT.

7. ADD REMAINING GRAPE SEED OIL.

8. POUR IN EGG MIXTURE.

9. WHEN THE EGGS ARE ALMOST SET ON THE SURFACE BUT STILL LOOK MOIST, COVER THE OMELET WITH THE WARM APPLES AND AND GARNISH WITH BRIE CHEESE.

10. PLACE IN OVEN AT BROIL FOR 1 TO 2 MINUTES TO MELT CHEESE.

Slide onto warm plate and serve with fruit salad and multi grain toasted bread.

SOFT BOILED EGGS
Mediterranean Style

8 EGGS, BOILED

8 OUNCES SMOKED HAM, FINELY SLICED

2 CUPS ZUCCHINI, GRILLED

2 CUPS CHERRY TOMATOES CUT IN HALF

4 TABLESPOONS FRESH CORIANDER

2 CUPS MANGO, RIPE & DICED

2 CUPS PEACH, RIPE & DICED

4 TABLESPOONS BALSAMIC VINEGAR

2 TABLESPOONS GRAPE SEED OIL

SEA SALT & PEPPER TO TASTE

READY TO COOK ⬇⬇⬇

1. BOIL THE EGGS FOR 9 MINUTES IN BOILING WATER. AFTER 9 MINUTES, PLACE IN COLD WATER FOR 2-3 MINUTES, PEEL AND SET ASIDE. 2. SLICE THE ZUCCHINI LENGTHWISE AND BRUSH WITH A SMALL AMOUNT OF OIL. 3. PLACE ON A RACK UNTIL THE OVEN GRILL AND GRILL ABOUT 3 MINUTES PER SIDE AT HIGH HEAT. 4. REMOVE FROM THE OVEN AND SET ASIDE. 5. TOSS THE CHERRY TOMATOES WITH A LITTLE OF THE SALT AND PEPPER, OIL AND BALSAMIC VINEGAR. 6. ROLL THE HAM SLICES INTO CIGAR SHAPES AND PLACE ON THE PLATES. 7. SPREAD A LAYER OF THE GRILLED ZUCCHINI OVER TOP. 8. PLACE 1/2 CUP PEACH, MANGO, TWO EGG HALVES AND CORIANDER IN THE MIDDLE OF EACH PLATE.

Served with a spread a little of the tomato and balsamic vinegar dressing over top.

HAM PIPERADE
with Potatoes

4 EGGS

4 EGG WHITES

1 CUP HAM, CHOPPED

2 CUPS SWEET RED PEPPERS, CHOPPED

2 CUPS GREEN BELL PEPPERS, CHOPPED

2 CUPS ONIONS, CHOPPED

2 CUPS FRESH TOMATOES, DICED

2 CUPS POTATOES, DICED

4 CLOVES GARLIC, FINELY CHOPPED

1 TEASPOON GRAPE SEED OIL

4 TABLESPOONS LOW FAT YOGURT

4 SLICES WHOLE WHEAT BREAD, TOASTED (*OPTIONAL*)

4 CUPS FRUIT SALAD (*OPTIONAL*) (*SEE RECIPE PAGE 59*)

READY TO COOK ⬇⬇⬇

1. HEAT OIL IN A LARGE FRYING PAN AND SAUTÉ ONIONS, RED AND GREEN PEPPERS, GARLIC AND POTATOES UNTIL JUST TENDER. 2. ADD TOMATOES, HAM, SEA SALT AND PEPPER AND COOK 3-4 MINUTES LONGER. 3. BEAT EGG WHITES UNTIL FLUFFY. 4. WHISK WHOLE EGGS AND FOLD INTO EGG WHITES. 5. POUR EGG MIXTURE OVER VEGETABLES AND COOK UNTIL EGG IS SET.

Serve with yogurt, whole wheat toast and a cup of fruit salad for a complete breakfast.

POTATO & EGG OMELET
with Leeks

8 WHOLE EGGS

4 EGG WHITES

2 CUPS POTATOES, PEELED & THINLY SLICED

2 CUPS FRESH TOMATOES, THINLY SLICED

2 CUPS LEEKS, CHOPPED

1 CUP RED ONIONS, THINLY SLICED

1 CUP GREEN ONIONS OR CHIVES, FINELY CHOPPED

1 TEASPOON GRAPE SEED OIL

4 SLICES WHOLE WHEAT BREAD, TOASTED (*OPTIONAL*)

4 CUPS FRESH BERRIES (*OPTIONAL*)

SEA SALT & PEPPER TO TASTE

READY TO COOK ↓↓↓

1. WHISK WHOLE EGGS AND EGG WHITES WITH SEA SALT AND PEPPER AND SET ASIDE. 2. IN A SMALL BOWL, POUR BOILING WATER OVER THINLY SLICED POTATOES AND LET SIT FOR 5 MINUTES. 3. DRAIN AND SET ASIDE. 4. ON STOVE TOP, COOK LEEKS AND RED ONIONS IN AN OVEN PROOF PAN WITH OIL UNTIL BOTH ARE JUST TENDER. 5. LAYER POTATOES ON TOP OF LEEK AND RED ONION MIXTURE. 6. ADD A LAYER OF THINLY SLICED TOMATOES. 7. POUR BEATEN EGGS OVER MIXTURE AND SPRINKLE WITH GREEN ONIONS OR CHIVES. 8. COVER THE PAN AND BAKE AT 300°F FOR APPROXIMATELY 10 MINUTES OR UNTIL EGGS ARE SET. 9. CUT IN WEDGES.

*Serve omelet with whole wheat toast
and a cup of mixed berries for a complete breakfast.*

STUFFED EGGS
with Tuna Salad

8 EGGS

1 CAN TUNA, CHOPPED

6 TABLESPOONS MAYONNAISE

3 TABLESPOONS FRESH CHIVES, FINELY CHOPPED

1 TEASPOON TABASCO SAUCE

6 CUPS LEBANESE CUCUMBERS, FINELY SLICED

3 TABLESPOONS WHITE VINEGAR

2 CUPS PEARS, DICED

4 WHOLE WHEAT BREAD SLICES, TOASTED (OPTIONAL)

SEA SALT & PEPPER TO TASTE

READY TO COOK

1. BOIL EGGS FOR 9 MINUTES, REMOVE AND PLACE IN COLD WATER TO COOL.

2. PEEL AND SET ASIDE.

3. COMBINE MAYONNAISE, CHIVES, WHITE VINEGAR AND TABASCO SAUCE.

4. DRAIN TUNA AND ADD TO MIXTURE.

5. CUT SHELLED EGGS IN HALF AND SCOOP OUT THE YOLKS.

6. MASH YOLKS IN A SMALL BOWL AND ADD TO MAYONNAISE MIXTURE ALONG WITH DICED PEARS.

7. STUFF EGG HALVES WITH MIXTURE.

8. SPREAD A LAYER OF FINELY SLICED CUCUMBERS ALONG THE BOTTOM OF 4 PLATES.

9. PLACE 3 PORTIONS OF STUFFED EGGS ON TOP.

SERVE STUFFED EGGS WITH WHOLE WHEAT TOAST.

THE WORST BREAKFAST
IS NO BREAKFAST.

EAT LIKE A CHAMPION
what a Breakfast

8 EGGS, BEATEN

1 CUP COOKED HAM, CUBED

2 CUPS POTATOES, PEELED & SLICED

2 CUPS FRESH TOMATOES, CUBED

2 CUPS ONIONS, CHOPPED

1 CUP GREEN BELL PEPPERS, CHOPPED

1 CUP SWEET RED PEPPERS, CHOPPED

1 TEASPOON GRAPE SEED OIL

1 TABLESPOON DRIED PARSLEY

1/2 CUP FRESH CHIVES, CHOPPED

4 SLICES MULTI GRAIN BREAD, TOASTED (*OPTIONAL*)

4 CUPS FRUIT SALAD (*OPTIONAL*) (*SEE RECIPE PAGE 59*)

SEA SALT & PEPPER TO TASTE

READY TO COOK

1. BOIL POTATO SLICES FOR 2-3 MINUTES.

2. REMOVE FROM HEAT AND DRAIN.

3. HEAT OIL IN A LARGE FRYING PAN AND SAUTÉ THE ONIONS WITH RED AND GREEN PEPPERS UNTIL TENDER.

4. ADD COOKED HAM, DRAINED BOILED POTATOES, FRESH TOMATOES, SEA SALT AND PEPPER.

5. SPREAD EVENLY OVER BOTTOM OF THE PAN.

6. ADD EGGS, COVER AND COOK ON LOW HEAT UNTIL DONE.

Serve with a dash of parsley and chives on top, a fruit salad and multi grain toasted bread on the side.

CHICKEN FRITTATA
with Fresh Herbs

16 OUNCES CHICKEN BREAST, CUBED

4 LARGE EGGS

4 EGG WHITES

2 CUPS GREEN ONIONS, CHOPPED

1 CUP GREEN PEPPERS, FINELY CHOPPED

1 CUP SWEET RED PEPPERS, FINELY CHOPPED

1 CUP FRESH SPINACH LEAVES, CHOPPED

1 CUP CELERY, CHOPPED

2 CUPS SWEET POTATOES, THINLY SLICED

2 TEASPOONS GRAPE SEED OIL

1/2 CUP SKIM MILK

1 TABLESPOON FRESH THYME, CHOPPED

1 TABLESPOON FRESH BASIL, CHOPPED

1 TABLESPOON FRESH SAVORY, CHOPPED

4 SLICES MULTI GRAIN BREAD, TOASTED (*OPTIONAL*)

4 CUPS MIXED BERRIES (*OPTIONAL*)

SEA SALT & PEPPER TO TASTE

READY TO COOK

1. HEAT OIL IN A FRYING PAN AND BROWN CHICKEN CUBES ON ALL SIDES.

2. COOK SWEET POTATOES FOR 1 MINUTE IN BOILING WATER.

3. DRAIN THE POTATOES AND PLACE THEM ON THE BOTTOM.

4. ADD THE CHICKEN TO THE CASSEROLE AND SPREAD EVENLY OVER POTATOES.

5. ADD GREEN ONIONS, RED AND GREEN PEPPERS, SPINACH, CELERY, FRESH HERBS, SEA SALT AND PEPPER.

6. BEAT EGGS, EGG WHITES AND MILK AND POUR OVER CHICKEN MIXTURE.

7. BAKE AT 350°F FOR 30 MINUTES.

Serve with mixed berries or multi grain toasted bread.

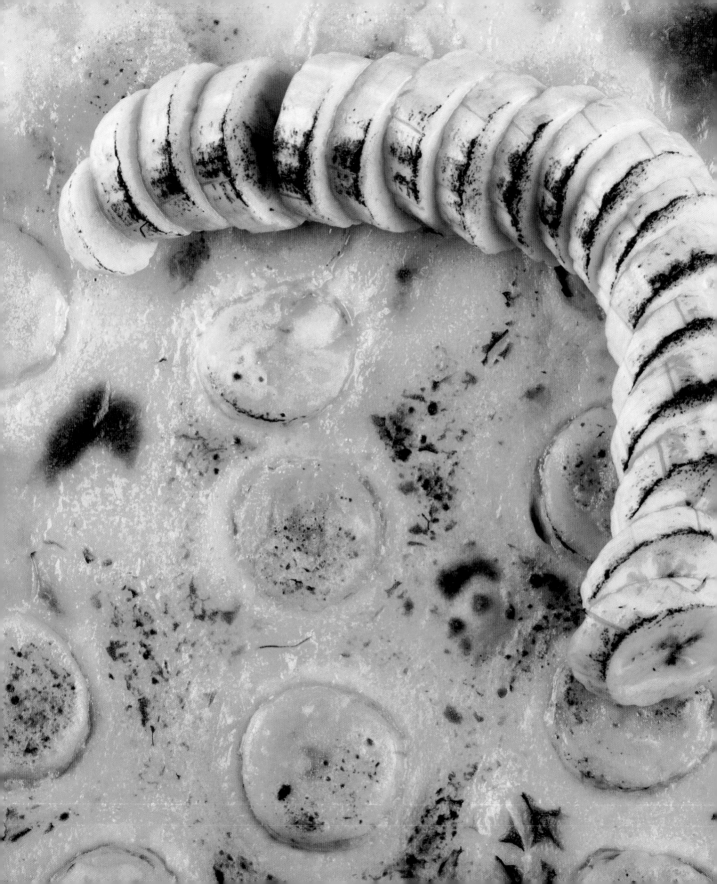

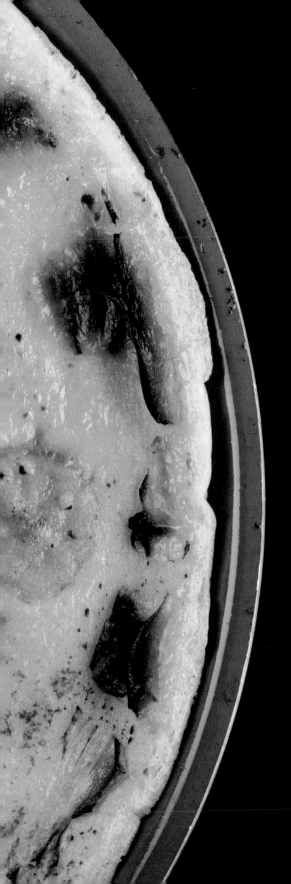

BANANA
OATMEAL
Crépes

2 BANANAS, PEELED & SLICED

1 PACKET ARTIFICIAL SWEETENER

1 CUP WHOLE WHEAT FLOUR

1/2 CUP QUICK OR OLD FASHIONED QUAKER OATS, UNCOOKED

1 TABLESPOON BAKING POWDER

1 CUP FAT FREE MILK

1 EGG, LIGHTLY BEATEN

2 TABLESPOONS GRAPE SEED OIL

2 BANANAS, SLICED *(OPTIONAL)*

1 CUP ALMOND SLICES *(OPTIONAL)*

SEA SALT & PEPPER TO TASTE

READY TO COOK

1. IN A BOWL, ADD 2 SLICED BANANAS AND SWEETENER, MIX.

2. SET ASIDE.

3. IN A SECOND BOWL, ADD FLOUR, OATS, BAKING POWDER AND SEA SALT AND BLEND WELL.

4. IN A THIRD BOWL, ADD MILK, EGG AND OIL AND BLEND WELL.

5. COMBINE ALL INGREDIENTS INTO ONE MIX.

6. HEAT A GRIDDLE OVER MEDIUM-HIGH HEAT AND ADD MIXTURE.

7. TURN PANCAKE WHEN TOP IS COVERED WITH BUBBLES.

SERVE WITH BANANA SLICES AND A DASH OF ALMONDS ON TOP.

MUSHROOM & SPINACH
Frittata

12 EGGS

3 CUPS SPINACH

4 CUPS MUSHROOMS, SLICED

1/4 CUP CHIVES, CHOPPED

1 CUP POTATOES, DICED & BOILED

1 CUP CHERRY TOMATOES, HALVED

1 TEASPOON GRAPE SEED OIL

1 TABLESPOON SKIM MILK

SEA SALT & PEPPER TO TASTE

READY TO COOK

1. SEPARATE EGG YOLKS FROM EGG WHITES.

2. WHISK EGG YOLKS WITH MILK, SEA SALT AND PEPPER UNTIL WELL BLENDED.

3. WHISK EGG WHITES UNTIL FLUFFY AND SET ASIDE.

4. COOK MUSHROOMS AND POTATOES WITH OIL IN A FRYING PAN UNTIL JUST TENDER.

5. ADD CHIVES, CHERRY TOMATOES, SPINACH AND TOSS.

6. FOLD EGG WHITES INTO EGG YOLKS AND POUR OVER THE MUSHROOM MIXTURE.

7. COOK ON STOVE TOP FOR ABOUT 3 MINUTES, STIRRING IN THE BEGINNING TO EVENLY MIX THE VEGETABLES AND EGGS.

8. TURN OFF THE HEAT AND COVER THE PAN WITH A TIGHT-FITTING LID.

9. LET SIT FOR ANOTHER 3-4 MINUTES. .

Serve frittata cut into wedges.

HAM & PEPPERS
Frittata

8 EGGS

2 CUPS HAM, CHOPPED

1 CUP RED PEPPERS, FINELY CHOPPED

1 CUP GREEN PEPPERS, FINELY CHOPPED

1 ONION, FINELY SLICED

2 CUPS GREEN ONIONS, CHOPPED

1 CUP FRESH TOMATOES, CHOPPED

3 CUPS SPINACH

1/2 CUP FRESH CILANTRO

1/2 CUP FRESH OREGANO

1/2 CUP PARMESAN CHEESE

4 CUPS MIXED BERRIES *(OPTIONAL)*

4 WHOLE WHEAT ENGLISH MUFFINS, CUT IN HALF & TOASTED *(OPTIONAL)*

SEA SALT & PEPPER TO TASTE

READY TO COOK

1. IN FRYING PAN, COOK ONIONS UNTIL TENDER.

2. ADD HAM, RED AND GREEN PEPPERS, SPINACH AND FRESH TOMATOES AND COOK FOR 2-3 MINUTES.

3. BEAT EGGS, SEA SALT AND PEPPER TOGETHER AND POUR OVER THE ONION MIXTURE.

4. SPRINKLE GREEN ONIONS, CILANTRO, OREGANO AND PARMESAN CHEESE OVER TOP.

5. COVER THE PAN AND COOK OVER LOW HEAT FOR ABOUT 10 MINUTES OR UNTIL THE EGGS ARE SET.

Serve frittata cut into wedges on English muffin, a bowl of mixed berries for a complete breakfast.

VERATI *Twist*

YOU CAN USE WHOLE WHEAT ENGLISH MUFFINS TO MAKE YOUR SANDWICHES.

CHEF
VERATi.

I ALWAYS SAY THAT YOU HAVE TO HAVE FUN WHILE COOKING... IS THERE ANYTHING MORE FUN THEN PREPARING A BREAKFAST WITH THE 3 LOVES OF MY LIFE?
-CHEF VERATI

CHEF
VERATi.

My inspiration: I teach people
how to flip «crêpes»,
Guess who taught me...?
Love you Dad! - Chef Verati

DAD'S
Savory Pancakes

3/4 CUP WHITE FLOUR

3/4 CUP WHOLE WHEAT FLOUR

1 TABLESPOON BAKING POWDER

4 EGGS

1 CUP SKIM MILK

1 TEASPOON GRAPE SEED OIL

1 TEASPOON BUTTER

1/2 CUP COOKED HAM, CHOPPED

1/2 CUP MUSHROOMS, SLICED

1 TEASPOON FRESH OREGANO, CHOPPED **OR 1/2 TEASPOON** DRIED OREGANO

1/2 CUP FRESH PARSLEY, CHOPPED **OR 1 TABLESPOON** DRIED PARSLEY

4 TABLESPOONS LOW FAT YOGURT

4 CUPS MIXED BERRIES (*OPTIONAL*)

SEA SALT & PEPPER TO TASTE

READY TO COOK

1. COOK SLICED MUSHROOMS IN BUTTER FOR 1-2 MINUTES, REMOVE FROM HEAT AND SET ASIDE.

2. IN A BOWL, BEAT THE EGGS.

3. ADD WHITE AND WHOLE WHEAT FLOUR, BAKING POWDER, MILK, SEA SALT AND PEPPER.

4. STIR WITH A FORK UNTIL MIXED.

5. ADD HAM, ONIONS, OREGANO AND PARSLEY.

6. POUR BATTER INTO A PRE-HEATED FRYING PAN TO FORM 4 EQUALLY SIZED PANCAKES.

7. COOK OVER MEDIUM HEAT UNTIL THE BOTTOM IS BROWN AND BUBBLES BEGIN TO FORM ON THE SURFACE.

8. FLIP PANCAKES OVER AND COOK OTHER SIDE UNTIL JUST BROWN.

9. REMOVE FROM HEAT.

Serve pancakes with low fat plain yogurt and a cup of mixed berries.

OVERATITRICK

IF THE BATTER IS TOO THICK, ADD A LITTLE MILK. IF IT'S TOO WATERY, ADD A LITTLE FLOUR. ALSO, WHEN POURING THE MIXTURE INTO THE FRYING PAN, MAKE SURE TO LEAVE ENOUGH SPACE IN BETWEEN PANCAKES. COOK IN BATCHES IF NECESSARY.

CHEF
VERATi.

CLUB BREAKFAST
with Fruit Salad

4 TEASPOONS MAYONNAISE

12 WHOLE WHEAT ENGLISH MUFFINS, CUT IN HALF & TOASTED

12 EGGS

4 ICEBERG LETTUCE LEAVES

4 FIRM TOMATO, RIPE & SLICES

12 STRIPS BACON, COOKED & CRISP

4 CUPS FRUIT SALAD (*OPTIONAL*) (*SEE RECIPE PAGE 59*)

SEA SALT & PEPPER TO TASTE

READY TO COOK

1. SPREAD ABOUT 1 TEASPOON OF MAYONNAISE ON 1 SIDE OF EACH TOASTED ENGLISH MUFFIN HALVES.

2. SET 1 ENGLISH MUFFIN HALF ON A PLATE, MAYONNAISE SIDE UP.

3. TOP WITH 3 SOFT-SCRAMBLED EGGS.

4. SPRINKLE LIGHTLY WITH SEA SALT AND PEPPER.

5. TOP THE EGGS WITH ANOTHER ENGLISH MUFFIN TOAST, ADD 1 ICEBERG LETTUCE LEAF, A SLICE OF TOMATO, 3 SLICES OF CRISP-COOKED BACON AND COVER WITH ANOTHER ENGLISH MUFFIN TOAST.

6. SECURE LAYERS WITH TOOTHPICKS AND CUT SANDWICH INTO HALVES OR QUARTERS.

7. REPEAT FOR ALL PLATES.

Serve with fruit salad.

A COMBINATION OF ALL
FOOD GROUPS IS PERMITTED
FOR BREAKFAST.

FRUIT SALAD
Strawberries + Mango

#1 STRAWBERRIES VANILLA ↓↓↓

1 CUP WATER	**4 CUPS** STRAWBERRIES, HULLED & HALVED
1 ORANGE, JUICED	**2 CUPS** BLUEBERRIES
1 ORANGE, ZESTED	**2 CUPS** RED GRAPES, HALVED
2 WHOLE VANILLA BEANS, CAVIAR SCRAPED OUT (OR 2 TEASPOONS VANILLA EXTRACT)	**2 CUPS** GREEN GRAPES, HALVED
	MINT LEAVES

READY TO COOK

1. PLACE THE WATER, ORANGE JUICE AND ORANGE ZEST INTO A SMALL SAUCEPAN. **2. STIR** AND BRING TO A BOIL **3. TURN** THE HEAT TO **LOW** AND SIMMER FOR 15-20 MINUTES TO THICKEN SLIGHTLY. **4. SET** ASIDE TO COOL, THEN STORE IN THE FRIDGE UNTIL COLD. **5. MIX** THE FRUITS IN A LARGE BOWL **6. POUR** THE SYRUP OVER THE FRUIT. **7. TOSS** GENTLY. **8. GARNISH** WITH MINT LEAVES.

• •

#2 MANGO GINGER ↓↓↓

2 CUPS PINEAPPLE, PEELED & CUBED	**1 TABLESPOON** LIME, JUICED
1 CUP MANGO, PEELED & CUBED	**1 TABLESPOON** LIME, ZESTED
1 CUP BANANA, SLICED	**1/8 TEASPOON** GROUND CINNAMON
1 CUP ORANGE, SECTIONED	**1/8 TEASPOON** GROUND CARDAMONE
1 TABLESPOON DARK BROWN SUGAR	**1/8 TEASPOON** GINGER

READY TO COOK

1. COMBINE LIME JUICE AND ZEST WITH THE SPICES. **2. ADD** ALL FRUITS IN A MEDIUM SIZE BOWL **3. TOSS** GENTLY TO COMBINE. **4. COVER** AND STORE IN THE FRIDGE FOR 1 HOUR.

A FRUIT SALAD IS A COMBINATION OF EVERY FRUIT YOU LOVE... SIMPLE AS THAT!
-CHEF VERATI

Ideal
SOUPS & SALADS

A DROP OF FREEDOM

...

TIPS & TRICKS

WRITE TO **CHEFVERATI@IDEALPROTEIN.COM**
FIND US ON **CHEF VERATI'S FACEBOOK PAGE**
VISIT **LOWFATLOWCARB.COM**

FAT
Best at lunch time

FACT # 1 ···································· 67

FESTIVE MINESTRONE CHICKEN SOUP ················ 71
ROASTED FENNEL GOAT CHEESE SALAD ·············· 72
CABBAGE SOUP FLAVOURED WITH BEEF ·············· 72
SUPER QUICK ITALIAN STYLE SOUP ·················· 73
CHICKEN & MOZZARELLA SALAD ····················· 74
CELERY & STILTON SOUP WITH SCALLOP SKEWERS ··· 75
RED VELVET FALLS OVER GOAT CHEESE ·············· 79
TOMATO & ORANGE SOUP WITH TURKEY PATTIES ···· 80
WARM SNOW PEA SALAD WITH CHICKEN SKEWERS ··· 81
AVOCADO SALAD WITH LIME VINAIGRETTE ············ 83
ITALIAN SAUSAGE WITH WARM SPINACH SALAD ······ 85
COBB SALAD WITH CRISP BACON & BLUE CHEESE CRUMBLE 86
ANTIPASTO PLATTER CHEF VERATI STYLE ·········· 87
FENNEL SALAD WITH GRILLED CHICKEN SKEWERS ··· 89
MARINATED VEGETABLE & SHRIMP SALAD ············ 90
SPICY CHICKEN & CABBAGE SOUP ···················· 91
SATAY CHICKEN SKEWERS WITH SPINACH SOUP ······ 93
SMOKED HAM CABBAGE SALAD ······················· 94
WARM CHICKEN SALAD ······························ 94
SALAD DRESSINGS RECIPES // LOW FAT + LOW CARB 95

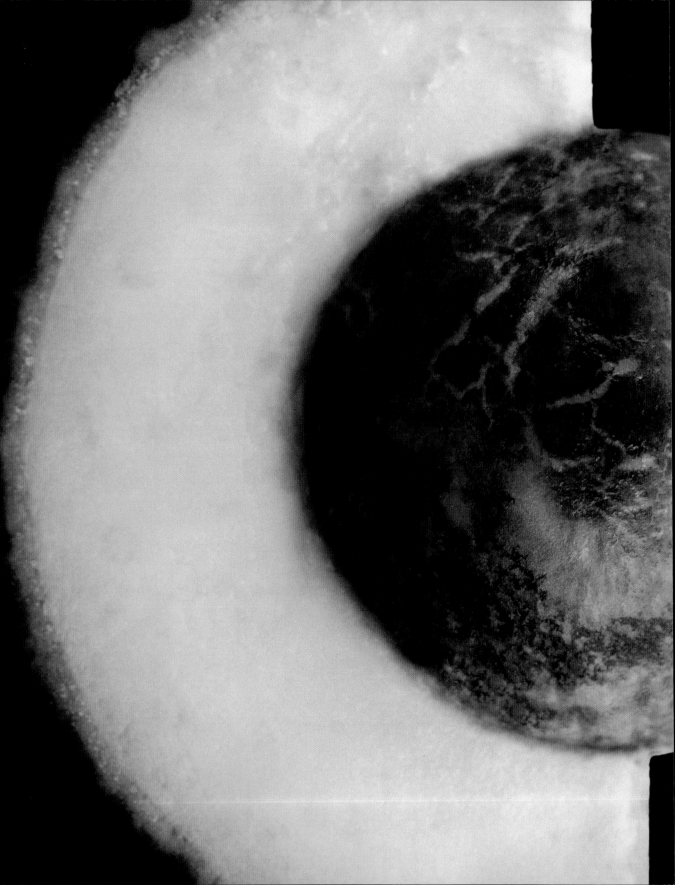

FAT

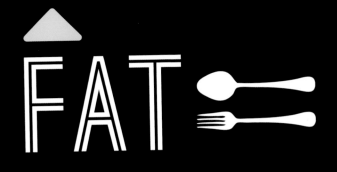

CARBS

best at lunch time

FACT #1

YOUR BRAIN

IS APPROXIMATELY TWO-THIRDS FAT. THEREFORE, YOU MUST GET CERTAIN ESSENTIAL FATTY ACIDS FROM YOUR DIET TO MAINTAIN ITS VITALITY. LET'S GET FISH, FLAX SEEDS, OLIVE OIL, AND SUNFLOWER SEEDS IN ARE MENUS.

CHEF
VERATI.

NOT ONLY DID [WE] HAVE TO BE CREATIVE WITH
THE RECIPES.... BUT ALSO WITH [THE] TOOLS WE USED
TO CREATE THE PERFEC[T] PHOTOS.
-CHEF VERATI

FESTIVE MINESTRONE

Chicken Soup

24 OUNCES CHICKEN BREASTS, CUBED

8 STRIPS OF BACON, CHOPPED IN 1" PIECES

1 TEASPOON GRAPE SEED OIL

2 CUPS GREEN ONIONS, FINELY CHOPPED

2 CUPS ZUCCHINI, CUBED

2 CLOVES GARLIC, FINELY CHOPPED

2 CUPS SAVOY CABBAGE, CHOPPED

1 CUP SMALL MUSHROOMS, WHOLE

1 CUP CELERY, CHOPPED

1 TEASPOON PAPRIKA

1 TEASPOON FRESH BASIL, CHOPPED

1 TEASPOON DRIED OREGANO

1 TEASPOON DRIED THYME

2 TABLESPOONS FRESH ITALIAN PARSLEY, CHOPPED

8 CUPS WATER OR CHICKEN BROTH

SEA SALT & PEPPER TO TASTE

READY TO COOK

1. HEAT OIL IN A PAN, ADD CHOPPED BACON AND COOK UNTIL CRISP. 2. REMOVE FROM PAN. SEASON THE CHICKEN CUBES WITH PAPRIKA AND BASIL AND COOK FOR 5 MINUTES, TURNING TO BROWN ALL SIDES. 3. REMOVE FROM PAN. 4. ADD ONIONS AND GARLIC AND COOK FOR 2-3 MINUTES UNTIL ONIONS BEGINS TO SOFTEN. DO NOT ALLOW GARLIC TO BROWN. 5. REMOVE FROM PAN. 6. PLACE COOKED BACON, CHICKEN AND GARLIC IN A LARGE POT, ADD CABBAGE, CELERY, MUSHROOMS, ZUCCHINI, OREGANO AND THYME AND STIR TO COMBINE. 7. ADD THE WATER OR CHICKEN BROTH, SEA SALT AND PEPPER AND SIMMER FOR 45 MINUTES. 8. SPRINKLE WITH PARSLEY AND SERVE WITH GREEN ONIONS ON TOP.

▶ PIG OUT

A SUNDAY BRUNCH ISN'T THE SAME WITHOUT BACON. SMELLS LIKE *Freedom*

SATURATED FATS FOUND IN BACON CAN INCREASE YOUR RISK OF HEART DISEASE IF CONSUMED IN EXCESS IT!

PER SERVING: 420 CALORIES// 27G FAT // 54G PROTEIN // 11G CARBOHYDRATE

ROASTED FENNEL
Goat Cheese Salad

4 CUPS	FENNEL, QUARTERED
4 OUNCES	GOAT CHEESE, SOFTENED
1 CUP	COOKED HAM, CUBED
2 CUPS	FRESH TOMATOES, DICED
4 CUPS	BABY SPINACH
1/2 CUP	FRESH CHIVES, CHOPPED
2 CLOVES	GARLIC, FINELY CHOPPED
1 TEASPOON	CAYENNE PEPPER
4 TABLESPOONS	GRAPE SEED OIL
3 TABLESPOONS	APPLE CIDER VINEGAR
SEA SALT & PEPPER TO TASTE	

READY TO COOK ⬇ ⬇ ⬇

1. PREHEAT OVEN TO 325⁰F. **2. WASH** THE FENNEL AND WRAP THEM IN FOIL. **3. BAKE** FOR 30 MINUTES. **4. REMOVE** FROM THE FOIL AND LET COOL. **5. MAKE** A DRESSING BY WHISKING TOGETHER THE APPLE CIDER VINEGAR, OIL, SEA SALT AND PEPPER. **6. RESERVE** 2 TABLESPOONS OF THE DRESSING AND POUR THE REMAINING DRESSING OVER THE FENNEL. **7. MIX** THE SOFTENED GOAT CHEESE WITH THE GARLIC, CHIVES AND CAYENNE PEPPER. **8. FORM** INTO FOUR SMALL BALLS AND SET ASIDE. **9. TOSS** TOGETHER THE SPINACH, CHOPPED TOMATOES, HAM AND THE RESERVED DRESSING. **10. HEAP** THE SPINACH, TOMATO AND HAM MIXTURE EVENLY ONTO THE MIDDLE OF 4 SERVING PLATES THEN SPREAD 1/4 OF THE FENNEL MIXTURE OVER EACH. **11. PLACE** A GOAT CHEESE BALL ON EACH.

Serve very hot.

PER SERVING: 397 CALORIES // 32G FAT // 20G PROTEIN // 10G CARBOHYDRATE

CABBAGE SOUP
Flavoured with Beef

24 OUNCES	LEAN GROUND BEEF
4 CUPS	BEEF STOCK
2 CUPS	TOMATOES, CHOPPED
1 CUP	GREEN PEPPERS, CHOPPED
1 CUP	GREEN ONIONS, CHOPPED.
4 CUPS	CABBAGE, CHOPPED
2 CUPS	SPICY CLAMATO JUICE
SEA SALT & PEPPER TO TASTE	

READY TO COOK ⬇ ⬇ ⬇

1. BROWN THE BEEF IN A LARGE SOUP POT. **2. DRAIN** OUT ALL FAT AFTER BROWNING. **3. ADD** THE BEEF STOCK, TOMATOES, CARROTS, GREEN PEPPERS, ONIONS, CABBAGE AND SEA SALT AND PEPPER. **4. BRING** TO A BOIL, REDUCE HEAT AND SIMMER FOR 2 HOURS. **5. ADD** THE CLAMATO JUICE AND SIMMER ANOTHER 10 MINUTES. **6. ADD** 1 CUP OF WATER OR BEEF STOCK IF TOO THICK.

Serve soup with a green onion garnish.

PER SERVING: 433 CALORIES // 29G FAT // 57G PROTEIN // 11G CARBOHYDRATE

SUPER QUICK
ITALIAN
Style Soup

2 CUPS ONIONS, CHOPPED

2 CLOVES GARLIC, FINELY CHOPPED

6 CUPS FROZEN MIXED VEGETABLES OF YOUR CHOICE (BROCCOLI, CAULIFLOWER, GREEN BEANS, SPINACH, CELERY, CABBAGE, CARROTS)

4 CUPS BEEF BROTH OR STOCK.

2 CUPS CANNED DICED TOMATOES

20 OUNCES COOKED POLISH COIL OR PEPPERONI, DICED

SEA SALT & PEPPER TO TASTE

READY TO COOK ⬇ ⬇ ⬇

1. IN A LARGE POT, GENTLY SAUTÉ THE ONIONS AND GARLIC UNTIL TRANSLUCENT. **2. ADD** BEEF BROTH OR STOCK AND THE POLISH COIL OR PEPPERONI. **3. SAUTÉ** FOR 2 MINUTES. **4. ADD** THE DICED TOMATOES AND FROZEN VEGETABLES AND COOK UNTIL THEY BEGIN TO SOFTEN (15-20 MINUTES).

Serve with goat cheese on top.

PER SERVING: 729 CALORIES // 43G FAT // 40G PROTEIN // 12G CARBOHYDRATE

CHICKEN & MOZZARELLA
Salad

24 **OUNCES** CHICKEN BREASTS, BONELESS, SKINLESS

1 **TEASPOON** HOT PAPRIKA

2 **CUPS** TOMATOES, CUBED

2 **CUPS** CUCUMBERS, CUBED

1 **CUP** RED PEPPERS, CUBED

3 **CUPS** LETTUCE GREENS, ROMAINE, ARUGULA, LEAF

1/2 **CUP** GREEN ONIONS, CHOPPED

1 **TABLESPOON** FRESH BASIL, CHOPPED

1 **TABLESPOON** FRESH CILANTRO, CHOPPED

2 **TABLESPOONS** GRAPE SEED OIL

1/2 **CUP** MOZZARELLA CHEESE, CUBED

2 **OUNCES** LOW FAT LOW CARB HOUSE DRESSING (*SEE PAGE 95*)

SEA SALT & PEPPER TO TASTE

READY TO COOK

1. **CUT** THE CHICKEN INTO 1" STRIPS.

2. **SEASON** WITH SEA SALT & PEPPER TO TASTE AND PAPRIKA AND COOK IN 1 TABLESPOON OF GRAPE SEED OIL UNTIL THE CHICKEN IS DONE.

3. **DRAIN** AND KEEP WARM.

4. **IN** A LARGE BOWL, COMBINE THE TOMATOES, CUCUMBERS, RED PEPPERS, GREEN ONIONS AND LETTUCE GREENS.

5. **ADD** THE BASIL AND CILANTRO AND TOSS WITH LOW FAT LOW CARB HOUSE DRESSING.

6. **ADD** THE COOKED CHICKEN STRIPS AND TOSS LIGHTLY.

7. **ADD** THE CUBED CHEESE AND TOSS AGAIN.

Serve immediately.

PER SERVING: 472 CALORIES // 22G FAT // 54G PROTEIN // 9G CARBOHYDRATE

CELERY & STILTON SOUP
with Scallop Skewers

20 OUNCES SCALLOPS

1 TABLESPOON LEMON JUICE

8 SKEWERS

2 CUPS CHERRY TOMATOES, WHOLE

5 CUPS CELERY, CHOPPED

1 CUP GREEN ONIONS, CHOPPED

1/4 CUP WALNUTS

4 TEASPOONS GRAPE SEED OIL

2 TEASPOONS FLOUR

4 CUPS CHICKEN OR VEGETABLE BROTH

1/4 CUP BLUE STILTON CHEESE

SEA SALT & PEPPER TO TASTE

READY TO COOK

1. **HEAT** 2 TEASPOONS OF THE OIL IN A SOUP PAN AND SAUTÉ THE CELERY UNTIL SOFT.

2. **REDUCE** HEAT AND STIR IN THE WALNUTS.

3. **ADD** THE FLOUR AND STIR QUICKLY, ADDING A LITTLE OF THE CHICKEN OR VEGETABLE BROTH TO KEEP LUMPS FROM FORMING.

4. **CONTINUE** TO STIR AS YOU ADD THE REMAINDER OF THE BROTH. BRING TO A BOIL. REDUCE HEAT IMMEDIATELY AND SIMMER FOR 20 MINUTES.

5. **ADD** SEA SALT AND PEPPER. BLEND UNTIL SMOOTH. RETURN THE SOUP TO THE SOUP PAN AND REHEAT. STIR IN THE STILTON CHEESE.

6. **PREHEAT** THE OVEN GRILL TO MEDIUM-HIGH.

7. **THREAD** THE SCALLOPS AND TOMATOES ON TO THE SKEWERS.

8. **BRUSH** WITH THE REMAINING 2 TEASPOONS OF OIL AND PLACE ONTO THE GRILL.

9. **GRILL** FOR 2-3 MINUTES PER SIDE, TURNING ONCE. DO NOT OVERCOOK.

10. **REMOVE** THE SKEWERS FROM THE OVEN AND DRIZZLE THE LEMON JUICE OVER THE SCALLOPS.

Serve 2 skewers on each bowl of soup with green onions on top.

VERATITRICK
SOAK YOUR SKEWERS BEFORE YOU LOAD THEM UP!

PER SERVING: 610 CALORIES // 28G FAT // 68G PROTEIN // 9G CARBOHYDRATE

CHEF
VERATI.

If there are no challenges, there is no creativity.... This was our first attempt.... and it was not our last....
-Chef Verati

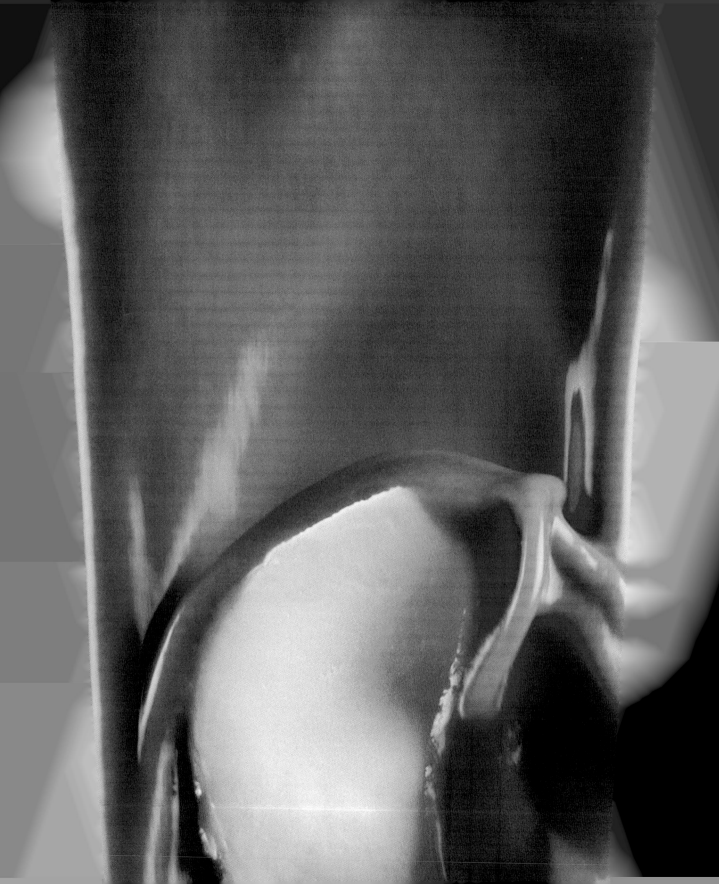

RED VELVET FALLS
over Goat Cheese

20 OUNCES SCALLOPS

4 OUNCES SOFT GOAT CHEESE

1 CUP BLACK OLIVES

4 BOSTON LETTUCE LEAVES

7 CUPS SWEET RED PEPPERS, CHOPPED

1 CUP GREEN ONIONS, CHOPPED

2 CLOVES GARLIC, CHOPPED

3 CUPS CHICKEN STOCK

1 CUP MILK

1 TABLESPOON TOMATO PASTE

1 TEASPOON OREGANO

1 TEASPOON GRAPE SEED OIL

2 TEASPOONS LEMON JUICE

SEA SALT & PEPPER TO TASTE

READY TO COOK

1. HEAT 1 TABLESPOON OF THE OIL IN A LARGE PAN AND GENTLY SAUTÉ THE GARLIC AND ONIONS UNTIL JUST SOFT.

2. ADD THE RED PEPPERS AND THE TOMATO PASTE AND COOK ANOTHER 2-3 MINUTES.

3. ADD THE CHICKEN STOCK, OREGANO, SEA SALT AND PEPPER. SIMMER 20 MINUTES,

4. ONCE THE RED PEPPERS ARE SOFT. ADD THE GOAT CHEESE AND MILK AND HEAT ANOTHER 1-2 MINUTES.

5. PLACE ALL THE INGREDIENTS IN A BLENDER AND PROCESS IN BATCHES UNTIL SMOOTH. RETURN TO THE PAN AND REHEAT.

6. HEAT THE REMAINING TABLESPOON OF OIL IN A FRYING PAN ON MEDIUM-HIGH HEAT.

7. SEASON THE SCALLOPS WITH LEMON JUICE AND COOK FOR ABOUT 2 MINUTES PER SIDE, TURNING TO BROWN.

8. PLACE 1 LETTUCE LEAF ON EACH OF 4 PLATES.

9. HEAP 1/4 OF THE SCALLOPS ON THE LETTUCE LEAF AND PLACE BLACK OLIVES AROUND THE EDGES OF THE PLATES.

SERVE PIPING HOT.

ENJOY YOUR SOUP...

HOT FOODS MAKE YOU FEEL FULL!

PER SERVING: 686 CALORIES // 39G FAT // 39G PROTEIN // 14G CARBOHYDRATE

TOMATO & ORANGE SOUP
with Turkey Patties

20 OUNCES GROUND TURKEY	**4 CUPS** VEGETABLE BROTH OR WATER
4 SLICES OF BACON	**1 TEASPOON** THYME
1 TABLESPOON GRAPE SEED OIL	**2 TEASPOONS** DRIED PARSLEY
6 CUPS TOMATOES, PEELED & QUARTERED	**1/4 TEASPOON** CHILI PEPPER
1 CUP GREEN ONIONS, FINELY CHOPPED	**8 TEASPOONS** SOUR CREAM
2 CLOVES GARLIC, FINELY CHOPPED	**1 TABLESPOON** ORANGE, ZESTED
1 CUP CELERY, CHOPPED	SEA SALT & PEPPER TO TASTE

READY TO COOK

1. **COOK** THE BACON IN A PAN UNTIL CRISP. REMOVE FROM THE PAN.

2. **POUR** A SMALL AMOUNT OF THE COOKING OIL ON AN OVEN TRAY AND SPREAD ON THE SURFACE.

3. **IN** A BOWL, COMBINE THE GROUND TURKEY, CHOPPED BACON, SEA SALT AND 1 TEASPOON DRIED PARSLEY.

4. **FORM** THE TURKEY MIXTURE INTO 4 BURGER PATTIES AND PLACE THEM ON THE OILED OVEN TRAY.

5. **BAKE** AT **350°F** ABOUT 10 MINUTES PER SIDE, TURNING ONCE, OR UNTIL THE TURKEY IS COOKED.

6. **HEAT** THE REMAINING TABLESPOON OF OIL IN A SOUP PAN AND SAUTÉ THE GARLIC UNTIL SOFT.

7. **ADD** THE TOMATOES, CELERY AND VEGETABLE BROTH OR WATER. ADD THYME, REMAINING TEASPOON OF PARSLEY, SEA SALT AND CHILI PEPPER AND SIMMER 15 MINUTES.

8. **STIR** IN THE ORANGE ZEST. REMOVE FROM HEAT AND BLEND IN BLENDER UNTIL SMOOTH.

Serve with a spoonful of sour cream in each bowl of soup and on each turkey patty.

WARM SNOW PEA SALAD
with Chicken Skewers

2 CUPS FRESH MUSHROOMS, SLICED	**1/2 CUP** FETA CHEESE, CRUMBLED
2 CUPS FRESH SNOW PEAS, STRINGS REMOVED	**1/4 CUP** PECANS, CHOPPED
1 CUP SWEET RED PEPPERS, CUBED	**24 OUNCES** CHICKEN BREASTS, BONELESS, SKINLESS & CUBED
4 CLOVES GARLIC, FINELY CHOPPED OR MINCED	**8** SKEWERS
4 CUPS FRESH WATERCRESS	**1 TEASPOON** OREGANO
1/4 CUP RICE VINEGAR	**1 TEASPOON** MARJORAM
2 TEASPOON GRAPE SEED OIL	SEA SALT & PEPPER TO TASTE

READY TO COOK

1. **IN** A BOWL, COMBINE THE OREGANO, MARJORAM, SEA SALT AND PEPPER. ROLL THE CHICKEN CUBES IN THE HERBS UNTIL WELL COATED.

2. **THREAD** THE CHICKEN PIECES ON THE SKEWERS ALONG WITH THE RED PEPPERS.

3. **GRILL** IN THE OVEN FOR 5 MINUTES PER SIDE OR UNTIL THE JUICES RUN CLEAR.

4. **REMOVE** FROM THE OVEN AND KEEP WARM.

5. **SAUTÉ** MUSHROOMS FOR 2 MINUTES IN OIL OR BUTTER.

6. **REMOVE** FROM PAN. SAUTÉ GARLIC UNTIL SOFT BUT NOT BROWN.

7. **ADD** THE SNOW PEAS AND CONTINUE TO COOK FOR 3-4 MINUTES. DO NOT OVERCOOK.

8. **ADD** MUSHROOMS BACK INTO THE PAN, ADD SEA SALT, AND STIR TO COMBINE.

9. **REMOVE** FROM HEAT AND PLACE IN SALAD BOWL.

10. **ADD** VINEGAR, WATERCRESS AND TOSS. SPRINKLE CRUMBLED FETA CHEESE AND CHOPPED PECANS OVER TOP.

Serve with 2 chicken skewers per person.

VERATITRICK
SOAK YOUR SKEWERS BEFORE YOU LOAD THEM UP!

PER SERVING: 536 CALORIES // 25G FAT // 57G PROTEIN // 10G CARBOHYDRATE

AVOCADO SALAD
with *Lime Vinaigrette*

24 OUNCES LARGE SHRIMP, DEVEINED & PEELED *(SEE PAGE 353)*

2 CLOVES GARLIC, FINELY CHOPPED

4 TEASPOONS GRAPE SEED OIL

4 CUPS ROMAINE LETTUCE, SHREDDED

1 CUP RED ONIONS, THINLY SLICED

1 CUP KALAMATA OLIVES, WHOLE

2 CUPS WHITE MUSHROOMS, THINLY SLICED

2 CUPS AVOCADO, SLICED

1 TEASPOON LIME, JUICE

1 TEASPOON GRAINY DIJON MUSTARD

2 TABLESPOONS LIME, ZEST

1/2 CUP FRESH PARSLEY, FINELY CHOPPED

SEA SALT & PEPPER TO TASTE

READY TO COOK

1. HEAT 2 TEASPOONS OF OIL IN A PAN.

2. SAUTÉ THE GARLIC UNTIL JUST SOFT.

3. ADD THE SHRIMP AND COOK UNTIL THEY TURN PINK.

4. REMOVE FROM THE HEAT AND SET ASIDE.

5. WHISK TOGETHER THE REMAINING OIL, LIME JUICE & DIJON MUSTARD.

6. IN A LARGE BOWL, COMBINE RED ONIONS, OLIVES, MUSHROOMS AND AVOCADO.

7. POUR THE OIL, LIME JUICE AND MUSTARD DRESSING OVER THE MIXTURE AND TOSS WELL.

8. DIVIDE THE LETTUCE AMONG 4 SERVING PLATES.

9. PUT 1/4 OF THE ONION, OLIVE, MUSHROOM AND AVOCADO MIXTURE ON EACH PLATE.

10. DIVIDE THE COOKED SHRIMP AMONG THE PLATES.

SERVE WITH A SPRINKLE OF LIME ZEST AND PARSLEY ON TOP.

PER SERVING: 447 CALORIES // 31G FAT // 36G PROTEIN // 9G CARBOHYDRATE

ITALIAN SAUSAGE
with Warm Spinach Salad

8 SAUSAGES, HOT ITALIAN

4 CUPS FRESH SPINACH, CHOPPED

8 STRIPS OF BACON

2 CUPS WHITE MUSHROOMS, THINLY SLICED

2 CUPS TOMATOES, CHERRY

1 TEASPOON OIL

2 CLOVES GARLIC, CRUSHED

2 TABLESPOONS WHITE VINEGAR

1/2 TEASPOON MUSTARD POWDER

1 TEASPOON DRIED THYME

SEA SALT & PEPPER TO TASTE

READY TO COOK

1. **HEAT** THE OIL IN A FRYING PAN.

2. **PRICK** THE SKINS OF THE SAUSAGES AND COOK UNTIL DONE (ABOUT 10-12 MINUTES)

3. **REMOVE** FROM THE PAN AND KEEP WARM.

4. **CUT** THE BACON INTO 1" PIECES AND COOK IN A FRYING PAN UNTIL CRISPY.

5. **REMOVE** FROM THE PAN AND DRAIN WELL.

6. **ADD** GARLIC AND COOK UNTIL GOLDEN BROWN.

7. **REMOVE** FROM THE PAN.

8. **PLACE** SPINACH IN A LARGE SALAD BOWL, ADD THE BACON, MUSHROOMS AND TOMATOES.

9. **IN** A SMALL SAUCEPAN, HEAT THE VINEGAR, MUSTARD POWDER, THYME, SEA SALT & PEPPER.

10. **POUR** THE HOT MIXTURE OVER THE SALAD AND TOSS.

Serve with the sausage.

PER SERVING: 658 CALORIES // 47G FAT // 40G PROTEIN // 6G CARBOHYDRATE

COBB SALAD
with Crisp Bacon and Blue Cheese Crumble

16 OUNCES CHICKEN BREASTS, BONELESS, SKINLESS

6 OUNCES BACON, CRISPY

4 EGGS HARD-BOILED

1 TEASPOON VINEGAR

1/2 CUP BLUE CHEESE, CRUMBLED

1 CUP ROMAINE LETTUCE, SLICED

1 CUP ICEBERG LETTUCE, SLICED

1 CUP WATERCRESS, CHOPPED

1 CUP FRESH TOMATOES, CHOPPED

1 CUP CHIVES, CHOPPED

2 CUPS AVOCADO, PEELED & SLICED

2 TEASPOONS GRAPE SEED OIL

1 TEASPOON SMOKED PAPRIKA

1/4 CUP MAYONNAISE

SEA SALT & PEPPER TO TASTE

READY TO COOK

1. **BOIL** A POT OF WATER AND COOK EGGS FOR 7-9 MINUTES.

2. **REMOVE** THE EGGS, COOL, PEEL AND CUT IN HALF.

3. **SET** ASIDE. CUT THE CHICKEN BREAST INTO 1/2" STRIPS.

4. **SEASON** WITH SEA SALT, PEPPER AND PAPRIKA.

5. **HEAT** THE OIL IN A FRYING PAN AND STIR-FRY THE CHICKEN STRIPS UNTIL DONE.

6. **REMOVE** FROM THE HEAT AND SET ASIDE.

7. **CUT** THE BACON INTO 1" PIECES AND COOK UNTIL CRISP.

8. **DRAIN** ON PAPER TOWEL AND SET ASIDE.

9. **IN** A LARGE BOWL, COMBINE THE ROMAINE AND ICEBERG LETTUCE, THE WATERCRESS, TOMATOES, CHIVES AND AVOCADO SLICES.

10. **FOLD** IN THE BACON, CHICKEN BREAST STRIPS AND BLUE CHEESE.

11. **TOSS** WITH MAYONNAISE.

Serve with cut hard boiled eggs over top of the salad.

PER SERVING: 632 CALORIES // 39G FAT // 60G PROTEIN // 7G CARBOHYDRATE

ANTIPASTO PLATTER
Chef Verati Style

2 CUPS FRESH ROMA TOMATOES, HALVED LENGTHWISE

1 CUP WHOLE MARINATED MUSHROOMS

1 JAR ARTICHOKE HEARTS, IN OIL

1 CUP KALAMATA OLIVES

2 CUPS ENGLISH CUCUMBER, PEELED & SLICED

4 HARD-BOILED EGGS, HALVED

16 OUNCES PROSCIUTTO, FINELY SLICED

1 CUP PICKLED EGGPLANT

SEA SALT & PEPPER TO TASTE

READY TO COOK

1. GROUP EACH INGREDIENT ON A LARGE PLATTER, MAKING SEPARATE SECTIONS IN A CIRCULAR FASHION AROUND THE PLATTER.

Serve directly on the table.

VERATI *Twist*
LET YOUR IMAGINATION RUN WILD. A VISIT TO THE DELI SECTION
OF YOUR GROCERY STORE MAKES THIS SALAD A SNAP.

PER SERVING: 670 CALORIES // 39G FAT // 36G PROTEIN // 14G CARBOHYDRATE

FENNEL SALAD
with Grilled Chicken Skewers

4 CUPS FENNEL, FINELY SLICED	**8** SKEWERS
1 TABLESPOON LEMON JUICE	**1 TEASPOON** GROUND CUMIN
3 TABLESPOONS GRAPE SEED OIL	**1 TEASPOON** GROUND CORIANDER
1 CUP RED ONIONS, FINELY SLICED	**1 TEASPOON** CURRY POWDER
1 CUP TOMATOES, DICED	**1 TEASPOON** GARLIC SALT
1 CUP SWEET RED PEPPERS, DICED	**1 TEASPOON** DIJON MUSTARD
1 CUP CUCUMBERS, DICED	**1 TEASPOON** PAPRIKA
4 EGGS, HARD-BOILED	SEA SALT & PEPPER TO TASTE
16 OUNCES CHICKEN BREASTS, BONELESS & SKINLESS	

READY TO COOK

1. **BOIL** THE EGGS FOR 10 MINUTES, REMOVE FROM HEAT, PLACE IN COLD WATER TO COOL AND REMOVE THE SHELLS.

2. **CUT** THE EGGS IN HALF LENGTHWISE AND SET ASIDE.

3. **WHISK** TOGETHER THE LEMON JUICE, 3 TABLESPOONS OF OIL, SEA SALT, PEPPER AND THE DIJON MUSTARD AND POUR OVER THE FENNEL.

4. **COMBINE** THE ONIONS, TOMATOES, RED PEPPERS AND CUCUMBERS AND ADD TO THE FENNEL.

5. **ALLOW** TO MARINATE WHILE YOU PREPARE THE CHICKEN SKEWERS.

6. **CUT** THE CHICKEN BREASTS INTO THIN STRIPS.

7. **COMBINE** THE CUMIN, CORIANDER, GARLIC SALT AND CURRY POWDER IN A SHALLOW BOWL AND COAT THE CHICKEN STRIPS WITH THE HERBS.

8. **THREAD** THE STRIPS ONTO THE SKEWERS AND GRILL IN THE OVEN FOR 5 MINUTES EACH SIDE OR UNTIL THE CHICKEN IS COOKED.

9. **DIVIDE** THE FENNEL AMONG 4 PLATES. PLACE 2 CHICKEN SKEWERS ON EACH PLATE ALONG WITH 2 EGG HALVES.

Sprinkle paprika over the eggs when serving.

VERATITRICK

SOAK YOUR SKEWERS BEFORE YOU LOAD THEM UP!

PER SERVING: 406 CALORIES // 31G FAT // 43G PROTEIN // 12G CARBOHYDRATE

MARINATED VEGETABLE
and Shrimp Salad

24 OUNCES SMALL SHRIMP, COOKED

1 CUP FETA CHEESE, CRUMBLED

1/2 CUP CELERY ROOT, FINELY JULIENNED

1/2 CUP BROCCOLI, FLORETS

1/2 CUP CAULIFLOWER, FLORETS

1/2 CUP RED CABBAGE, FINELY SLICED

1 CUP SWEET RED PEPPERS, FINELY SLICED

1 CUP GREEN ONIONS, FINELY CHOPPED

1 CLOVE GARLIC, FINELY CHOPPED

4 CUPS CHERRY TOMATOES, HALVED

4 TABLESPOONS CIDER VINEGAR

4 TABLESPOONS GRAPE SEED OIL

1 TEASPOON CURRY POWDER

SEA SALT & PEPPER TO TASTE

READY TO COOK

1. **BRING** A POT OF WATER AND COOK THE BROCCOLI AND CAULIFLOWER FOR 3 MINUTES.

2. **DRAIN,** RINSE WITH COLD WATER AND DRAIN AGAIN.

3. **PLACE** THE CABBAGE, RED PEPPERS, GREEN ONIONS, GARLIC AND CHERRY TOMATOES IN A LARGE BOWL.

4. **ADD** THE CELERY ROOT, CAULIFLOWER AND BROCCOLI AND TOSS TO MIX.

5. **WHISK** WHISK TOGETHER THE CIDAR VINEGAR, OIL, CURRY POWDER, SEA SALT AND PEPPER.

6. **POUR** THE MIXTURE OVER THE VEGETABLES, ADD THE SHRIMP AND TOSS WELL.

7. **COVER** AND ALLOW TO MARINATE IN THE REFRIGERATOR FOR 3-4 HOURS.

Serve chilled.

PER SERVING: 412 CALORIES; 29G FAT; 38G PROTEIN; 12G CARBOHYDRATE

SPICY CHICKEN
and Cabbage Soup

20 OUNCES GROUND CHICKEN	**7 CUPS** CHICKEN BROTH OR STOCK
3 CUPS CHINESE CABBAGE, FINELY CHOPPED	**4 TABLESPOONS** FRESH GINGER, GRATED
2 CUPS GREEN ONIONS, FINELY CHOPPED	**2 TEASPOONS** CHINESE GARLIC CHILI SAUCE
2 CLOVES GARLIC, FINELY CHOPPED	**1/2 CUP** FRESH CILANTRO, CHOPPED
1 CUP SWEET RED PEPPERS, CHOPPED	**4 TABLESPOONS** FISH SAUCE (*OPTIONAL*)
1 CUP CELERY, CHOPPED	**1 TABLESPOON** GRAPE SEED OIL
1 CUP FRESH TOMATOES, CHOPPED	SEA SALT & PEPPER TO TASTE

READY TO COOK

1. **IN** A LARGE POT, HEAT THE OIL AND SAUTÉ THE GROUND CHICKEN UNTIL IT BEGINS TO BROWN.

2. **REMOVE** FROM THE PAN AND DRAIN ANY EXCESS FAT.

3. **IN** THE REMAINING OIL, SAUTÉ THE ONIONS AND GARLIC FOR 2-3 MINUTES.

4. **ADD** THE CHICKEN BACK INTO THE PAN AND ADD THE CABBAGE, RED PEPPERS, CELERY AND TOMATOES.

5. **SIMMER** 10-15 MINUTES, STIRRING OCCASIONALLY.

6. **ADD** THE CHICKEN BROTH, GINGER, GARLIC, CHILI SAUCE, FISH SAUCE (IF USING), SEA SALT AND PEPPER.

7. **COVER** AND SIMMER FOR 25 MINUTES.

Serve with the chopped cilantro over top.

IF YOU DON'T EAT YOUR VEGETABLES NO DESSERT!!

PER SERVING: 557 CALORIES // 35G FAT // 52G PROTEIN // 8G CARBOHYDRATE

SATAY CHICKEN SKEWERS
with Spinach Soup

20 OUNCES CHICKEN, BONELESS, SKINLESS, SLICED

8 SKEWERS

2 TABLESPOONS LEMON JUICE

4 TABLESPOONS COCONUT MILK

4 TABLESPOONS YOGURT

1 TABLESPOON PEANUT BUTTER

6 CUPS FRESH SPINACH

1 CUP GREEN ONIONS, CHOPPED

1 CUP CAULIFLOWER, CHOPPED

2 CLOVES GARLIC, CHOPPED

3 CUPS CHICKEN OR VEGETABLE BROTH OR STOCK

1/2 CUP CREAM

2 TEASPOONS GRAPE SEED OIL

SEA SALT & PEPPER TO TASTE

READY TO COOK

1. IN A SHALLOW BOWL, COMBINE THE LEMON JUICE, 1 TEASPOON OF THE OIL, THE COCONUT MILK, YOGURT AND PEANUT BUTTER, WHISKING WELL TO BLEND WITH THE PEANUT BUTTER.

2. MARINATE THE CHICKEN STRIPS IN THE MARINADE FOR 30 MINUTES.

3. THREAD THE CHICKEN ONTO THE SKEWERS RESERVING ANY REMAINING MARINADE.

4. PLACE THE SKEWERS ON A RACK OVER AN OVEN PAN AND POSITION UNDER THE OVEN BROILER AND GRILL 5 MINUTES PER SIDE, TURNING ONCE AND BASTING WITH THE REMAINING MARINADE.

5. HEAT 1 TEASPOON OF THE OIL IN A LARGE PAN. GENTLY SAUTE THE GARLIC UNTIL SOFT.

6. ADD THE CHICKEN OR VEGETABLE BROTH ALONG WITH THE SPINACH AND CAULIFLOWER, SEA SALT AND PEPPER. SIMMER FOR 15 MINUTES.

7. ADD THE CREAM AND COOK FOR ANOTHER 5 MINUTES.

8. PROCESS THE SOUP IN A BLENDER (IN BATCHES IF NECESSARY) UNTIL SMOOTH, CHECKING THE SEASONING AT THE END.

SERVE THE SOUP WITH 2 SKEWERS OF SATAY CHICKEN POSITIONED ACROSS THE BOWL AND GREEN ONIONS FOR GARNISH.

SOAK YOUR SKEWERS BEFORE YOU LOAD THEM UP!

PER SERVING: 554 CALORIES // 26G FAT // 68G PROTEIN // 8G CARBOHYDRATE

SMOKED HAM
Cabbage Salad

24 OUNCES	SMOKED COOKED HAM, SLICED
6 CUPS	GREEN CABBAGE, FINELY SLICED
1 CUP	RED ONIONS, FINELY SLICED
1 CUP	GREEN APPLES, UNPEELED, DICED
2 CLOVES	GARLIC, FINELY CHOPPED
1/2 CUP	CAPERS
1/2 CUP	FRESH PARSLEY, CHOPPED
1/2 CUP	FRESH CHIVES, CHOPPED
4 TABLESPOONS	GRAPE SEED OIL
1 TABLESPOON	DIJON MUSTARD
3 TABLESPOONS	CIDER VINEGAR
2 TABLESPOONS	RED WINE VINEGAR
	SEA SALT & PEPPER TO TASTE

READY TO COOK ⬇ ⬇ ⬇

1. COMBINE THE CABBAGE, RED ONIONS AND APPLES IN A LARGE BOWL. **2. WHISK** TOGETHER THE MUSTARD, OIL, CIDER AND RED WINE VINEGARS, SEA SALT AND PEPPER. **3. POUR** THE DRESSING OVER THE CABBAGE MIXTURE AND REFRIGERATE FOR 1 HOUR. **4. JUST** BEFORE SERVING ADD THE SMOKED HAM AND TOSS WELL.

Serve with red onions on top.

PER SERVING: 463 CALORIES // 29G FAT // 30G PROTEIN // 11G CARBOHYDRATE

WARM CHICKEN
Salad

24 OUNCES	CHICKEN BREASTS, SLICED
1 CUP	CELERY, FINELY CHOPPED
1 CUP	GREEN ONIONS, FINELY CHOPPED
1 TABLESPOON	CAPERS, CHOPPED
1 CUP	SWEET RED PEPPERS, CHOPPED
1 CUP	GREEN BELL PEPPERS, CHOPPED
1/2 CUP	MAYONNAISE
1/2 CUP	YOGURT
4 CUPS	CRISP BOSTON LETTUCE LEAVES (ABOUT 16 LEAVES)
1 TEASPOON	PAPRIKA
1 TABLESPOON	GRAPE SEED OIL
	SEA SALT & PEPPER TO TASTE

READY TO COOK ⬇ ⬇ ⬇

1. HEAT THE OIL IN A PAN. **2. SEASON** THE CHICKEN WITH SEA SALT, PEPPER AND PAPRIKA AND STIR-FRY UNTIL THE CHICKEN IS COOKED. **3. REMOVE** FROM THE PAN AND KEEP WARM. **4. COMBINE** THE ONIONS, CELERY, CAPERS, GREEN AND RED PEPPERS. **5. ADD** THE MAYONNAISE AND YOGURT AND MIX WELL. **6. DIVIDE** THE LETTUCE LEAVES AMONG 4 PLATES. **7. PUT** 1/4 OF THE VEGETABLE MIXTURE ON EACH PLATE. **8. DIVIDE** THE CHICKEN INTO EQUAL PORTIONS AND PLACE ON TOP OF THE VEGETABLES.

Serve warm or cold.

PER SERVING: 411 CALORIES // 17G FAT // 52G PROTEIN // 5G CARBOHYDRATE

SALAD DRESSINGS
Low Fat + Low Carb

#1 CITRUS FREEDOM ⬇⬇⬇

90 CALORIES // 10G FAT // 0.1 PROTEIN // 16G CARBOHYDRATE

1 LARGE NAVEL ORANGE
2 TABLESPOONS LEMON, JUICE
1 CLOVE GARLIC, MINCED
2 TABLESPOONS WHITE WINE VINEGAR

1/4 TEASPOON DIJON MUSTARD
12 TABLESPOONS GRAPESEED OIL
SEA SALT & PEPPER TO TASTE

#2 EASY OIL AND VINEGAR ⬇⬇⬇

90 CALORIES // 10G FAT // 0.0G PROTEIN // 0.1G CARBOHYDRATE

4 TABLESPOONS APPLE CIDER VINEGAR
12 TABLESPOONS GRAPESEED OIL
1 CLOVE GARLIC, MINCED

1/4 TEASPOON DIJON MUSTARD
SEA SALT & PEPPER TO TASTE

#3 FUN RANCH ⬇⬇⬇

17 CALORIES // 2G CARBOHYDRATE // 1G PROTEIN // 0.5G FAT

1/2 CUP FAT FREE MAYONNAISE
1 CUP LOW FAT BUTTERMILK
1 TEASPOON CHIVES, CHOPPED
1 TEASPOON PARSLEY, CHOPPED

1/4 TEASPOON GARLIC POWDER
1/4 TEASPOON ONION POWDER
SEA SALT & PEPPER TO TASTE

#4 CREAMY CUCUMBER ⬇⬇⬇

29 CALORIES // 2.6G CARBOHYDRATE // 0.8G PROTEIN // 1.1G FAT

2/3 CUP FAT FREE YOGURT
1/4 CUP LOW FAT MAYONNAISE
1 CUP CUCUMBERS, PEELED, SEEDED & FINELY CHOPPED

1/2 TEASPOON FRESH DILL, CHOPPED
SEA SALT & PEPPER TO TASTE

READY TO COOK

1. COMBINE ALL THE INGREDIENTS IN A BOWL. **2. REFRIGERATE** UNTILL READY TO USE. **3. ENJOY** 1 OUNCE AT A TIME!

*THESE ARE EASY RECIPES AND
A GREAT BASE FOR EXPLORATION... FEEL FREE
TO LET YOUR IMAGINATION GO WILD!
—CHEF VERATI*

CARBS

↓ ↓ ↓ ↓ ↓ ↓ ↓ ↓ ↓

FAT

best at dinner time

FACT #2

LOW CARBOHYDRATE

TO ACHIEVE A BALANCED LIFE-STYLE, YOU MUST INTRODUCE CARBOHYDRATES INTO YOUR DAILY DIET AS THEY ARE ESSENTIAL. LET'S INCLUDE WHOLE-GRAIN BREADS AND CEREALS IN OUR MENUS AND KEEP THE BAKED GOODS FOR THE FUN DAY!

BALANCE

Freedom

RED POTATO SALAD
with Fresh Dill and Sesame Shrimp

32 OUNCES SHRIMP, PEELED & DEVEINED *(SEE PAGE 353)*	**1 1/2 CUPS** GREEN ONIONS, FINELY CHOPPED
8 SKEWERS	**1 CUP** RED PEPPERS, CHOPPED
1 EGG WHITE	**2 TABLESPOONS** WHITE VINEGAR
1/2 CUP SESAME SEEDS	**1/2 CUP** LOW FAT MAYONNAISE
1/2 TEASPOON CAYENNE	**2 TABLESPOONS** OLIVE OIL
1/2 TEASPOON SESAME OIL	**1 TABLESPOON** LEMON ZEST, GRATED
4 CUPS RED POTATOES, PEELED & CUBED	**1/4 CUP** FRESH DILL, CHOPPED
1 1/2 CUPS CELERY, FINELY CHOPPED	SEA SALT & PEPPER TO TASTE

READY TO COOK

1. BOIL POTATOES UNTIL JUST TENDER, DRAIN AND REFRIGERATE UNTIL COLD. 2. CUT THE POTATOES INTO CUBES AND PLACE THEM IN A LARGE BOWL WITH THE CELERY, GREEN ONIONS, RED PEPPERS, SEA SALT AND PEPPER. 3. SPRINKLE WITH VINEGAR, MAYONNAISE AND OIL, ADD LEMON ZEST AND FRESH DILL AND MIX WELL. 4. REFRIGERATE UNTIL READY TO SERVE. 5. THREAD THE SHRIMP ONTO THE SKEWERS. 6. WHISK THE EGG WHITE WITH THE SESAME OIL UNTIL FLUFFY. 7. COMBINE THE CAYENNE AND THE SESAME SEEDS ON A SHALLOW PLATE. 8. DIP THE SHRIMP SKEWERS FIRST INTO THE EGG WHITE, THEN INTO THE SESAME SEEDS. 9. PLACE ON AN OILED OVEN RACK AND GRILL 5 MINUTES PER SIDE OR UNTIL THE SHRIMP ARE DONE. 10. SERVE SHRIMP SKEWERS WITH RED POTATO AND DILL SALAD.

▶ OH, SWEET POTATO
MASHED, FRIED, BAKED; POTATOES ARE COMFORT FOOD ON A PLATE. TASTES LIKE *Freedom*
A POTATO IS NOT NECESSARILY BAD FOR YOU, JUST BE CAREFULL WITH WHAT AND HOW YOU EAT IT!

PER SERVING: 489 CALORIES // 36G CARBOHYDRATE // 51G PROTEIN // 12G FAT

BEEF & VEGETABLE SOUP
with a Pinch of Parmesan

24 OUNCES LEAN BEEF, CUBED

2 CUPS CARROTS, PEELED & CUBED

2 CUPS POTATOES, CUBED

1 CUP CELERY, CUBED

2 CUPS ONIONS, FINELY CHOPPED

1 CUP GREEN PEPPERS, FINELY CHOPPED

4 CLOVES GARLIC, FINELY CHOPPED

2 CUPS TOMATO SAUCE

1 CUP COOKED KIDNEY BEANS

1/2 CUP PASTA, COOKED (*OPTIONAL*) (*SEE PAGE 215*)

1 TEASPOON DRIED OREGANO

1 TEASPOON DRIED MARJORAM

1 TEASPOON DRIED BASIL

8 CUPS WATER

1 TABLESPOON LOW FAT PARMESAN CHEESE

1 TEASPOON GRAPE SEED OIL

SEA SALT & PEPPER TO TASTE

READY TO COOK

1. **HEAT** THE OIL IN A LARGE SOUP POT AND SAUTÉ THE BEEF, ONIONS AND GARLIC FOR ABOUT 7 MINUTES.

2. **ADD** THE CARROTS, POTATOES, CELERY AND GREEN PEPPERS AND SAUTÉ ANOTHER 5 MINUTES.

3. **ADD** THE TOMATO SAUCE, BEANS, OREGANO, MARJORAM, BASIL, SEA SALT AND PEPPER AND SIMMER ANOTHER 5 MINUTES.

4. **ADD** THE WATER, COVER AND COOK, COVERED FOR 30 MINUTES.

5. **PLACE** ALL THE INGREDIENTS IN A LARGE POT AND BRING TO A BOIL.

6. **REDUCE** HEAT AND SIMMER APPROXIMATELY 45 MINUTES OR UNTIL THE VEGETABLES ARE COOKED.

7. **ADD** PASTA AND SERVE (*OPTIONNAL*)

Serve with a sprinkle of grated low fat parmesan cheese over top.

PER SERVING: 596 CALORIES // 39G CARBOHYDRATE // 60G PROTEIN // 11G FAT

CARROT & GINGER SOUP
with Cajun Grilled Shrimp

24 OUNCES SHRIMP, PEELED & DEVEINED (*SEE PAGE 353*)

8 SKEWERS

1 TEASPOON DRIED OREGANO

1 TEASPOON CAYENNE PEPPER

1 TEASPOON GRAPE SEED OIL

6 CUPS CARROTS, PEELED & CUBED

2 CUPS POTATOES, PEELED & CUBED

1 1/2" PIECE FRESH GINGER, PEELED & CHOPPED

1 CUP SKIM MILK.

6 CUPS WATER

SEA SALT & PEPPER TO TASTE

READY TO COOK

1. **COOK** CARROTS, POTATOES AND GINGER IN WATER UNTIL VEGETABLES ARE SOFT.

2. **BLEND** THE VEGETABLES IN BATCHES, ADDING PART OF THE COOKING LIQUID, A SMALL AMOUNT OF SEA SALT AND MILK TO EACH BATCH.

3. **WHEN** THE VEGETABLES ARE BLENDED, STIR AND ADJUST THE SEASONING BY ADDING MORE MILK OR ANY REMAINING COOKING LIQUID.

4. **BRUSH** THE DEVEINED AND PEELED SHRIMP WITH THE OIL.

5. **SEASON** WITH OREGANO AND CAYENNE PEPPER.

6. **PLACE** IN THE OVEN AND GRILL FOR 2 MINUTES PER SIDE.

Serve soup with 2 shrimp skewers across each bowl.

VERATI**TIPS**
WHEN BLENDING THE VEGETABLES, THE END PRODUCT SHOULD
BE FAIRLY THICK AND THE GINGER TASTE SHOULD BE NOTICEABLE.

PER SERVING: 383 CALORIES // 28G CARBOHYDRATE // 40G PROTEIN // 9G FAT

CRAB ON THE BEACH
Golden Rice Salad

1 CUP BASMATI RICE	4 TABLESPOONS LOW FAT MAYONNAISE
2-3 CUPS WATER	1 TABLESPOON LIME JUICE
16 OUNCES CRAB MEAT, CANNED & CHOPPED	1 TEASPOON DRIED BASIL
1 CUP GREEN ONIONS, CHOPPED	1 TEASPOON DRIED THYME
1 CUP SWEET RED PEPPERS, FINELY CHOPPED	1/2 CUP FRESH CILANTRO, CHOPPED
1 CUP CELERY, FINELY CHOPPED	1 TEASPOON TABASCO SAUCE
1 CUP RADISH, FINELY CHOPPED	3 CUPS BOSTON LETTUCE
1 CUP AVOCADO, CHOPPED	SEA SALT & PEPPER TO TASTE

READY TO COOK

1. COOK BASMATI RICE IN SALTED WATER.
2. COVER AND SIMMER ABOUT 20 MINUTES OR UNTIL THE RICE IS SOFT AND THE WATER ABSORBED.
3. TRANSFER TO A LARGE BOWL AND ADD THE CRAB MEAT, GREEN ONIONS, RED PEPPERS, CELERY, RADISH AND AVOCADO.
4. WHISK TOGETHER THE OIL, LIME JUICE, MAYONNAISE, BASIL, THYME, TABASCO, SEA SALT AND PEPPER.
5. POUR OVER THE RICE MIXTURE.
6. STIRRING WELL TO COMBINE.
7. FOLD IN THE FRESH CHOPPED CILANTRO.

SERVE SALAD WARM OR COLD ON BOSTON LETTUCE LEAVES.

MICROWAVE RICE IS EASY...
HIGH TEMPERATURE + 4 MINUTES INCREMENTS
ADDING MORE WATER IF NECESSARY.

PER SERVING: 362 CALORIES // 23G CARBOHYDRATE // 37G PROTEIN // 9G FAT

FRESH LOBSTER
on Quinoa Tabbouleh

24 OUNCES LOBSTER MEAT, COOKED

1 CUP QUINOA

2 CUPS WATER

1 CUP GREEN ONIONS, FINELY CHOPPED

2 CLOVES GARLIC, FINELY CHOPPED

2 CUPS CUCUMBERS, DICED

2 CUPS FRESH TOMATOES, DICED

3 CUPS FRESH PARSLEY, FINELY CHOPPED

1 CUP YELLOW BELL PEPPERS, DICED

1/2 CUP FRESH MINT, CHOPPED

3 TABLESPOONS LEMON JUICE

1 TABLESPOON LEMON ZEST, GRATED

1 TEASPOON SMOKED PAPRIKA

2 TABLESPOONS GRAPE SEED OIL

SEA SALT & PEPPER TO TASTE

READY TO COOK

1. **BOIL** THE WATER, ADD A PINCH OF SEA SALT AND COOK THE QUINOA.

2. **COOK** ON MEDIUM HEAT FOR 15-20 MINUTES OR UNTIL THE QUINOA IS SOFT.

3. **DRAIN** ANY EXCESS LIQUID AND SET ASIDE.

4. **WHISK** TOGETHER THE LEMON JUICE, LEMON ZEST, OIL, PAPRIKA, MINT, SEA SALT AND PEPPER.

5. **COMBINE** THE CUCUMBERS, TOMATOES, PARSLEY, YELLOW PEPPERS, GREEN ONIONS AND GARLIC IN A LARGE BOWL.

6. **POUR** THE LEMON JUICE AND OIL MIXTURE OVER TOP, MIX WELL AND REFRIGERATE FOR 1 HOUR.

7. **CUT** THE LOBSTER MEAT INTO SMALL PIECES.

Serve tabbouleh topped with pieces of lobster meat.

PER SERVING: 404 CALORIES // 38G CARBOHYDRATE // 31G PROTEIN // 11G FAT

SHRIMP SOUP
Chinese Style

24 OUNCES SHRIMP, PEELED & DEVEINED *(SEE PAGE 353)*		**1/2 CUP** FRESH CILANTRO, CHOPPED	
1/2 CUP CARROTS, GRATED		**2" PIECE** FRESH GINGER, PEELED & FINELY CHOPPED	
1 CUP RED PEPPERS, SLICED		**1 TEASPOON** CHINESE HOT CHILI SAUCE	
2 CUPS FRESH TOMATOES, DICED		**4 TABLESPOONS** CHINESE HOISIN SAUCE	
1 CUP CELERY, CHOPPED		**7 1/2 CUPS** WATER	
1 1/2 CUP GREEN ONIONS, CHOPPED		**2 TEASPOONS** CORN STARCH	
2 CUPS MUSHROOMS, SLICED		**4 OUNCES** VERMICELLI NOODLES	
2 CLOVES GARLIC, FINELY CHOPPED		**1 TEASPOON** GRAPE SEED OIL	
1/4 CUP BLACK BEAN SAUCE		SEA SALT & PEPPER TO TASTE	

READY TO COOK

1. **HEAT** THE OIL IN A SOUP PAN.

2. **ADD** THE MUSHROOMS, GARLIC AND GINGER AND SAUTÉ FOR 3-4 MINUTES.

3. **ADD** 7 CUPS OF WATER, SEA SALT AND PEPPER, CARROTS, RED PEPPERS, TOMATOES, CELERY AND BLACK BEAN SAUCE AND SIMMER ANOTHER 5 MINUTES.

4. **ADD** THE CILANTRO, HOT CHILI SAUCE, HOISIN SAUCE AND VERMICELLI NOODLES.

5. **COOK** AT MEDIUM TEMPERATURE FOR ANOTHER 10-12 MINUTES OR UNTIL PASTA IS DONE.

6. **ADD** THE SHRIMP AND COOK UNTIL THEY ARE PINK.

7. **DISSOLVE** THE CORNSTARCH IN 1/2 CUP WATER AND ADD TO THE SOUP, STIRRING CONSTANTLY.

8. **SIMMER** ANOTHER 3-4 MINUTES.

Serve in bowls with sprinkled green onions on top.

SEARED SCALLOPS
with Cucumber Salad

32 OUNCES LARGE SCALLOPS

8 SKEWERS

2 TEASPOONS GRAPE SEED OIL

3 CUPS CHERRY TOMATOES, WHOLE

4 CUPS ENGLISH CUCUMBERS, PEELED & SLICED

1 CUP GREEN ONIONS, FINELY CHOPPED

4 CLOVES GARLIC, FINELY CHOPPED

1/4 CUP HOT CHILI PEPPERS, SEEDED & FINELY CHOPPED

1/2 CUP FRESH MINT, CHOPPED

1/2 CUP FRESH CORIANDER, CHOPPED

1 CUP SWEET RED PEPPERS, FINELY CHOPPED

1 CUP GREEN PEPPERS, FINELY CHOPPED

1 TEASPOON LIME JUICE

1/8 CUP PEANUTS

SEA SALT & PEPPER TO TASTE

READY TO COOK

1. **PLACE** CUCUMBERS IN A LARGE BOWL AND ADD THE GREEN ONIONS, RED AND GREEN PEPPERS, GARLIC, HOT CHILI PEPPER, MINT AND CORIANDER.
2. **MIX** WELL, ADDING 1 TABLESPOON OF GRAPE SEED OIL AND LIME JUICE.
3. **REFRIGERATE** 30 MINUTES TO 1 HOUR.
4. **THREAD** THE SCALLOPS AND CHERRY TOMATOES ALTERNATELY ONTO THE SKEWERS. BRUSH WITH THE REMAINING GRAPE SEED OIL, SEASON WITH SEA SALT AND PEPPER AND PLACE ON A RACK IN A PRE-HEATED **425ºF** OVEN.
5. **GRILL** FOR 2 MINUTES PER SIDE OR UNTIL THE SCALLOPS ARE DONE.

Serve scallop skewers with cucumber salad topped with peanuts.

VERATITRICK
SOAK YOUR SKEWERS BEFORE YOU LOAD THEM UP!

PER SERVING: 339 CALORIES // 22G CARBOHYDRATE // 42G PROTEIN // 7G FAT

CHUNKY VEGETABLE
and Beef Soup

24 OUNCES LEAN GROUND BEEF	**2 CUPS** TOMATO JUICE
2 CUPS ONIONS, CHOPPED	**4 CLOVES** GARLIC, CHOPPED
1 CUP CARROTS, CHOPPED	**1 TEASPOON** DRIED OREGANO
1 CUP CELERY, CHOPPED	**1 TEASPOON** DRIED MARJORAM
2 CUPS POTATOES, CHOPPED IN 1" PIECES	**6 CUPS** WATER
1 CUP TURNIP OR SQUASH, CHOPPED IN 1" PIECES	**1 TEASPOON** GRAPE SEED OIL
1 CUP ZUCCHINI, CHOPPED	**4 TABLESPOONS** FRESH PARSLEY, CHOPPED
2 CUPS FRESH TOMATOES, DICED	SEA SALT & PEPPER TO TASTE

READY TO COOK

1. **HEAT** THE OIL IN A LARGE POT AND BROWN THE BEEF UNTIL IT LOSES ITS PINK COLOR.
2. **DRAIN** ANY EXCESS OIL FROM THE PAN AND ADD THE ONIONS AND GARLIC AND SAUTÉ FOR 2-3 MINUTES.
3. **ADD** THE CARROTS, CELERY, POTATOES, TURNIP OR SQUASH, DICED TOMATOES, TOMATO JUICE, OREGANO, MARJORAM, SEA SALT, PEPPER AND WATER.
4. **SIMMER** GENTLY FOR ABOUT 20 MINUTES OR UNTIL THE VEGETABLES ARE COOKED.
5. **ADD** THE ZUCCHINI AND COOK ANOTHER 5 MINUTES.
6. **ADJUST** THE SEASONING IF NECESSARY BY ADDING MORE SALT AND PEPPER.

Serve soup sprinkled with chopped parsley over top.

HOMEMADE SOUP IS A GREAT WAY TO MAKE USE OF LEFTOVER VEGETABLES.

PER SERVING: 515 CALORIES // 32G CARBOHYDRATE // 57G PROTEIN // 13G FAT

CHEF VERATI.

COOKING WITH MY FRIEND JOHN IS ALWAYS
A PLEASURE. WE SURE KNOW HOW TO BE PRODUCTIVE!!
-CHEF VERATI

TOMATO SOUP SPLASH
with Open-Face Tuna Sandwich

2 CANS CHUNK TUNA, PACKED IN WATER

1 GREEN APPLE, UNPEELED & FINELY CHOPPED

1/2 CUP GREEN ONIONS, CHOPPED

2 WHOLE GRAIN ROLLS, CUT IN HALF

2 TABLESPOONS LOW FAT MAYONNAISE

1 TEASPOON CURRY POWDER

6 CUPS FRESH TOMATOES, PEELED & DICED

1 CUP ONIONS, CHOPPED

2 CLOVES GARLIC, FINELY CHOPPED

1 CUP CARROTS, PEELED & CHOPPED

6 CUPS WATER OR VEGETABLE STOCK

2 TABLESPOONS PLAIN LOW FAT YOGURT

4 SPRIGS FRESH PARSLEY, CHOPPED

SEA SALT & PEPPER TO TASTE

READY TO COOK

1. **SAUTÉ** CHOPPED ONIONS AND GARLIC IN A LARGE PAN UNTIL SOFT.

2. **ADD** THE DICED TOMATOES, CARROTS AND WATER OR VEGETABLE STOCK.

3. **SIMMER** 20 MINUTES UNTIL CARROTS AND TOMATOES ARE COOKED.

4. **ADD** 2 TABLESPOONS OF PLAIN YOGURT.

5. **REMOVE** FROM HEAT AND BLEND OR PURÉE THE VEGETABLE MIXTURE UNTIL SMOOTH.

6. **DRAIN** THE CANS OF TUNA AND PLACE THE FISH IN A BOWL.

7. **MIX** IT WITH THE CHOPPED APPLE, GREEN ONIONS, MAYONNAISE AND CURRY POWDER.

8. **TOAST** THE WHOLE GRAIN ROLL HALVES AND SPREAD THE TUNA MIXTURE ON EACH OF THE ROLLS.

Serve the tuna sandwich with tomato soup topped with fresh parsley.

VERATITRICK
TO REMOVE SKIN, PLACE TOMATOES IN A POT OF BOILING WATER FOR A FEW SECONDS THEN USE A KNIFE TO REMOVE THE SKIN.

PER SERVING: 368 CALORIES // 38G CARBOHYDRATE // 27G PROTEIN // 10G FAT

POTATO SALAD
Farmer's Style

4 CUPS MEDIUM SIZE POTATOES, SLICED

4 EGGS, HARD BOILED

4 CUPS LEAN HAM, COOKED

4 CUPS ARUGULA

1/2 CUP SHALLOTS OR GREEN ONIONS, FINELY CHOPPED

1/2 CUP FRESH TARRAGON, FINELY CHOPPED

1/4 CUP CIDER VINEGAR

1 TEASPOON DIJON MUSTARD

2 TABLESPOONS CAPERS

2 TEASPOONS GRAPE SEED OIL

SEA SALT & PEPPER TO TASTE

READY TO COOK ⬇⬇⬇

1. BRING A POT OF WATER TO A BOIL, REDUCE THE HEAT AND BOIL THE SLICED POTATOES FOR 3-4 MINUTES. BE CAREFUL NOT TO OVERCOOK. **2. REMOVE** THE POTATOES AND RINSE WITH COLD WATER, DRAIN AND LEAVE TO COOL. **3. PUT** THE EGGS IN THE BOILING WATER AND COOK 7-9 MINUTES. **4. COOL**, SHELL AND WHEN THE EGGS ARE COOL ENOUGH TO HANDLE, CUT THEM IN HALF LENGTHWISE. **5. WHISK** TOGETHER THE CIDER VINEGAR, DIJON MUSTARD, GRAPE SEED OIL, SEA SALT AND PEPPER. **6. ADD** THE SHALLOTS OR GREEN ONIONS, TARRAGON AND CAPERS AND MIX WELL. **7. PLACE** A BORDER OF COOLED POTATOES AROUND THE OUTSIDE OF THE SERVING PLATE. **8. PLACE** THE ARUGULA IN THE MIDDLE.

Serve ham and two egg halves on top of the arugula and drizzle the dressing over everything.

PER SERVING: 482 CALORIES // 31G CARBOHYDRATE // 33G PROTEIN // 14G FAT

LENTIL & HAM
What a Soup

8 CUPS VEGETABLE STOCK OR BROTH

24 OUNCES COOKED HAM, CHOPPED

2 CUPS ONIONS, CHOPPED

4 CLOVES GARLIC, FINELY CHOPPED

2 CUPS CELERY, FINELY CHOPPED

2 CUPS POTATOES, PEELED & CUBED

1 CUP RED PEPPERS, FINELY CHOPPED

1 CUP CARROTS, CHOPPED

1 CUP DRIED PARSLEY, CHOPPED

2 CUPS COOKED LENTILS

1 TEASPOON GRAPE SEED OIL

SEA SALT & PEPPER TO TASTE

READY TO COOK ⬇⬇⬇

1. ADD THE ONIONS AND GARLIC TO THE PAN AND SAUTÉ IN GRAPE SEED OIL FOR 2-3 MINUTES, UNTIL THEY ARE SOFT BUT NOT BROWNED. **2. ADD** THE CELERY, POTATOES, RED PEPPERS, CARROTS, VEGETABLE STOCK OR BROTH, LENTILS, SEA SALT AND PEPPER. **3. SIMMER** FOR 20 MINUTES OR UNTIL THE VEGETABLES ARE COOKED. **4. WARM** THE HAM IN THE SOUP FOR ABOUT 2-3 MINUTES.

Serve soup sprinkled with parsley over top.

PER SERVING: 401 CALORIES // 27G CARBOHYDRATE // 36G PROTEIN // 12G FAT

HAM & PEA SOUP
Comfort Style

1 HAM BONE

1 ONION, UNPEELED & QUARTERED

2 **STICKS** CELERY, CUT IN HALF

2 CARROTS, CUT IN HALF

2 **CUPS** CARROTS, FINELY CHOPPED

8 **CUPS** WATER

2 **CUPS** ONIONS, CHOPPED

2 **CUPS** CELERY, LEAVES ON & FINELY CHOPPED

24 **OUNCES** RESERVED HAM, CHOPPED

2 **CUPS** YELLOW SPLIT-PEAS

SEA SALT & PEPPER TO TASTE

READY TO COOK ⬇ ⬇ ⬇

1. PLACE THE HAM BONE IN A LARGE POT OF WATER WITH THE ONION QUARTERS, CELERY STICKS AND CARROT HALVES.. **2. BRING** TO A BOIL AND SIMMER FOR 1-2 HOURS OR UNTIL ANY MEAT LEFT ON THE BONE IS READY TO FALL OFF. **3. DRAIN** THE LIQUID THROUGH A SIEVE, KEEPING THE LIQUID BUT DISCARDING THE BONE, ONION QUARTERS, CELERY STICKS AND CARROT HALVES. **4. REMOVE** ANY LARGER PIECES OF HAM AND PUT ASIDE. **5. POUR** THE LIQUID BACK INTO THE POT AND PLACE ON THE STOVE. **6. ADD** THE CHOPPED ONIONS, CELERY, CARROTS AND SPLIT PEAS. **7. SIMMER** THE SOUP FOR 45 MINUTES TO 1 HOUR OR UNTIL THE PEAS ARE VERY SOFT. **8. REMOVE** ONE CUP OF THE SOUP AND PROCESS IN A FOOD PROCESSOR OR BLENDER UNTIL SMOOTH. ADD BACK INTO THE SOUP AND REHEAT.

Serve this soup in a big ceramic pot in the center of the table.

PER SERVING: 454 CALORIES // 57G CARBOHYDRATE // 48G PROTEIN // 7G FAT

SEAFOOD QUICHE
with a Dash of Nutmeg

1 X 9" PREPARED PIE SHELL (*SEE PAGE 397*)

8 **OUNCES** SHRIMP, COOKED

8 **OUNCES** CRABMEAT, COOKED

10 EGGS, BEATEN

2 **CUPS** SKIM MILK

DASH OF NUTMEG

8 **CUPS** MIXED GREENS

2 **OUNCES** LOW FAT LOW CARB HOUSE DRESSING (*SEE PAGE 95*)

SEA SALT & PEPPER TO TASTE

READY TO COOK ⬇ ⬇ ⬇

1. BAKE PIE SHELL AT **350⁰F** FOR 15 MINUTES. **2. REMOVE** FROM OVEN AND ALLOW TO COOL FOR 10-15 MINUTES. **3. BEAT** THE EGGS WITH THE MILK, SEA SALT, PEPPER AND NUTMEG. **4. CUT** THE SHRIMP AND CRABMEAT INTO BITE-SIZED PIECES AND PLACE ON THE BOTTOM OF THE COOLED PIE SHELL. **5. POUR** THE EGG MIXTURE OVER THE SHRIMP AND CRABMEAT. **6. BAKE** AT 375 FOR ABOUT 20-30 MINUTES OR UNTIL THE EGGS ARE SET.

Serve quiche with green salad topped with low fat house dressing.

PER SERVING: 472 CALORIES // 31G CARBOHYDRATE // 35G PROTEIN // 17G FAT

CHEF
VERATi.
POACHING IS MY HEALTHY WAY
TO COOK MY EGGS!
-CHEF VERATI

BROCCOLI SOUP
with Poached Eggs

6 CUPS BROCCOLI, CUBED

2 CUPS POTATOES, PEELED & CUBED

2 CUPS FRESH SPINACH

6 CUPS WATER

1 CUP SKIM MILK OR VEGETABLE BROTH

8 EGGS

2 TEASPOONS VINEGAR

4 SLICES WHOLE GRAIN BREAD, TOASTED

1 TEASPOON PAPRIKA

1 TEASPOON BUTTER

SEA SALT & PEPPER TO TASTE

READY TO COOK ⬇ ⬇ ⬇

1. BRING 6 CUPS OF WATER TO A BOIL IN A LARGE POT AND ADD THE BROCCOLI, SPINACH AND POTATOES. **2. SIMMER** FOR 10-15 MINUTES OR UNTIL THE POTATOES ARE SOFT. **3. REMOVE** FROM HEAT AND ALLOW TO COOL FOR A FEW MINUTES. **4. BLEND** IN BATCHES, ADDING SOME OF THE COOKING LIQUID, SEA SALT AND A PORTION OF MILK TO EACH BATCH. **5. WHEN** THE VEGETABLES ARE BLENDED, STIR AND ADJUST SEASONING BY ADDING MORE SEA SALT IF NECESSARY AND THEN ADD THE BUTTER. **6. RETURN** THE BLENDED SOUP TO THE PAN AND REHEAT. **7. IN** A SHALLOW PAN, BRING ANOTHER 6 CUPS OF WATER TO A BOIL, ADDING THE VINEGAR. **8. GENTLY** POACH THE EGGS THEN PLACE 2 EGGS ON EACH SLICE OF TOASTED BREAD. **9. SPRINKLE** PAPRIKA OVER THE EGGS.

Serve soup with poached eggs on toast.

PER SERVING: 300 CALORIES // 28G CARBOHYDRATE // 22G PROTEIN // 10G FAT

APPLE COLESLAW
with Beef Skewers

24 OUNCES BEEF, SLICED

8 SKEWERS

2 TABLESPOONS SOY SAUCE

1/2 TEASPOON SESAME OIL

1 TEASPOON GROUND GINGER

1 ORANGE, JUICED

4 CUPS GREEN CABBAGE, CHOPPED OR THINLY SLICED

1 CUP GREEN ONIONS, CHOPPED

3 CUPS APPLES, CHOPPED

2 TABLESPOONS LEMON JUICE

1/2 CUP COLESLAW DRESSING, LOW FAT

1 TABLESPOON CARAWAY SEEDS

SEA SALT & PEPPER TO TASTE

READY TO COOK ⬇ ⬇ ⬇

1. COMBINE THE SOY SAUCE, SESAME OIL, GINGER AND ORANGE JUICE IN A BOWL. **2. ADD** THE BEEF AND MARINATE FOR 30 MINUTES. **3. THREAD** THE BEEF PIECES ONTO THE SKEWERS AND BROIL UNDER THE OVEN GRILL FOR 3 MINUTES PER SIDE. **4. IN** A LARGE BOWL, COMBINE THE CABBAGE, GREEN ONIONS, APPLES AND LEMON JUICE WITH COLESLAW DRESSING. **5. TOSS** WELL AND ALLOW TO SIT FOR 20-30 MINUTES. **6. DIVIDE** THE SALAD AMONG 4 SERVING PLATES. **7. ADD** 2 BEEF SKEWERS TO EACH PLATE.

Serve beef skewers sprinkled with caraway seeds and coleslaw on the side.

PER SERVING: 487 CALORIES // 29G CARBOHYDRATE // 54G PROTEIN // 12G FAT

CUCUMBER SOUP
with Smoked Fish

20 OUNCES	SMOKED SALMON
4 CUPS	CUCUMBERS, PEELED & CHOPPED
2 CUPS	CUCUMBERS, SKIN ON & CHOPPED
2 CUPS	WATER
3 HEADS	BOSTON LETTUCE, ROUGHLY CHOPPED
2 CLOVES	GARLIC, CHOPPED
3 TABLESPOONS	LIME JUICE
1 CUP	LOW FAT YOGURT
5 TABLESPOONS	FRESH DILL
1 TABLESPOON	FRESH MINT
4	CRUSTY BREAD ROLLS
	SEA SALT & PEPPER TO TASTE

READY TO COOK ⬇⬇⬇

1. BRING WATER TO A BOIL AND COOK THE LETTUCE FOR 2-3 MINUTES. **2. REMOVE** FROM THE HEAT AND DRAIN OFF HALF THE WATER INTO A SEPARATE PAN. **3. ADD** THE CUCUMBERS, GARLIC, LIME JUICE, YOGURT, DILL, SEA SALT AND PEPPER. **4. PROCESS** IN A BLENDER IN BATCHES, ADDING THE RESERVED WATER IF NECESSARY. **5. THE** SOUP SHOULD BE VERY SMOOTH. **6. AT** THIS POINT CHECK THE SEASONING AND ADD MORE SEA SALT AND PEPPER IF NECESSARY. **7. WHEN** ALL THE SOUP IS BLENDED, PLACE IN A LARGE BOWL IN THE REFRIGERATOR AND CHILL FOR 1 HOUR. **8. LADLE** THE SOUP INTO 4 BOWLS AND SPRINKLE SOME CHOPPED FRESH MINT ON TOP.

Serve with the smoked salmon and crusty bread rolls.

PER SERVING: 452 CALORIES // 48G CARBOHYDRATE // 39G PROTEIN // 8G FAT

EGG FU YUNG
with Vegetables

4	EGGS
16 OUNCES	SHRIMP, COOKED
2 CUPS	MUSHROOMS, SLICED
2 CUPS	WHITE PARTS OF LEEKS, SLICED
1 CUP	CELERY, FINELY CHOPPED
1 CUP	GREEN ONIONS, CHOPPED
2 CUPS	BEAN SPROUTS
1 TABLESPOON	LIGHT SOY SAUCE
1/4 CUP	CHICKEN OR VEGETABLE BROTH
1 TABLESPOON	CORNSTARCH
1 TABLESPOON	GRAPE SEED OIL
1/2 TEASPOON	SESAME OIL
	SEA SALT & PEPPER TO TASTE

READY TO COOK ⬇⬇⬇

1. HEAT HALF THE GRAPE SEED OIL IN A FRYING PAN AND SAUTÉ THE LEEKS AND CELERY UNTIL SOFT. **2. ADD** THE MUSHROOMS AND COOK ANOTHER 2-3 MINUTES. **3. STIR** THE CORN STARCH INTO THE BROTH. **4. ADD** THE BEAN SPROUTS, SOY SAUCE, COOKED SHRIMP AND BROTH AND COOK ANOTHER 2-3 MINUTES. **5. BEAT** THE EGGS UNTIL FLUFFY. **6. IN** ANOTHER PAN, HEAT THE REMAINING GRAPE SEED OIL ON **MEDIUM-HIGH** HEAT AND COOK THE EGGS UNTIL GOLDEN ON EACH SIDE. **7. REMOVE** FROM THE PAN AND CUT INTO STRIPS. **8. ADD** TO THE VEGETABLE AND SHRIMP MIXTURE.

Serve egg fu yung topped with green onions and sesame oil.

PER SERVING: 314 CALORIES // 24G CARBOHYDRATE // 38G PROTEIN // 9G FAT

SPICY LENTIL SALAD
with Smoked Turkey

1 CUP BROWN LENTILS	**2 CUPS** RED ONIONS, FINELY CHOPPED
2 1/2 CUPS WATER	**2 CUPS** CELERY, FINELY CHOPPED
1/2 CUP ONIONS, FINELY CHOPPED	**1 CUP** FRESH PARSLEY, FINELY CHOPPED
2 CLOVES GARLIC, FINELY CHOPPED	**2 CUPS** SMOKED COOKED TURKEY, CUBED
1/2 CUP CARROTS, DICED	**2 TABLESPOONS** GRAPE SEED OIL
1 TEASPOON FRESH THYME	**3 TABLESPOONS** VINEGAR
2 BAY LEAVES	**1 TEASPOON** CAYENNE PEPPER
2 CUPS SWEET RED PEPPERS, FINELY CHOPPED	**1 TEASPOON** GROUND CUMIN
2 CUPS GREEN BELL PEPPERS, FINELY CHOPPED	SEA SALT & PEPPER TO TASTE

READY TO COOK

1. **PUT** THE LENTILS, ONIONS, GARLIC, CARROTS, THYME AND BAY LEAVES IN BOILING WATER AND SIMMER FOR 25-35 MINUTES OR UNTIL THE LENTILS ARE SOFT.
2. **STIR** OCCASIONALLY, CHECKING THE WATER LEVEL AND ADDING MORE IF NECESSARY.
3. **WHISK** TOGETHER THE OIL, VINEGAR, CAYENNE PEPPER, CUMIN, SEA SALT AND PEPPER.
4. **COMBINE** THE CHOPPED RED PEPPERS, GREEN PEPPERS, RED ONIONS, CELERY AND PARSLEY IN A BOWL.
5. **POUR** THE OIL AND VINEGAR MIXTURE OVER THE VEGETABLES.
6. **ADD** THE PARSLEY, COOKED LENTILS AND SMOKED TURKEY.
7. **COMBINE** WELL.

Served very hot, it makes a beautiful winter dish.

BE ADVENTUROUS, EXPLORE NEW SPICES TO ADD FLAVOR TO YOUR DISHES.

PER SERVING: 569 CALORIES // 48G CARBOHYDRATE // 47G PROTEIN // 12G FAT

QUICK SHRIMP
Chowder

24 OUNCES SHRIMP, PEELED & DEVEINED *(SEE PAGE 353)*	**2 CUPS** MUSHROOMS, SLICED
1 CUP ONIONS, FINELY DICED	**1 TABLESPOON** GRAPE SEED OIL
1 CUP CELERY, FINELY DICED	**2 CUPS** SKIM MILK
1 CUP POTATOES, DICED	**2 CUPS** WATER
1 CUP SWEET RED PEPPERS, CHOPPED	**1 TABLESPOON** CORN STARCH
1 CUP GREEN BELL PEPPERS, CHOPPED	**2 TABLESPOONS** FRESH CILANTRO, CHOPPED
4 CLOVES GARLIC, FINELY CHOPPED	SEA SALT & PEPPER TO TASTE
2 CUPS FROZEN MIXED ORIENTAL VEGETABLES	

READY TO COOK

1. **HEAT** THE OIL IN A SOUP POT AND SAUTÉ THE ONIONS, CELERY, POTATOES AND GARLIC UNTIL SOFT.

2. **ADD** THE MUSHROOMS, PEPPERS, AND COOK ANOTHER 2-3 MINUTES

3. **COOK** FROZEN VEGETABLES IN ANOTHER POT UNTIL JUST TENDER, DRAIN AND ADD TO THE ONION MIXTURE.

4. **DISSOLVE** CORN STARCH IN THE WATER AND ADD TO THE SOUP POT.

5. **BRING** TO A BOIL AND IMMEDIATELY REDUCE THE HEAT TO SIMMER.

6. **STIR** IN THE MILK AND REHEAT.

7. **SEASON** WITH SEA SALT AND PEPPER TO TASTE.

8. **ADD** THE SHRIMP AND SIMMER UNTIL THE SHRIMP ARE HEATED THROUGH.

Serve chowder with fresh cilantro sprinkled over top.

VIETNAMESE SALAD
with Chicken

24 OUNCES CHICKEN BREASTS, SLICED

8 SKEWERS

1/2 TEASPOON CAYENNE PEPPER

2 CUPS GREEN ONIONS, CHOPPED

2 CUPS CUCUMBERS, DICED

4 MEDIUM CARROTS, GRATED

1 LARGE HANDFUL FRESH CILANTRO, CHOPPED

1 LARGE HANDFUL FRESH MINT, CHOPPED

2 CUPS COOKED VERMICELLI OR RICE NOODLES

2 LIMES, JUICED

2 TABLESPOONS CHINESE MIRIN

1 TEASPOON HOT CHILI PEPPER

1/2 TEASPOON SESAME OIL

SEA SALT & PEPPER TO TASTE

READY TO COOK

1. **THREAD** THE STRIPS OF CHICKEN ON SKEWERS AND SEASON WITH SEA SALT AND CAYENNE PEPPER.

2. **PLACE** ON AN OVEN RACK UNDER THE GRILL AND COOK FOR 5 MINUTES PER SIDE OR UNTIL THE CHICKEN IS DONE.

3. **BRING** A POT OF WATER TO A BOIL AND COOK THE VERMICELLI OR RICE NOODLES FOR ABOUT 3 MINUTES OR UNTIL SOFT.

4. **IN** A BLENDER, PROCESS THE LIME JUICE, MIRIN AND CHILI PEPPER.

5. **POUR** INTO A LARGE GLASS BOWL.

6. **ADD** NOODLES, CUCUMBERS, CARROTS, GREEN ONIONS, CILANTRO AND MINT AND TOSS WELL.

7. **SPRINKLE** SESAME OIL OVER THE MIXTURE.

Serve salad with 2 skewers of chicken per person.

VERATITRICK

SOAK YOUR SKEWERS BEFORE YOU LOAD THEM UP!

PER SERVING: 490 CALORIES // 37G CARBOHYDRATE // 51G PROTEIN // 11G FAT

CHEF
VERATI.

I NEVER SPILL ANYTHING! BUT MY ASSISTANT
ON THE OTHER HAND... WITHOUT HER
WE NEVER WOULD HAVE MADE THIS SHOT!
-CHEF VERATI

TARRAGON & MINT PEA SOUP
with Beef Tenderloin

20 OUNCES BEEF TENDERLOIN, CUBED	**1 TABLESPOON** CORNSTARCH
2 CUPS GREEN ONIONS, CHOPPED	**1/2 CUP** FRESH TARRAGON, CHOPPED
2 CUPS WHITE PART OF LEEKS, CHOPPED	**1/2 CUP** FRESH MINT, CHOPPED
4 CUPS FROZEN GREEN PEAS	**4** FRESH MINT LEAVES, WHOLE
2 CUPS CHICKEN STOCK	**2 TEASPOONS** GRAPE SEED OIL
2 CUPS SKIM MILK	SEA SALT & PEPPER TO TASTE

READY TO COOK

1. **HEAT** 1 TABLESPOON OF OIL IN A LARGE POT.

2. **SAUTÉ** THE LEEKS UNTIL THEY BEGIN TO SOFTEN, BUT NOT BROWN.

3. **ADD** THE PEAS AND THE CHICKEN STOCK.

4. **DISSOLVE** THE CORNSTARCH IN THE MILK, STIRRING UNTIL SMOOTH.

5. **ADD** TO THE POT AND SIMMER, COVERED FOR 25-30 MINUTES.

6. **COMBINE** THE GREEN ONIONS, TARRAGON, MINT, 1 TEASPOON OF SEA SALT AND 1/2 TEASPOON OF PEPPER AND COOK ANOTHER 2-3 MINUTES.

7. **HEAT** THE REMAINING TABLESPOON OF OIL IN A PAN UNTIL VERY HOT AND SEAR THE BEEF ON ALL SIDES.

8. **REMOVE** FROM THE HEAT WHEN MEAT IS MEDIUM RARE.

9. **DIVIDE** THE BEEF AMONG 4 SOUP BOWLS.

Serve beef topped with soup, each bowl garnished with one fresh mint leaf.

PASTA & VEGETABLE
Tuna Salad

2 CUPS SMALL PASTA (PENNE, MACARONI) *(SEE PAGE 215)*

2 CANS CHUNK TUNA

1/2 CUP PITTED OLIVES

2 CUPS CUCUMBERS, CUBED

2 CUPS RADISH, DICED

2 CUPS CARROTS, GRATED

2 CUPS SWEET RED PEPPERS, FINELY CHOPPED

2 TABLESPOONS LEMON JUICE

1 TEASPOON SOY SAUCE

1 TEASPOON DIJON MUSTARD

1 CLOVE GARLIC, FINELY CHOPPED

1/2 CUP SHALLOTS OR GREEN ONIONS, FINELY CHOPPED

1/2 CUP FRESH PARSLEY, FINELY CHOPPED

1/2 CUP FRESH BASIL, FINELY CHOPPED

4 TABLESPOONS LOW FAT MAYONNAISE

SEA SALT & PEPPER TO TASTE

READY TO COOK

1. **COOK** THE PASTA AND DRAIN.

2. **ADD** THE CUCUMBERS, RADISH, CARROTS, RED PEPPERS AND OLIVES.

3. **WHISK** TOGETHER THE LEMON JUICE, SOY SAUCE, MUSTARD, GARLIC, SHALLOTS OR GREEN ONIONS, PARSLEY, MAYONNAISE, SEA SALT AND PEPPER.

4. **BREAK** THE TUNA INTO PIECES AND ADD TO THE DRESSING. POUR THE DRESSING OVER THE PASTA AND VEGETABLES AND ALLOW TO REST AT ROOM TEMPERATURE FOR 15-20 MINUTES BEFORE SERVING.

Serve with a sprinkle of fresh basil.

BOSTON LETTUCE SALAD
with Lobster Meat

16 LEAVES BOSTON LETTUCE

16 OUNCES LOBSTER MEAT

2 CUPS YELLOW CHERRY TOMATOES, HALVES

2 CUPS RED CHERRY TOMATOES, HALVES

1 CUP SWEET RED PEPPERS, FINELY SLICED

1 CUP GREEN ONIONS, CHOPPED

2 CUPS CORN, CANNED

1/2 CUP CHIVES, FINELY CHOPPED

1/2 CUP FRESH TARRAGON, FINELY CHOPPED

1 TABLESPOON DIJON MUSTARD

1 TABLESPOON GRAPE SEED OIL

1/4 CUP LEMON, JUICED

1 TABLESPOON BUTTER

1 TEASPOON PAPRIKA

SEA SALT & PEPPER TO TASTE

READY TO COOK

1. IN A LARGE BOWL, COMBINE THE CHERRY TOMATOES, RED PEPPERS, CORN, GREEN ONIONS AND CHIVES.

2. WHISK TOGETHER THE MUSTARD, OIL, TARRAGON, LEMON JUICE, SEA SALT AND PEPPER.

3. ADD TO THE CHERRY TOMATO MIXTURE AND TOSS.

4. HEAT THE BUTTER IN A FRYING PAN.

5. SEASON THE LOBSTER MEAT WITH PAPRIKA AND COOK THE LOBSTER QUICKLY, TOSSING CONSTANTLY.

6. PLACE 4 LEAVES OF LETTUCE ON EACH OF THE 4 SERVING PLATES.

7. ADD 1/4 OF THE TOMATO AND DRESSING MIXTURE TO EACH PLATE.

8. DIVIDE THE LOBSTER AMONG THE 4 PLATES.

SERVE LOBSTER WITH A DASH OF LIQUID BUTTER OVER TOP.

PER SERVING: 299 CALORIES // 23G CARBOHYDRATE // 19G PROTEIN // 8G FAT

QUINOA SOUP
with Chicken and Eggs

1 **CUP** QUINOA

2 **CUPS** WATER

4 **CUPS** CHICKEN BROTH

16 **OUNCES** CHICKEN, CUBED

4 **EGGS**, HARD BOILED

1 **CUP** RED ONIONS, CHOPPED

2 **CUPS** WHITE PART OF LEEKS, CHOPPED

4 **CLOVES** GARLIC, FINELY CHOPPED

1 **CUP** KERNEL CORN

1 **CUP** SWEET RED PEPPERS, CHOPPED

3 **CUPS** MUSHROOMS, SLICED

1/4 **CUP** LEMON, JUICED

1 **TABLESPOON** LEMON ZEST

1 **TEASPOON** GROUND CUMIN

1 **TEASPOON** FRESH CORIANDER

1 **TEASPOON** HOT PAPRIKA

2 **TABLESPOONS** GRAPE SEED OIL

SEA SALT & PEPPER TO TASTE

READY TO COOK

1. **BOIL** THE EGGS, SHELL AND SET ASIDE.

2. **SEASON** THE CHICKEN CUBES WITH CUMIN AND CORIANDER AND STIR-FRY IN 1 TABLESPOON OF THE OIL UNTIL DONE.

3. **HEAT** THE REMAINING TABLESPOON OF OIL IN A LARGE POT AND SAUTÉ THE RED ONIONS, GARLIC AND LEEKS FOR ABOUT 4 MINUTES.

4. **ADD** THE MUSHROOMS, RED PEPPERS, CORN, SEA SALT AND PEPPER AND COOK ANOTHER 1-2 MINUTES.

5. **ADD** THE QUINOA, WATER, CHICKEN BROTH AND COOKED CHICKEN, INCLUDING THE COOKING JUICES, COVER AND SIMMER FOR 25-30 MINUTES.

6. **ADJUST** THE SEASONING IF NECESSARY BY ADDING MORE SEA SALT AND PEPPER AND ADD LEMON JUICE AND LEMON ZEST

7. **SLICE** THE HARD-BOILED EGGS AND DISTRIBUTE AMONG THE 4 BOWLS WHEN SERVING.

Serve soup with a sprinkle of paprika over top.

VERATI**TIPS**
THE QUINOA MUST BE RINSED THOROUGHLY IN WATER TO REMOVE THE COATING AROUND THE GRAIN WHICH IS SLIGHTLY BITTER.

PER SERVING: 552 CALORIES // 43G CARBOHYDRATE // 53G PROTEIN // 13G FAT

BLANCH VEGETABLES
How + Why

1 GALLON WATER

12 OUNCES VEGETABLES (LISTED BELOW)

ARTICHOKE - GLOBE HEARTS: 7 MINUTES
ARTICHOKE - JERUSALEM: 3-5 MINUTES
ASPARAGUS - SMALL STALK: 2 MINUTES
ASPARAGUS - MEDIUM STALK: 3 MINUTES
ASPARAGUS - LARGE STALK: 4 MINUTES
BEANS - GREEN, SNAP OR WAX: 3 MINUTES.
BEANS - LIMA, BUTTER OR PINTO - SMALL: 2 MINUTES
BEANS - LIMA, BUTTER OR PINTO - MEDIUM: 3 MINUTES
BEANS - LIMA, BUTTER OR PINTO - LARGE: 4 MINUTES.
BEETS - SMALL*: 30 TO 35 MINUTES
BEETS - MEDIUM*: 45 TO 50 MINUTES
BROCCOLI: 3 MINUTES.
BRUSSEL SPROUTS - SMALL HEADS: 3 MINUTES
BRUSSEL SPROUTS - MEDIUM HEADS: 4 MINUTES
BRUSSEL SPROUTS - LARGE HEADS: 5 MINUTES
CABBAGE OR CHINESE CABBAGE - SHREDDED: 1 1/2 MINUTES
CABBAGE OR CHINESE CABBAGE - WEDGES: 3 MINUTES
CARROTS - WHOLE: 5 MINUTES
CARROTS - DICED, SLICED, OR LENGTHWISE STRIPS: 2 MINUTES.
CAULIFLOWER: 3 MINUTES.
CELERY: 3 MINUTES

CORN-ON-THE-COB - SMALL EARS: 7 MINUTES
CORN-ON-THE-COB - LARGE EARS: 11 MINUTES
CORN - WHOLE KERNEL OR CREAM STYLE**: 4 MINUTES
EGGPLANT: 4 MINUTES
GREENS - COLLARDS: 3 MINUTES
MUSHROOMS - WHOLE (STEAMED): 9 MINUTES
MUSHROOMS - BUTTONS OR QUARTERS (STEAMED): 9 MINUTES
MUSHROOMS - SLICES (STEAMED): 5 MINUTES
OKRAS: 3 MINUTES
ONIONS: 3-7 MINUTES
PARSNIPS: 3 MINUTES
PEAS, SHELLED: 1-2 MINUTES
PEPPERS, SWEET - HALVES: 5 MINUTES
PEPPERS, SWEET - STRIPS OR RINGS: 3 MINUTES
POTATOES: 3-5 MINUTES
RAPINIS: 2 MINUTES
RUTABAGAS: 3 MINUTES
SNAP PEAS: 1 1/2 MINUTES.
SPINACH & ALL GREENS: 2 MINUTES.
SUMMER SQUASH: 3 MINUTES.
TURNIPS: 3 MINUTES

READY TO COOK

1. **WASH** THE VEGETABLES 2. **PEEL,** TRIM AND CUT VEGETABLES INTO UNIFORM SIZES. 3. **BRING** WATER TO A VIGOROUS BOIL 4. **PUT** VEGETABLES INTO A BLANCHER*** 5. **LOWER** VEGETABLES INTO BOILING WATER. 6. **KEEP** ON HIGH HEAT. 7. **WHEN** BLANCHING IS COMPLETE. PUT VEGETABLES IN COLD WATER TO STOP THE COOKING PROCESS.

* IF YOU LEAVE THE STEM ON TOP, THEY WON'T BLEED INTO THE WATER AS MUCH.
** EARS BLANCHED BEFORE CUTTING CORN FROM THE COB. ***WIRE BASKET OR METAL STRAINER.

BLANCHING IS AN EASY TECHNIQUE THAT MANY COOKS USE TO KEEP VEGETABLES CRISP AND TENDER. IT PRESERVES TEXTURE, COLOR AND FLAVOR.
-CHEF VERATI

TIPS
TRICKS

WRITE TO **CHEFVERATI@IDEALPROTEIN.COM**
FIND US ON **CHEF VERATI'S FACEBOOK PAGE**
VISIT **LOWFATLOWCARB.COM**

EAT

Best at lunch time

FACT # 3 ·· 139

A HEALTHY STACK PASTA FREE LASAGNA ············ 143

CHICKEN MARINATED IN YOGURT ····················· 145

ASIAN CHICKEN WITH GINGER ························ 146

OKRA CASSEROLE & SWISS CHARD ··················· 146

MUSHROOM SMOTHERED CHICKEN BREASTS ············ 147

OVEN BAKED CHICKEN LEGS ························· 147

STIR IT UP! ORIENTAL CHICKEN STIR-FRY ············ 151

PARMESAN CHICKEN WITH ROASTED RED PEPPERS ···· 152

SAFFRON PAELLA WITH SEAFOOD & ITALIAN SAUSAGE · 153

TOUCHDOWN GARLIC WINGS & VEGETABLE CHOW MEIN · 155

ECLIPSED...TURKEY STUFFED EGGPLANT ·············· 157

PARMESAN CRUSTED CHICKEN & CRUSTLESS MUSHROOM PIE 158

SPINACH STUFFED CHICKEN WITH LEMON-CREAM SAUCE 159

"CHILI STYLE" CHICKEN WITH MIXED VEGETABLES ···· 160

CHICKEN TAGINE WITH FRESH HERBS ················· 161

COMFORT IN A PLATE WITH CORNISH GAME HENS ····· 163

MUSTARD CRUSTED RABBIT LEGS WITH FENNEL ······· 165

CURRY KABOBS WITH VEGETABLES ··················· 166

BACON STUFFED CHICKEN BREASTS ·················· 166

BRAISED RABBIT WITH SAVOY CABBAGE ·············· 167

BUTTERMILK & PAPRIKA WITH GREEN BEANS ·········· 167

CHICKEN & SHRIMP FUNKY WRAPS ··················· 169

ROAST CHICKEN WITH BRUSSELS SPROUTS ············ 170

HOMEY CASSEROLE WITH LEEKS ····················· 170

FIERY CHICKEN WINGS WITH TURNIP CHIPS ··········· 171

MUSTARD CHICKEN & BRAISED ENDIVES ·············· 172

SPICE BLENDS / CHILI + CURRY + TAGINE ············ 173

CARBS
Best at dinner time

TURKEY BURGER A REAL ONE ······················ 177

SPLASH OF WINE COQ AU VIN ······················ 179

HERBED CHICKEN WITH VEGETABLES ················ 180

SPICY SLOPPY JOES WITH GREEN SALAD ············ 180

TURKEY A L'ORANGE WITH ZUCCHINI ················ 181

MOUNT CHICKEN WITH SIMMERED APRICOTS ·········· 183

CHICKEN & SWISS CHARD ROMANO BEAN CASSEROLE · 184

MEXICAN TURKEY TABBOULEH ······················ 185

GRANDMA'S CHICKEN & WHITE BEAN CASSEROLE ····· 187

CHICKEN PENNE WITH VEGETABLES ················· 188

BROWN RICE & CHICKPEA CHICKEN CASSEROLE ······· 188

SESAME CHICKEN WITH SNOW PEAS ················· 189

CHICKEN, MUSHROOM & LEEK PIE ···················· 189

SPICY CHICKEN STRIPS & BRUSSELS SPROUTS ······· 191

CREAMY CHICKEN & VEGETABLE STEW ··············· 192

CHICKEN WRAPS WITH BROWN RICE & LENTILS ····· 193

OPEN-FACED CHICKEN WHAT A SANDWICH! ·········· 195

DIJON CHICKEN WITH BUTTERNUT SQUASH ·········· 196

LEMON GINGER CHICKEN WITH RAPINI ··············· 196

YOGURT CHICKEN DRUMSTICKS ······················ 197

SATAY CHICKEN WITH PEANUT SAUCE ··············· 198

TURKEY SCALLOPINI WITH CAULIFLOWER ············ 199

HOISIN CHICKEN WITH COCONUT SAUCE ·············· 201

LEMON ROASTED WHOLE CHICKEN ···················· 202

CRISPY CHICKEN SAUTÉ WITH WALNUTS & BROWN RICE 203

MEDITERRANEAN STYLE CHICKEN STEW ·············· 204

SPICY BUTTERMILK MARINATED CHICKEN WITH COLE SLAW· 205

OVEN FRESH CHICKEN PIZZA ························· 207

TURKEY TETRAZZINI WITH LOW FAT PARMESAN CHEESE 208

CITRUS CHICKEN WITH WHOLE WHEAT COUSCOUS ···· 209

MAKE IT POP! GRILLED CHICKEN BREASTS WITH CORN
ON THE COB ··· 211

THE DAY AFTER...THANKSGIVING ····················· 212

LEFTOVER TURKEY SHEPHERD'S PIE ·················· 213

ROLL IT ! INDIVIDUAL SPINACH LASAGNA ·············· 214

PIZZA CRUST + FRESH PASTA // BASIC ············· 215

Each recipe serves four.

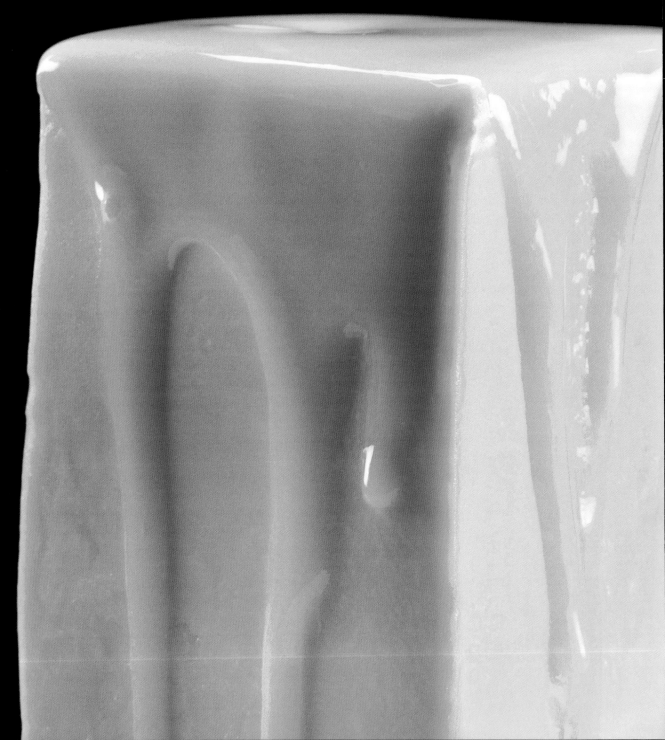

FAT

↓ ↓ ↓ ↓ ↓ ↓ ↓ ↓ ↓

CARBS

— *best at lunch time* —

FACT # 3

KNOW YOUR

ESSENTIAL FATS! IF IT SWIMS, IT'S AN OMEGA 3: LOVE THAT COLD WATER FISH. IF IT GROWS, IT'S AN OMEGA 6: THINK OF YOUR VEGETABLE OILS. YOU MUST KNOW WHAT YOUR EATING TO ASSURE PROPER INTAKE.

ESSENTIAL

CHEF
VERATi.

I can melt cheese beautifully for a meal...
Melting cheese for a photo shoot...That was a challenge!
Turn to the next page & see our perfect shot....
-Chef Verati

Pasta Free Lasagna

24 OUNCES TURKEY (4 BREASTS), BONELESS, SKINLESS & SLICED

4 ZUCCHINI, SLICED LENGTHWISE, NOODLE SHAPE

1 CUP GREEN ONIONS, FINELY CHOPPED

2 CLOVES GARLIC, FINELY CHOPPED

2 CUPS MUSHROOMS, SLICED

1 CUP SPINACH, CHOPPED

1 CUP TOMATO SAUCE

1 CUP FRESH TOMATOES, CHOPPED

1 CUP CHEESE (MOZZARELLA OR WHITE CHEDDAR)

1 TEASPOON BASIL

1 TEASPOON THYME

2 TABLESPOONS GRAPE SEED OIL

1 TABLESPOON BUTTER

4 CUPS MIXED GREEN SALAD

4 OUNCES LOW FAT LOW CARB HOUSE DRESSING (*SEE PAGE 95*)

SEA SALT & PEPPER TO TASTE

READY TO COOK

1. HEAT HALF THE OIL IN A PAN AND SAUTÉ THE GARLIC UNTIL SOFT, BUT NOT BROWNED. 2. ADD THE CHOPPED SPINACH AND COOK 1-2 MINUTES OR UNTIL THE SPINACH IS COMPLETELY WILTED. 3. ADD SEA SALT, PEPPER, BASIL AND THYME, GREEN ONIONS AND STIR TO MIX. 4. IN A SEPARATE PAN, HEAT THE REMAINDER OF THE OIL AND QUICKLY SAUTÉ THE TURKEY STRIPS. 5. REMOVE THE TURKEY AND COOK THE MUSHROOMS FOR 1-2 MINUTES. 6. ADD THE TURKEY TO THE PAN WITH THE ONIONS, GARLIC AND SPINACH. 7. BLANCH THE ZUCCHINI NOODLES UNTIL SOFT. 8. REMOVE AND COOL IN COLD WATER FOR 1 MINUTE. 9. WHEN THE NOODLES ARE COOL ENOUGH TO HANDLE, IN A PAN SMALL ENOUGH TO CONTAIN THE NOODLES SO THAT THEY JUST TOUCH ONE ANOTHER, SPREAD A LAYER OF ZUCCHINI NOODLES. 10. COVER THE ZUCCHINI NOODLES WITH A PORTION OF THE ONION, GARLIC, SPINACH AND TURKEY MIXTURE AND ALTERNATE LAYERS. 11. ONCE THE LAYERS ARE COMPLETED, SPREAD MUSHROOMS OVER TOP. 12. ADD THE FRESH CHOPPED TOMATOES AND POUR THE TOMATO SAUCE EVENLY OVER THE NOODLES. 13. TOP WITH THE CHEESE AND DOLLOPS OF BUTTER. 14. BAKE, UNCOVERED, IN A 350°F OVEN FOR 45 MINUTES UNTIL BUBBLY AND THE CHEESE IS MELTED. 15. SERVE WITH MIXED GREEN SALAD AND A LOW CARBOHYDRATE SALAD DRESSING.

▶SAY CHEESE

CHEESE CURDS, CHEESE DIPS, CHEESE SLICES; WHITE, BLUE OR YELLOW. OVER 900 KINDS; THAT'S *Freedom*
PRIORITIZE HARD CHEESES; AS THEY ARE LOWER IN FAT.

PER SERVING: 407 CALORIES // 25G FAT // 43G PROTEIN // 12G CARBOHYDRATE

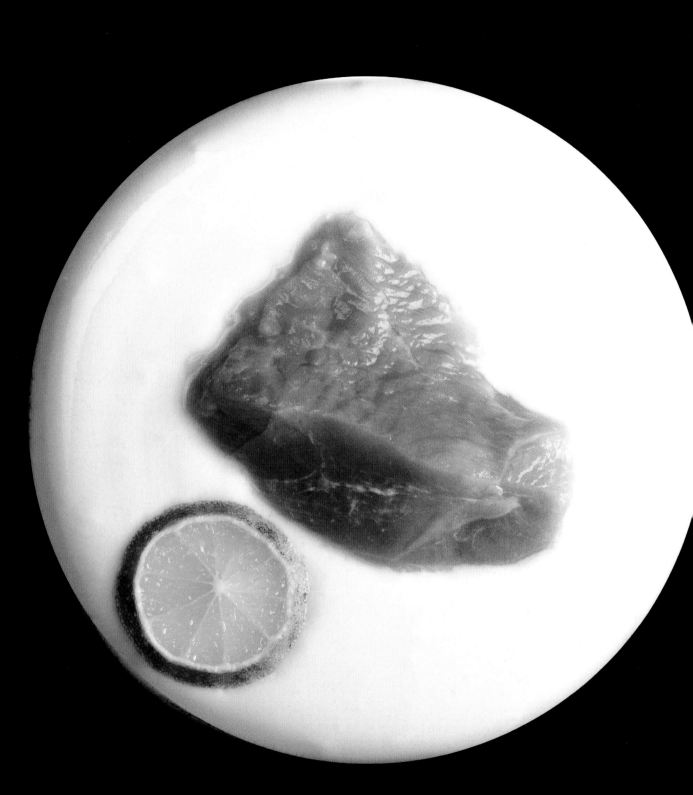

CHICKEN

Marinated in Yogurt

32 OUNCES CHICKEN THIGHS OR DRUMSTICKS, SKINLESS	1 TEASPOON DRIED CORIANDER
1 TEASPOON GRAPE SEED OIL	4 CUPS BROCCOLI, FLORETS
1 CUP PLAIN LOW FAT YOGURT	4 CUPS MUSHROOMS, SLICED
1 TEASPOON LIME JUICE	1/8 TEASPOON SESAME OIL
1 TEASPOON CURRY POWDER OR CURRY BLEND (SEE PAGE 173)	1 TEASPOON BUTTER
1 TEASPOON DRIED CUMIN	SEA SALT & PEPPER TO TASTE

READY TO COOK

1. MARINATE THE CHICKEN FOR 1 HOUR IN PLAIN YOGURT, LIME JUICE, CURRY POWDER, DRIED CUMIN, DRIED CORIANDER, SEA SALT AND PEPPER.
2. HEAT THE OIL IN A PAN.
3. REMOVE THE CHICKEN FROM THE MARINADE AND BROWN ON ALL SIDES.
4. PLACE ON A RACK IN THE OVEN AND BAKE AT 350°F FOR 20 MINUTES,
5. TURNING ONCE.
6. STEAM BROCCOLI UNTIL JUST TENDER ABOUT 4-5 MINUTES.
7. SAUTÉ MUSHROOMS 2 MINUTES IN BUTTER.
8. DRAIN THE BROCCOLI AND PUT THEM IN A SERVING BOWL WITH THE MUSHROOMS.

SERVE WITH A DASH OF SESAME OIL.

MARINATE OVERNIGHT, COVERED, IN YOUR REFRIGERATOR FOR BEST RESULTS!

PER SERVING: 555 CALORIES // 24G FAT // 69G PROTEIN // 10G CARBOHYDRATE

ASIAN CHICKEN
with Ginger

24 OUNCES	CHICKEN (4 BREASTS), BONELESS & SKIN ON
2 TABLESPOONS	GRAPE SEED OIL
1" PIECE	FRESH GINGER, PEELED & FINELY CHOPPED
4 CLOVES	GARLIC, FINELY CHOPPED
1 TABLESPOON	ASIAN BLACK BEAN SAUCE
1 TABLESPOON	ASIAN CHILI GARLIC SAUCE
1 TEASPOON	LEMON JUICE
1/8 CUP	WATER
1 TEASPOON	CORN STARCH
4 CUPS	BABY BOK CHOY
4 CUPS	FRESH YARD LONG ASIAN BEANS
	TABASCO TO TASTE (*OPTIONAL*)
	SEA SALT & PEPPER TO TASTE

READY TO COOK ⬇ ⬇ ⬇

1. SAUTÉ THE CHICKEN BREASTS IN THE OIL UNTILL PARTIALLY COOKED, 6 MINUTES. **2. ADD** GINGER AND GARLIC AND SAUTÉ **3. ADD** WATER, LEMON JUICE, BLACK BEAN SAUCE AND CHILI GARLIC SAUCE TO THE PAN AND STIR TO COAT THE CHICKEN. **4. ADD** THE BOK CHOY AND GREEN BEANS TO THE PAN AND SIMMER UNTIL THE CHICKEN IS COOKED. **5. DISSOLVE** CORN STARCH IN 3 TEASPOONS OF WATER AND THICKEN SAUCE.

Serve in a bowl. If you like you asian dishes spicy, you can add some tabasco.

PER SERVING: 480 CALORIES // 31G FAT // 66G PROTEIN // 14G CARBOHYDRATE

OKRA CASSEROLE
and Swiss Chard

24 OUNCES	CHICKEN (4 BREASTS), BONELESS, SKINLESS & CUBED
2 CUPS	OKRA
2 CUPS	GREEN ONIONS, CHOPPED
1 CUP	CELERY, CHOPPED
1 CUP	CELERY ROOT, CHOPPED
2 CUPS	SWISS CHARD, CHOPPED
2 CUPS	CHICKEN BROTH
1 TEASPOON	THYME
1 TEASPOON	OREGANO
1 TEASPOON	BASIL
2 TABLESPOONS	OIL
2 TEASPOONS	BUTTER
	SEA SALT & PEPPER TO TASTE

READY TO COOK ⬇ ⬇ ⬇

1. SEASON CHICKEN WITH SEA SALT AND PEPPER. **2. HEAT** THE OIL AND BUTTER IN A FRYING PAN AND BROWN THE CHICKEN ON ALL SIDES. **3. REMOVE** THE CHICKEN AND ADD THE OKRA AND BROWN LIGHTLY. **4. PLACE** THE BROWNED CHICKEN, OKRA AND ONIONS IN AN OVEN-PROOF CASSEROLE DISH. **5. ADD** CELERY, CELERY ROOT, SWISS CHARD, CHICKEN BROTH, THYME, OREGANO AND BASIL. **6. COVER** AND BAKE FOR 45-50 MINUTES AT **350° F**.

Served really hot, swiss chard is a vegetable to be discovered.

PER SERVING: 489 CALORIES // 22G FAT // 57G PROTEIN // 11G CARBOHYDRATE

MUSHROOM SMOTHERED
Chicken Breasts

24 OUNCES	CHICKEN (4 BREASTS), BONELESS & SKINLESS
2 CUPS	GREEN ONIONS, FINELY CHOPPED
4 CLOVES	GARLIC, FINELY CHOPPED
1 CUP	CELERY ROOT, DICED
1 CUP	CELERY, DICED
4 CUPS	SHITAKE MUSHROOMS, SLICED
1/2 CUP	CHICKEN BROTH
1 CUP	SOUR CREAM
1 TEASPOON	PAPRIKA
1 TEASPOON	MARJORAM
1 TEASPOON	GRAPE SEED OIL
SEA SALT & PEPPER TO TASTE	

READY TO COOK ⬇⬇⬇

1. HEAT THE OIL IN A LARGE FRYING PAN. **2. SEASON** THE CHICKEN BREASTS WITH SEA SALT AND PEPPER, PAPRIKA AND MARJORAM AND BROWN ON BOTH SIDES. **3. REMOVE** FROM THE PAN AND KEEP WARM. **4. ADD** THE ONIONS AND GARLIC TO THE PAN AND SAUTÉ UNTIL SOFT. **5. ADD** THE MUSHROOMS AND COOK FOR 2 MINUTES. **6. RETURN** THE CHICKEN BREASTS TO THE PAN **7. ADD** THE CELERY ROOT AND CELERY. **8. REDUCE** THE HEAT TO SIMMER. **9. ADD** THE CHICKEN BROTH AND SOUR CREAM AND STIR WELL. **10. COVER** AND SIMMER FOR 30 MINUTES. **11. COOK** MUSHROOMS.

Serve with any type of mushrooms. I personnaly love shitaki mushrooms for this recipe.

PER SERVING: 484 CALORIES // 25G FAT // 54G PROTEIN // 10G CARBOHYDRATE

OVEN BAKED
Chicken Legs

32 OUNCES	CHICKEN LEGS, THIGHS ATTACHED & SKINLESS
4 TABLESPOONS	MUSTARD, DIJON
1/2 TEASPOON	FRESH THYME, CHOPPED
1 CLOVE	GARLIC, CHOPPED
1" PIECE	FRESH GINGER, PEELED & CHOPPED
1 TEASPOON	OIL
1 TEASPOON	BUTTER
8 CUPS	ZUCCHINI, SLICED
1 TABLESPOON	SESAME SEEDS
SEA SALT & PEPPER TO TASTE	

READY TO COOK ⬇⬇⬇

1. PUT CHICKEN LEGS WITH PAPER TOWEL TO DRY. **2. BRUSH** WITH OIL. **3. SEASON** WITH SEA SALT AND PEPPER ON EACH SIDE. **4. PLACE** ON RACK UNDER THE OVEN BROILER AND BROIL FOR 15 MINUTES. **5. COAT** THE COOKED SIDE WITH A GENEROUS AMOUNT OF MUSTARD MARINADE AND RETURN TO THE OVEN FOR A ANOTHER 5 MINUTES. **6. TURN** THE LEGS OVER AND REPEAT ON THE OTHER SIDE. **7. TURN** UP THE HEAT AND BROIL EACH SIDE 2-3 MINUTES MORE, WATCHING CAREFULLY SO THEY DO NOT BURN. **8. SAUTÉ** THE ZUCCHINI IN BUTTER AND OIL TILL COOKED, 4-5 MINUTES.

Serve with a sprinkle of sesame seeds.

PER SERVING: 539 CALORIES // 29G FAT // 71G PROTEIN // 13G CARBOHYDRATE

CHEF
VERATi.

My daughter really knows how to surprise me.... And once again she did!!!! She flipped those vegetables like a real chef!
-Chef Verati

STIR IT UP!
Oriental Chicken Stir-Fry

24 OUNCES CHICKEN (4 BREASTS), BONE IN & SKINLESS

1 CUP BEAN SPROUTS

1 CUP YELLOW ONIONS, CHOPPED

1 CUP GREEN ONIONS, FINELY CHOPPED

2 CLOVES GARLIC, FINELY CHOPPED

1 CUP SWEET RED PEPPERS, CUBED

2 CUPS MUSHROOMS, SLICED

2 CUPS SNOW PEAS

2 TABLESPOONS SOY SAUCE

1 TEASPOON CHILI GARLIC SAUCE

1 TABLESPOON REGULAR OR RICE WINE VINEGAR

1 TEASPOON CORN STARCH

2" PIECE FRESH GINGER, PEELED & CHOPPED

1/4 CUP SLIVERED ALMONDS

1 TABLESPOON DARK SESAME OIL

2 TEASPOONS GRAPE SEED OIL

SEA SALT & PEPPER TO TASTE

READY TO COOK

1. HEAT THE GRAPE SEED OIL IN A PAN AND BROWN THE CHICKEN PIECES.

2. ADD THE YELLOW ONIONS AND GARLIC AND SAUTÉ UNTIL THE ONIONS ARE SOFT BUT NOT BROWNED.

3. ADD THE MUSHROOMS AND COOK 8-10 MINUTES OR UNTIL CHICKEN IS COOKED.

4. IN A SMALL BOWL, COMBINE THE SOY SAUCE, VINEGAR, CORN STARCH AND CHILI GARLIC SAUCE.

5. ADD THE SWEET RED PEPPERS, GINGER AND SNOW PEAS AND SIMMER FOR 2 MINUTES.

6. ADD THE BEAN SPROUTS AND ALMONDS TO THE PAN WITH THE CHICKEN.

7. POUR THE SOY SAUCE MIXTURE OVER TOP AND RE-HEAT.

SERVE WITH A SPINKLE OF SESAME OIL OVER THE TOP.

PER SERVING: 527 CALORIES // 24G FAT // 61G PROTEIN // 11G CARBOHYDRATE

PARMESAN CHICKEN
with Roasted Red Peppers

24 OUNCES CHICKEN (4 BREASTS), BONELESS & SKINLESS	**1 TEASPOON** DRIED THYME
4 RED PEPPERS, SEEDED & HALVES	**1 TABLESPOON** GRAPE SEED OIL
1 RED ONION, SLICED	**1/2 CUP** CHICKEN BROTH
2 CUPS CELERY, CHOPPED	**2 TEASPOONS** LEMON ZEST
1 CUP GREEN ONIONS, CHOPPED	**2 TABLESPOONS** DRIED PARSLEY
1/4 CUP PARMESAN CHEESE, GRATED	SEA SALT & PEPPER TO TASTE
1 TEASPOON DRIED BASIL	PAPER BAG

READY TO COOK

1. **COMBINE** THE SEA SALT, PEPPER, BASIL, THYME AND PARMESAN CHEESE IN A BOWL.

2. **COAT** THE CHICKEN BREASTS WITH THE MIXTURE.

3. **HEAT** HALF THE OIL IN A PAN AND BROWN THE CHICKEN ON BOTH SIDES.

4. **PRE-HEAT** THE OVEN BROILER TO HIGH.

5. **WIPE** THE SURFACE OF THE PEPPERS WITH A LITTLE OF THE REMAINING OIL AND PLACE, CUT SIDE DOWN, ON A BAKING SHEET.

6. **WATCHING** CAREFULLY, CHAR THE OUTSIDE OF THE PEPPERS.

7. **WHEN** THEY ARE BLACK, REMOVE FROM THE OVEN AND PLACE IN A PAPER BAG FOR 5 MINUTES OR UNTIL COOL ENOUGH TO PEEL.

8. **REMOVE** THE SKIN AND SLICE THE PEPPERS IN STRIPS.

9. **COMBINE** THE PEPPER STRIPS AND THE RED ONION SLICES AND PUT IN THE PAN WITH THE CHICKEN BREASTS.

10. **ADD** CHICKEN BROTH AND SIMMER, COVERED, 35-40 MINUTES OR UNTIL THE CHICKEN IS DONE.

Serve chicken and roasted peppers topped with lemon zest and parsley.

PER SERVING: 405 CALORIES // 19G FAT // 54G PROTEIN // 8G CARBOHYDRATE.

SAFFRON PAELLA
with Seafood and Italian Sausage

16 OUNCES CHICKEN (4 BREASTS), BONELESS & SKINLESS, CUBED

4 OUNCES SHRIMPS, PEELED & DEVEINED (*SEE PAGE 353*)

4 OUNCES (2) HOT ITALIAN SAUSAGES

8 OUNCES MUSSELS, WASHED & DEBEARDED (*SEE PAGE 353*)

2 CLOVES GARLIC, FINELY CHOPPED

2 CUPS FRESH TOMATOES, CHOPPED

1 TEASPOON SAFFRON

1 TABLESPOON GRAPE SEED OIL

1 TABLESPOON BUTTER

1/4 CUP CHICKEN BROTH

1 CUP GREEN PEPPERS, CHOPPED

1 CUP RED PEPPERS, CHOPPED

1 CUP GREEN ONIONS, CHOPPED

4 CUPS MIXED GREEN SALAD

1 OUNCES LOW FAT LOW CARB HOUSE DRESSING (*SEE PAGE 95*)

SEA SALT & PEPPER TO TASTE

READY TO COOK

1. **PUT** SAFFRON IN A SMALL BOWL, POUR 1 TABLESPOON OF BOILING WATER OVER TOP AND SET ASIDE.

2. **HEAT** 1 TABLESPOON OF THE OIL AND BUTTER IN A FRYING PAN.

3. **SEASON** CHICKEN WITH SEA SALT AND PEPPER AND BROWN FOR 5-6 MINUTES. REMOVE FROM PAN AND KEEP WARM.

4. **PUT** THE SAUSAGE IN THE PAN AND COOK FOR ABOUT 10 MINUTES OR UNTIL DONE, TURNING FREQUENTLY.

5. **REMOVE** FROM THE PAN AND CUT EACH SAUSAGE INTO 4 PIECES.

6. **ADD** THE TOMATOES, GREEN PEPPERS, RED PEPPERS AND GARLIC AND CONTINUE TO COOK ON **MEDIUM** HEAT.

7. **ADD** THE 1/4 CUP OF CHICKEN BROTH TO THE PAN ALONG WITH THE SAFFRON.

8. **RETURN** THE CHICKEN AND SAUSAGE TO THE PAN AND SIMMER FOR 10 MINUTES.

9. **ADD** THE SHRIMPS AND MUSSELS AND COOK, COVERED, FOR 8-10 MORE MINUTES OR UNTIL THE MUSSELS HAVE OPENED.

10. **DISCARD** ANY MUSSELS WHICH DO NOT OPEN.

11. **TOP** WITH GREEN ONIONS.

Serve with mixed green salad topped with low fat low carb house dressing.

TOUCHDOWN GARLIC WINGS
and Vegetable Chow Mein

48 OUNCES CHICKEN WINGS	**1 TEASPOON** GROUND STAR ANISE (*OPTIONAL*)
1 TABLESPOON GRAPE SEED OIL	**1 CUP** GREEN ONIONS, CHOPPED
4 CLOVES GARLIC, FINELY CHOPPED	**1 CUP** CELERY, CHOPPED
1/8 CUP SOY SAUCE **+ 1 TABLESPOON**	**1 CUP** CELERY ROOT, DICED
2 CUPS CHICKEN BROTH	**3 CUPS** MUSHROOMS, SLICED
1 TABLESPOON CORN STARCH	**2 CUPS** FRESH BEAN SPROUTS
2 TABLESPOONS FRESH GINGER, FINELY CHOPPED	SEA SALT & PEPPER TO TASTE

READY TO COOK

1. **IN** A LARGE BOWL, SEASON THE CHICKEN WINGS WITH THE OIL.
2. **SPREAD** THE WINGS ON A BAKING SHEET AND PLACE IN A PRE-HEATED **400°F** OVEN AND BAKE FOR ABOUT 20 MINUTES, TURNING OCCASIONALLY.
3. **IN** A SAUCE PAN COMBINE THE SOY SAUCE, CHICKEN BROTH, GARLIC, GINGER AND ANISE.
4. **MIX** THE CORN STARCH AND WATER AND ADD TO THE PAN.
5. **BRING** TO A BOIL AND REDUCE HEAT.
6. **ADD** THE CHICKEN WINGS AND SIMMER FOR ABOUT 15 MINUTES.
7. **IN** A FRYING PAN, COOK THE CELERY, MUSHROOMS AND CELERY ROOT UNTIL TENDER.
8. **ADD,** SEA SALT, PEPPER AND BEAN SPROUTS, AND THE TABLESPOON OF SOY SAUCE.

Serve the wings with the sauce and sprinkle the chopped green onions on vegetables.

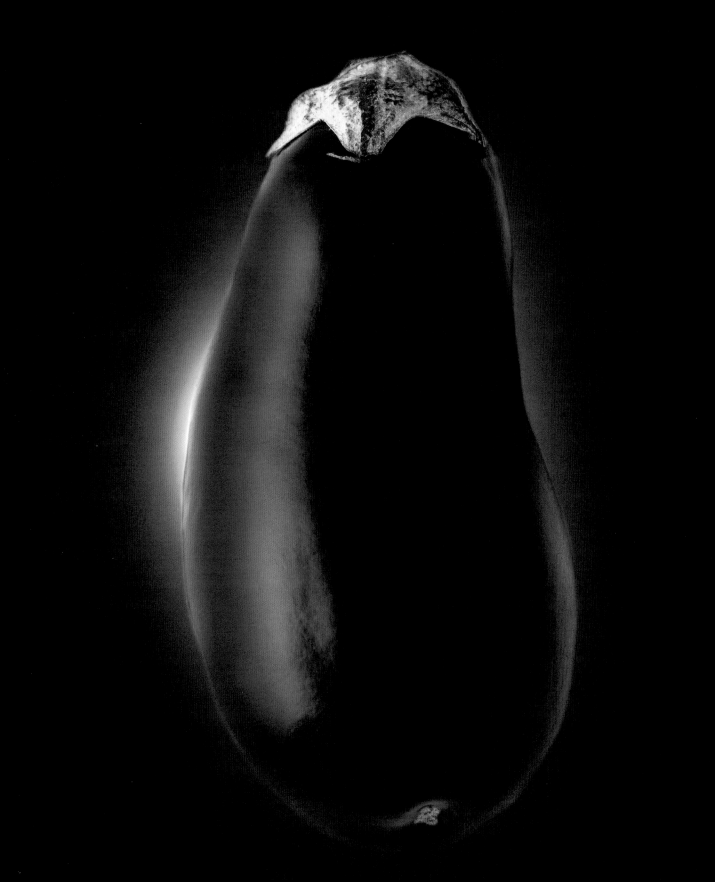

ECLIPSED
Turkey Stuffed Eggplant

24 OUNCES GROUND TURKEY	2 TEASPOONS GRAPE SEED OIL
1 CUP ONIONS, FINELY CHOPPED	1 CUP WATER
2 CLOVES GARLIC, FINELY CHOPPED	1/2 CUP CHEESE, GRATED
1 TEASPOON OREGANO	1/2 CUP CHICKEN BROTH
1 TEASPOON THYME	4 CUPS ARUGULA AND SPINACH
1 TEASPOON BASIL	4 OUNCES LOW FAT LOW CARB HOUSE DRESSING (*SEE PAGE 95*)
2 MEDIUM SIZE EGGPLANTS, CUT IN HALF	SEA SALT & PEPPER TO TASTE

READY TO COOK

1. SCOOP OUT THE 4 EGGPLANT HALVES, LEAVING ABOUT 1/2 INCH OF THE EGGPLANT AROUND THE EDGES.
2. DICE THE EGGPLANT WHICH HAS BEEN REMOVED.
3. HEAT THE OIL IN A PAN AND BROWN THE TURKEY.
4. ADD DICED EGGPLANTS, ONIONS AND GARLIC AND COOK UNTIL SOFT.
5. ADD THE OREGANO, THYME AND SEA SALT.
6. PUT 1/4 OF THE MIXTURE INTO EACH OF THE EGGPLANT HALVES.
7. PLACE THE EGGPLANT HALVES IN AN OVEN PAN, ADD THE CHICKEN BROTH TO THE BOTTOM OF THE PAN AND BAKE, COVERED FOR ABOUT 30 MINUTES AT 350° F.
8. REMOVE THE COVER AND SPREAD THE CHEESE EVENLY OVER EACH OF THE EGGPLANTS.
9. PUT BACK IN THE OVEN AND COOK FOR ANOTHER 20 MINUTES OR UNTIL THE EGGPLANT IS SOFT AND THE CHEESE HAS MELTED.

SERVE WITH SPINACH AND ARUGULA SALAD WITH LOW FAT LOW CARB HOUSE DRESSING.

PER SERVING: 516 CALORIES // 25G FAT // 56G PROTEIN // 10G CARBOHYDRATE

PARMESAN CRUSTED CHICKEN
and Crustless Mushroom Pie

20 OUNCES CHICKEN (4 BREASTS), BONELESS & SKINLESS	**2** BAY LEAVES
1 TEASPOON OIL	**1 CUP** MILK
1 CUP ONIONS, CHOPPED	**1/2 CUP** CHICKEN BROTH
1 CUP CELERY, FINELY CHOPPED	**1 1/2 TABLESPOONS** CORN STARCH
1 CUP CELERY ROOT, DICED	**1 TABLESPOON** BUTTER
1 CUP FENNEL, CHOPPED	**1/8 TEASPOON** NUTMEG
4 CUPS MUSHROOMS, SLICED	**4 TEASPOONS** PARMESAN CHEESE, GRATED
1/2 CUP FRESH PARSLEY, CHOPPED	**4 SLICES** PARMESAN CHEESE
2 TEASPOONS FRESH SAGE, CHOPPED	SEA SALT & PEPPER TO TASTE

READY TO COOK

1. **IN** A SMALL PAN, BOIL THE CELERY, CELERY ROOT AND FENNEL UNTIL TENDER, BUT NOT OVERCOOKED. DRAIN AND SET ASIDE.

2. **HEAT** OIL IN ANOTHER PAN AND SAUTÉ THE ONIONS UNTIL SOFT.

3. **ADD** THE MUSHROOMS AND SAUTE, 2-3 MINUTES.

4. **REMOVE** FROM THE PAN.

5. **CUT** THE CHICKEN BREASTS INTO CUBES, SEASON WITH SEA SALT AND PEPPER AND SAUTÉ UNTIL BROWNED ON ALL SIDES.

6. **REMOVE** FROM THE PAN.

7. **MELT** THE BUTTER IN THE PAN.

8. **IN** A BOWL, ADD THE CORN STARCH TO THE MILK AND POUR INTO THE PAN WITH THE CHICKEN BROTH, STIRRING CONSTANTLY UNTIL YOU GET A SMOOTH SAUCE.

9. **ADD** NUTMEG AND BAY LEAVES.

10. **COMBINE** THE CELERY, FENNEL, CELERY ROOT, ONIONS, MUSHROOMS AND THE CHICKEN IN A LARGE CASSEROLE.

11. **ADD** THE FRESH SAGE AND CHOPPED PARSLEY.

12. **POUR** THE SAUCE OVER ALL THE INGREDIENTS AND MIX WELL.

13. **TOP** WITH PARMESAN CHEESE AND BROIL IN OVEN UNTIL GOLDEN BROWN.

Serve with a slice of fresh parmesan on each plate.

PER SERVING: 424 CALORIES // 31G FAT // 48G PROTEIN // 16G CARBOHYDRATE.

SPINACH STUFFED CHICKEN
with Lemon-Cream Sauce

24 OUNCES CHICKEN (4 BREASTS), BONELESS & SKINLESS	**2 CUPS** FENNEL BULBS, SLICED & BLANCHED (*SEE PAGE 129*)
2 TEASPOONS GRAPE SEED OIL	**2 CUPS** CELERY ROOT, SLICED & BLANCHED (*SEE PAGE 129*)
3 CUPS FRESH SPINACH, CHOPPED	**1 CUP** MILK
1 CUP ONIONS, FINELY CHOPPED	**1 1/2 TABLESPOONS** CORN STARCH
2 CLOVES GARLIC, FINELY CHOPPED	**2 TABLESPOONS** BUTTER
2 TEASPOONS FRESH SAGE LEAVES, FINELY CHOPPED	**1/4 CUP** LEMON JUICE
4 TEASPOONS GRAINY MUSTARD	SEA SALT & PEPPER TO TASTE

READY TO COOK

1. **COOK** ONIONS IN 1 TEASPOON OF GRAPE SEED OIL UNTIL ALMOST SOFT.

2. **ADD** GARLIC AND COOK FOR 1 MINUTE LONGER.

3. **ADD** THE SPINACH, FRESH SAGE, SEA SALT AND PEPPER AND COOK UNTIL THE SPINACH IS WILTED, ABOUT 1-2 MINUTES.

4. **REMOVE** FROM THE HEAT AND ALLOW TO COOL FOR A FEW MINUTES.

5. **CUT** EACH CHICKEN BREAST THROUGH THE MIDDLE LENGTHWISE.

6. **SPREAD** 1 TEASPOON GRAINY MUSTARD ON ONE SIDE OF THE CUT BREAST.

7. **PUT** 1/4 OF THE SPINACH MIXTURE ON TOP OF THE MUSTARD.

8. **PUT** THE SECOND HALF OF THE BREAST ON TOP OF THE MIXTURE AND SECURE WITH STRING. REPEAT WITH THE OTHER 3 CHICKEN BREASTS.

9. **BRUSH** BOTH SIDES OF EACH BREAST WITH THE REMAINING TEASPOON OF OIL AND PLACE ON A RACK IN A **350°F** OVEN FOR
   20-25 MINUTES OR UNTIL THE CHICKEN IS DONE, TURNING ONCE DURING THE COOKING TIME.

10. **BLANCH** OR STEAM CELERY ROOT AND FENNEL.

11. **MELT** THE BUTTER IN A SAUCEPAN.

12. **STIR** THE CORN STARCH INTO THE MILK AND ADD TO THE PAN, STIRRING CONSTANTLY TO PREVENT LUMPS. ADD SEA SALT, PEPPER
    AND LEMON JUICE AND CONTINUE TO STIR UNTIL THE SAUCE IS SMOOTH AND CREAMY.

Serve stuffed chicken topped with creamy lemon sauce, vegetables on the side.

"CHILI STYLE" CHICKEN
with Mixed Vegetables

24 OUNCES CHICKEN LEGS, SKINLESS	**2 TEASPOONS** CUMIN
1 TEASPOON GRAPE SEED OIL	**2 CUPS** FRESH MUSHROOMS, SLICED
2 CUPS ONIONS, DICED	**2 TEASPOONS** DRIED OREGANO
4 CLOVES GARLIC, FINELY CHOPPED	**2 TEASPOONS** DRIED MARJORAM
2 CUPS FRESH TOMATOES, CHOPPED	**1/4 TEASPOON** GROUND CLOVES
1 CUP TOMATO JUICE	**1 TEASPOON** GROUND CINNAMON
1 CUP GREEN PEPPERS, DICED	**1 CUP** FRESH CILANTRO LEAVES, CHOPPED
1 CUP SWEET RED PEPPERS, DICED	SEA SALT & PEPPER TO TASTE
2 TABLESPOONS CHILI POWDER (*SEE PAGE 173*)	

READY TO COOK

1. **BROWN** THE CHICKEN PIECES IN THE OIL.
2. **REMOVE** FROM PAN AND SET ASIDE.
3. **COOK** THE ONIONS IN THE PAN UNTIL JUST BEGINNING TO SOFTEN.
4. **ADD** THE GARLIC AND SAUTÉ FOR 1 MINUTE.
5. **ADD** THE MUSHROOMS AND SAUTÉ ANOTHER 2 MINUTES.
6. **IN** A LARGE POT, PUT THE ONIONS, GARLIC, MUSHROOMS, CHOPPED TOMATOES, TOMATO JUICE, RED, GREEN AND CHILI PEPPERS AND COOK ANOTHER 2 MINUTES.
7. **ADD** THE OREGANO, MARJORAM, CLOVES, CINNAMON, CUMIN, SALT AND PEPPER.
8. **PLACE** THE CHICKEN PIECES ON TOP OF THE SAUCE, COVER AND SIMMER FOR 1 HOUR.

Serve chicken topped with cilantro leaves, vegetables on the side.

CHICKEN TAGINE
with Fresh Herbs

24 OUNCES CHICKEN BREAST, BONELESS, SKINLESS & CUBED	**4 CUPS** CHICKEN BROTH
2 CUPS GREEN ONIONS, CHOPPED	**5 1/4 TABLESPOONS** VERATI'S TAGINE BLEND (SEE RECIPE PAGE 173)
4 CLOVES GARLIC, FINELY CHOPPED	**2 TABLESPOONS** LEMON JUICE
2 CUPS CABBAGE, SLICED	**2 TABLESPOONS** GRAPE SEED OIL
2 CUPS FRESH GREEN BEANS, WHOLE	**2 TEASPOONS** BUTTER
2 CUPS SMALL UNPEELED EGGPLANT, CUBED	**1 CUP** FRESH CORIANDER, CHOPPED
1 TEASPOON PAPRIKA	SEA SALT & PEPPER TO TASTE

READY TO COOK

1. **HEAT** THE OIL AND BUTTER IN A LARGE HEAVY POT.

2. **SEASON** THE CHICKEN CUBES WITH SEA SALT, PEPPER AND PAPRIKA AND BROWN ON ALL SIDES.

3. **MOVE** THE CHICKEN PIECES TO ANOTHER PAN.

4. **IN** THE OIL AND CHICKEN DRIPPINGS, ADD THE EGGPLANT, GREEN ONIONS, GARLIC, CABBAGE AND GREEN BEANS AND SAUTÉ ANOTHER 2-3 MINUTES.

5. **ADD** THE CHICKEN BROTH AND LEMON JUICE AND BRING TO A BOIL.

6. **IMMEDIATELY** REDUCE THE HEAT AND ADD THE VERATI'S BLEND.

7. **COVER** THE PAN AND SIMMER FOR 1 HOUR.

Serve chicken tagine with a dash of fresh coriander over top.

DON'T GO GROCERY SHOPPING
ON AN EMPTY STOMACH

PER SERVING: 460 CALORIES // 21G FAT // 59G PROTEIN // 9G CARBOHYDRATE

CHEF
VERATI

MY TEAM ATE THAT GARLIC
AS IF IT WAS CANDY...THEY
TOLD ME THAT THE RECIPE
NEEDED TO BE IN THIS
BOOK! SEE THE TWIST
ON THE NEXT PAGE...
-CHEF VERATI

COMFORT IN A PLATE
with Cornish Game Hens

2 CORNISH GAME HENS, CUT IN HALF

2 TABLESPOONS ROSEMARY

2 TABLESPOONS THYME

2 TABLESPOONS BASIL

15 CLOVES GARLIC, WHOLE & PEELED

2 TEASPOONS GRAPE SEED OIL

3 CUPS LEEKS

5 CUPS GREEN BEANS

2 TABLESPOONS WATER

SEA SALT & PEPPER TO TASTE

READY TO COOK

1. **WASH** THE LEEKS WELL AND SLICE IN ROUNDS, DISCARDING THE TOUGHER GREEN ENDS.

2. **SAUTÉ** IN 1 TEASPOON OF THE OIL AND 2 TABLESPOONS OF WATER UNTIL SOFT.

3. **RUB** THE GAME HENS WITH THE OIL AND SEASON WITH SEA SALT, PEPPER, ROSEMARY, THYME AND BASIL.

4. **PLACE** THE GARLIC IN THE BOTTOM OF AN OVEN PAN.

5. **TOP** WITH THE LEEKS AND PLACE THE GAME HENS ON TOP.

6. **COVER** THE PAN WITH FOIL AND BAKE AT **350⁰F** FOR APPROXIMATELY 50 MINUTES OR UNTIL THE GAME HENS ARE COOKED.

Serve with steamed fresh green beans.

VERATI *Twist*

YOU CAN ALSO MAKE THE GARLIC "CONFIT"! CUT OFF THE TOP AND ADD A BIT OF OIL. SIMPLY PUT THE BULB ON A COOKING SHEET FOR 40 MINUTES IN A 400F OVEN. USE IT FOR THIS RECIPE OR ADD IT TO ANY MEAL. MY TEAMS FAVORITE IS THE "ELEPHANT" GARLIC!

PER SERVING: 600 CALORIES // 31G FAT // 66G PROTEIN // 14G CARBOHYDRATE

MUSTARD CRUSTED
Rabbit Legs with Fennel

4 RABBIT LEGS

1/4 CUP SALTED BUTTER, MELTED

2 TABLESPOONS GRAPE SEED OIL

1/2 CUP DIJON MUSTARD

1/4 CUP FRESH THYME, CHOPPED

1/4 CUP PARSLEY, CHOPPED

1/2 TEASPOON PAPRIKA

4 CUPS FENNEL, SLICED

3 CUPS CELERY ROOT

1 CUP GREEN ONIONS, CHOPPED

SEA SALT & PEPPER TO TASTE

READY TO COOK

1. PREHEAT THE OVEN TO 375°F.

2. SEASON THE RABBIT LEGS WITH SEA SALT, PEPPER AND PAPRIKA.

3. IN A BOWL, COMBINE THE BUTTER AND GRAPE SEED OIL WITH THE DIJON MUSTARD.

4. REMOVE 1/4 OF THE MIXTURE TO A SMALL BOWL AND SET ASIDE.

5. IN ANOTHER BOWL, COMBINE THE FRESH THYME, BLACK PEPPER AND PAPRIKA.

6. ROLL THE RABBIT LEGS FIRST IN THE MAIN MUSTARD MIXTURE AND THEN IN THE HERB MIXTURE.

7. PLACE THE RABBIT ON A RACK OVER A BAKING SHEET IN THE OVEN AND BAKE FOR 40 MINUTES,

8. TURNING ONCE.

9. REMOVE FROM THE OVEN, TENT THE PAN WITH FOIL AND ALLOW THE LEGS TO REST FOR 15 MINUTES.

10. STEAM THE SLICED FENNEL AND CELERY ROOT FOR 10 MINUTES OR UNTIL DONE. DRAIN.

11. POUR THE RESERVED BUTTER AND MUSTARD MIXTURE OVER THE HOT FENNEL AND CELERY ROOT AND MIX WELL.

SERVE THE RABBIT OVER A BED OF THE VEGETABLES AND PARSLEY AND CHOPPED GREEN ONIONS.

PER SERVING: 640 CALORIES // 29G FAT // 66G PROTEIN // 10G CARBOHYDRATE

CURRY KABOBS
with Vegetables

24 OUNCES CHICKEN (4 BREASTS), BONELESS, SKINLESS & CUBED

2 CUPS CHERRY TOMATOES, WHOLE

2 CUPS GREEN PEPPERS, CUBED

2 CUPS GREEN ONIONS, WHITE ONLY, SLICED

2 CUPS SWEET RED PEPPERS, CUBED

1 TEASPOON CUMIN

1 TEASPOON CORIANDER

1 TEASPOON CURRY POWDER

1 CUP ROMAINE LETTUCE

1 CUP ARUGULA

4 CUPS MIXED GREEN SALAD

4 OUNCES LOW FAT LOW CARB HOUSE DRESSING (*SEE PAGE 95*)

SKEWERS

READY TO COOK ⬇⬇⬇

1. SEASON THE CHICKEN WITH CUMIN, CORIANDER, CURRY POWDER, SEA SALT AND PEPPER TO TASTE. **2. THREAD** THE CHICKEN, ONIONS, TOMATOES AND GREEN AND RED PEPPERS ALTERNATELY ONTO THE SKEWERS. **3. BROIL** UNDER THE OVEN GRILL UNTIL THE CHICKEN IS COOKED, **4. ABOUT** 10 MINUTES PER SIDE.

Serve on a bed of romaine lettuce and arugula leaves with a side of salad.

PER SERVING: 428 CALORIES // 21G FAT // 55G PROTEIN // 10G CARBOHYDRATE

BACON STUFFED
Chicken Breasts

24 OUNCES CHICKEN (4 BREASTS), BONELESS & SKIN ON

4 STRIPS BACON, CHOPPED

1/2 CUP GREEN ONIONS, FINELY CHOPPED

1 TEASPOON FRESH THYME, CHOPPED

1 TEASPOON FRESH SAGE, CHOPPED

1 TEASPOON FRESH OREGANO, CHOPPED

2 TEASPOONS GRAPE SEED OIL

1 TEASPOON PAPRIKA

1/2 TEASPOON CHILI POWDER (*OPTIONAL*) (*SEE PAGE 173*)

8 CUPS BROCCOLI, FLORETS & BLANCHED (*SEE PAGE 129*)

SEA SALT & PEPPER TO TASTE

READY TO COOK ⬇⬇⬇

1. CUT DOWN THE MIDDLE OF THE BREASTS, LENGTHWISE, ALMOST THROUGH. **2. OPEN** THE CHICKEN BREASTS IN "BUTTERFLY" FASHION AND SEASON WITH SEA SALT AND PEPPER. **3. COOK** THE BACON UNTIL CRISP. **4. IN** A BOWL, COMBINE THE, ONION, THYME, SAGE AND OREGANO AND THE BACON, INCLUDING SOME OF THE OIL FROM COOKING AND MIX WELL. **5. SPREAD** THE MIXTURE ON ONE HALF OF EACH OF THE CHICKEN BREASTS. **6. FOLD** THE SECOND HALF OVER TOP. **7. SECURE** WITH MEAT SKEWERS IF NECESSARY. **8. SEASON** THE CHICKEN BREASTS WITH PAPRIKA AND CHILI POWDER. **9. BROWN** ON EACH SIDE IN THE GRAPE SEED OIL. **10. REMOVE** TO AN OVEN PAN AND BAKE FOR ABOUT 35 MINUTES OR UNTIL THE CHICKEN IS DONE. **11. BLANCH** THE BROCCOLI.

Serve with broccoli.

PER SERVING: 557 CALORIES // 24G FAT // 61G PROTEIN // 10G CARBOHYDRATE

BRAISED RABBIT
with Savoy Cabbage

2 **WHOLE** RABBITS, CUT INTO 8 PORTIONS

4 **SLICES** BACON, CUT IN 1" PIECES

2 **TABLESPOONS** GRAPE SEED OIL

2 **TEASPOONS** BUTTER

6 **CLOVES** GARLIC, CHOPPED

2 **CUPS** GREEN ONIONS, THICKLY SLICED

2 **CUPS** FENNEL, THICKLY SLICED

2 **CUPS** CELERY, THICKLY SLICED

2 **CUPS** SAVOY CABBAGE, THICKLY SLICED

2 **TABLESPOONS** FLOUR

6 **CUPS CHICKEN** STOCK

2 **BAY LEAVES**

1 **TEASPOON** GROUND BLACK PEPPER

1 **TABLESPOON** LEMON JUICE

READY TO COOK ⬇⬇⬇

1. **HEAT** THE OIL IN A LARGE HEAVY POT. 2. **SEASON** THE RABBIT PIECES WITH SEA SALT AND PEPPER AND BROWN ON ALL SIDES. 3. **REMOVE** FROM THE POT AND SET ASIDE. 4. **PLACE** THE BACON IN THE POT AND STIRRING CONSTANTLY, COOK UNTIL BEGINNING TO CRISP. 5. **ADD** THE GARLIC, FENNEL AND CELERY. 6. **SPRINKLE** THE FLOUR OVER TOP AND STIR INTO THE MIXTURE, ADDING ONE CUP OF THE CHICKEN STOCK AS YOU STIR. 7. **WHEN** THE MIXTURE BEGINS TO THICKEN, ADD THE REMAINDER OF THE CHICKEN STOCK AND THE BAY LEAVES. 8. **BRING** TO A BOIL AND IMMEDIATELY REDUCE THE HEAT TO SIMMER. 9. **ADD** THE CABBAGE AND THE RABBIT TO THE POT, COVER AND PLACE IN A 350⁰F OVEN FOR 1 1/4 TO 1 1/2 HOURS OR UNTIL THE RABBIT IS COOKED. 10. **BEFORE** SERVING, STIR IN THE 2 TEASPOONS BUTTER, THE FRESHLY GROUND BLACK PEPPER, GREEN ONIONS AND THE LEMON JUICE.

Serve on a top of braised vegetables.

PER SERVING: 668 CALORIES // 31G FAT // 65G PROTEIN // 14G CARBOHYDRATE

BUTTERMILK & PAPRIKA
with Green Beans

24 **OUNCES** CHICKEN (4 BREASTS), BONELESS & SKINLESS

1 **CUP** BUTTERMILK

2 **TABLESPOONS** PAPRIKA

2 **TEASPOONS** OIL

3 **CUPS** FRESH GREEN BEANS

3 **CUPS** MUSHROOMS, SLICED

1 **CUP** SWEET RED PEPPERS, FINELY CHOPPED

1 **CUP** GREEN ONIONS, CHOPPED

SEA SALT & PEPPER TO TASTE

READY TO COOK ⬇⬇⬇

1. **MARINATE** THE CHICKEN BREASTS IN BUTTERMILK FOR 1 HOUR (OR OVERNIGHT IN THE REFRIGERATOR). 2. **COMBINE** SEA SALT, PEPPER AND PAPRIKA IN A SMALL BOWL. 3. **REMOVE** THE CHICKEN BREASTS FROM THE BUTTERMILK AND DIP INTO THE PAPRIKA MIXTURE. 4. **BROWN** THE CHICKEN ON BOTH SIDES IN OIL. 5. **MOVE** CHICKEN TO A RACK IN OVEN AND BAKE AT 350⁰F FOR 30-35 MINUTES OR UNTIL JUICES RUN CLEAR. 6. **COOK** THE MUSHROOMS IN REMAINING OIL IN PAN IN WHICH CHICKEN WAS COOKED. 7. **REMOVE** FROM HEAT. 8. **BOIL** THE GREEN BEANS UNTIL JUST TENDER. 9. **DRAIN** AND TOSS WITH THE COOKED MUSHROOMS. 10. **ADD** SWEET RED PEPPERS AND GREEN ONIONS AND TOSS AGAIN.

Serve with fresh green onions on top.

PER SERVING: 484 CALORIES // 25G FAT // 54G PROTEIN // 10G CARBOHYDRATE

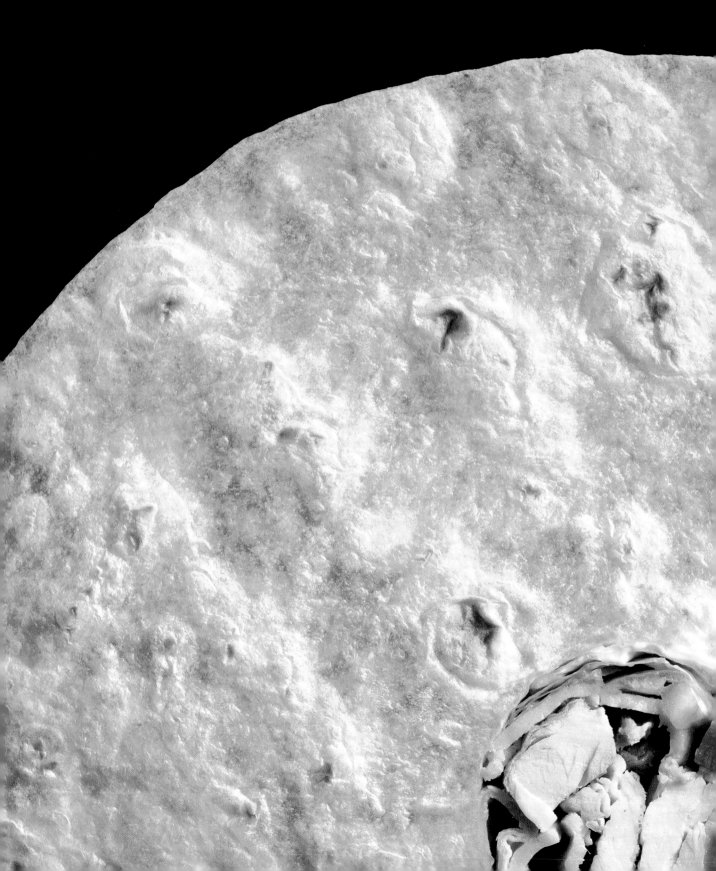

CHICKEN & SHRIMP
Funky Wraps

12 OUNCES COOKED CHICKEN, STRIPPED	**8 LARGE** LETTUCE LEAVES, BOSTON OR ICEBERG
12 OUNCES SHRIMP, PEELED, DEVEINED & COOKED *(SEE PAGE 353)*	**8 OUNCES** FETA CHEESE
1 CUP RED ONIONS, THINLY SLICED	**5 CUPS** CUCUMBERS
1 CUP AVOCADO, PEELED	**1/2 LIME**, JUICED
2 TABLESPOONS MAYONNAISE	**1 TEASPOON** SOY SAUCE
1 TEASPOON LEMON JUICE	**1 TEASPOON** SESAME OIL
1 TEASPOON CHILI SAUCE	SEA SALT & PEPPER TO TASTE
1 CUP CHOPPED FRESH TOMATOES	

READY TO COOK

1. **MASH** THE AVOCADO WITH THE MAYONNAISE.
2. **ADD** LEMON JUICE AND CHILI SAUCE.
3. **SPREAD** A LITTLE OF THE MIXTURE ON EACH OF THE LETTUCE WRAPS.
4. **DIVIDE** THE CHICKEN, SHRIMP, RED ONIONS AND FRESH TOMATOES AMONG THE 8 WRAPS.
5. **SPREAD** FETA CHEESE OVER TOP.
6. **SEASON** WITH SEA SALT AND PEPPER AND ROLL UP EACH WRAP.
7. **MARINATE** CUCUMBERS IN SOY, LIME AND SESAME OIL.

Serve wraps with cucumber salad.

VERATI**TIPS**
MAKE YOUR OWN HOMEMADE SAUCES AND VINAIGRETTES AS THEY ARE LOWER IN SODIUM, PRESERVATIVES, FATS, SUGARS AND ARE MUCH MORE FLAVORABLE!

PER SERVING: 389 CALORIES // 21G FAT // 45G PROTEIN // 8G CARBOHYDRATE

ROAST CHICKEN
with Brussels Sprouts

1	WHOLE CHICKEN
2 TABLESPOONS	DRIED ROSEMARY
2 TABLESPOONS	DRIED TARRAGON
2 TABLESPOONS	BUTTER, SOFTENED
2	WHOLE LEMONS, HALVED
8 CUPS	BRUSSELS SPROUTS, BLANCHED (*SEE PAGE 129*)
2 TABLESPOONS	GRAPE SEED OIL
SEA SALT & PEPPER TO TASTE	

READY TO COOK ⬇ ⬇ ⬇

1. RINSE THE CAVITY OF THE CHICKEN IN COLD WATER AND DRAIN WELL. **2. PUT** THE LEMONS IN THE CAVITY OF THE CHICKEN. **3. IN** A BOWL, COMBINE ROSEMARY, TARRAGON, SEA SALT AND PEPPER WITH SOFTENED BUTTER. **4. LOOSEN** THE SKIN AROUND THE BREAST OF THE CHICKEN IN 3 OR 4 PLACES AND PRESS SOME OF THE BUTTER MIXTURE UNDER THE SKIN. **5. BRUSH** THE SURFACE OF THE CHICKEN WITH OIL AND PLACE IN THE OVEN BREAST DOWNWARDS, ON A RACK OVER A ROASTING PAN. **6. BAKE** AT 350° F FOR ABOUT 45 MINUTES. **7. TURN** THE CHICKEN BREAST SIDE UP AND COOK FOR ANOTHER 15 MINUTES OR UNTIL THE JUICES ARE CLEAR. **8. BLANCH** THE BRUSSEL SPROUTS.

Serve roasted chicken with brussels sprouts.

PER SERVING: 545 CALORIES // 29G FAT // 69G PROTEIN // 15G CARBOHYDRATE

HOMEY CASSEROLE
with Leeks

24 OUNCES	CHICKEN THIGHS OR DRUMSTICKS, SKIN REMOVED
12 LARGE CLOVES	GARLIC, WHOLE & PEELED
4 CUPS	LEEKS, SLICED
4 CUPS	FRESH GREEN BEANS
1 TEASPOON	FRESH SAVORY
1 TEASPOON	FRESH BASIL
1 TEASPOON	THYME
4 TABLESPOONS	LEMON JUICE
2 TEASPOONS	OIL
SEA SALT & PEPPER TO TASTE	

READY TO COOK ⬇ ⬇ ⬇

1. BROWN THE CHICKEN PIECES IN THE OIL. **2. ADD** LEEKS AND SAUTÉ FOR 3-4 MINUTES UNTIL THEY BEGIN TO SOFTEN. **3. PLACE** THE CLOVES OF WHOLE GARLIC IN THE BOTTOM OF A CASSEROLE DISH WITH THE LEMON JUICE. **4. PUT** THE CHICKEN ON TOP OF THE GARLIC. **5. ADD** THE LEEKS, GREEN BEANS, SEA SALT AND PEPPER, SAVORY, BASIL AND THYME. **6. BAKE** IN THE OVEN AT 350° F FOR 45 MINUTES OR UNTIL THE CHICKEN IS COOKED.

Serve the casserole in the middle of the table.

PER SERVING: 545 CALORIES // 29G FAT // 69G PROTEIN // 15G CARBOHYDRATE

FIERY CHICKEN WINGS
with Turnip Chips

36 OUNCES CHICKEN WINGS

2 TABLESPOONS GRAPE SEED OIL

2 TABLESPOONS CHILI POWDER* (*SEE PAGE 173*)

2 TABLESPOONS GARLIC POWDER

2 TABLESPOONS SMOKED PAPRIKA

1 TABLESPOON ONION SALT

1 TABLESPOON FLOUR

1 SMALL RUTABAGA

6 CUPS MIXED GREENS

SEA SALT & PEPPER TO TASTE

VERA TIT RICK

IT IS THE CHILI THAT BRINGS THE PIQUANCY AND FLAVOR TO DISHES. IT IS RESPONSIBLE FOR THAT FIERY TASTE! IF YOU PREFER YOUR WINGS MILDLY FIERY, USE LESS BUT IF YOU WANT LIGHT YOUR MOUTH ON FIRE, ADD MORE!!

* CHILI POWDER IS ONE OF MANY CHILI PEPPER VARIETIES, AND SOMETIMES IS COMBINED WITH OTHER SPICES. WANT TO MAKE YOUR OWN CHILI POWDER MIX?

(SEE PAGE 173)

READY TO COOK ⬇ ⬇ ⬇

1. PEEL THE RUTABAGA AND CUT INTO POTATO CHIP SIZE LENGTHS. **2. COOK** IN BOILING WATER FOR 5 MINUTES. **3. DRAIN** AND TOSS WITH 1 TABLESPOON OF THE OIL. **4. IN** A BOWL, COMBINE THE CHILI POWDER, GARLIC POWDER, ONION SALT AND SMOKED PAPRIKA. **5. DREDGE** THE RUTABAGA PIECES IN THE CHILI MIXTURE, SHAKE OFF EXCESS AND PLACE ON A GREASED OVEN PAN. **6. BAKE** AT 350⁰ F, TURNING OCCASIONALLY UNTIL THE TURNIP IS COOKED AND CRISP. **7. ADD** ONE TABLESPOON OF FLOUR TO THE SPICE MIXTURE. **8. DREDGE** THE CHICKEN WINGS IN THE MIXTURE. **9. SHAKE** OFF EXCESS AND PLACE ON AN OILED PAN IN THE OVEN. **10. BAKE** AT 350⁰ F, TURNING OCCASIONALLY UNTIL THE CHICKEN WINGS ARE COOKED AND CRISP.

Serve chicken wings with turnip "chips" and green salad with low fat low carb house dressing.

PER SERVING: 580 CALORIES // 27G FAT // 66G PROTEIN // 12G CARBOHYDRATE

MUSTARD CHICKEN
and Braised Endives

24 OUNCES CHICKEN THIGHS	**4 CUPS** ROMAINE LETTUCE
1 TEASPOON GRAPE SEED OIL	**1/2 CUP** RED ONIONS, FINELY SLICED
8 ENDIVES	**1/2 CUP** TOMATOES, CHOPPED
1/2 CUP CHICKEN BROTH	**1/2 CUP** RED PEPPERS, CHOPPED
4 TABLESPOONS DIJON MUSTARD	**2 TABLESPOONS** OLIVE OIL
1 TABLESPOON + 2 TEASPOONS LEMON JUICE	**1 TEASPOON** OREGANO
SEA SALT & PEPPER TO TASTE	**1/2 CUP** LOW FAT FETA CHEESE PIECES

READY TO COOK

1. **SEASON** THE CHICKEN PIECES WITH SEA SALT AND PEPPER AND BROWN IN THE GRAPE SEED OIL ON BOTH SIDES.

2. **REMOVE** THE CHICKEN AND SET ASIDE.

3. **PUT** THE ENDIVES IN THE PAN AND SAUTÉ FOR ABOUT 5 MINUTES, TURNING TO COOK EACH SIDE.

4. **ADD** THE CHICKEN BROTH AND SIMMER FOR ANOTHER 5 MINUTES.

5. **MIX** THE DIJON MUSTARD AND 1 TABLESPOON OF LEMON JUICE AND COAT THE CHICKEN THIGHS WITH THE MIXTURE.

6. **PLACE** THE CHICKEN ON TOP OF THE ENDIVES IN THE PAN, COVER AND COOK FOR ABOUT 45 MINUTES.

7. **SHRED** THE LETTUCE AND TOSS WITH FETA.

8. **WHISK** 2 TEASPOONS OF LEMON JUICE WITH THE OLIVE OIL AND OREGANO AND POUR OVER THE SALAD. ADD THE CHOPPED TOMATOES, RED PEPPERS AND RED ONIONS.

Serve chicken with braised endives and side of salad.

PER SERVING: 490 CALORIES // 26G FAT // 54G PROTEIN // 7G CARBOHYDRATE

SPICE BLENDS
Chili + Curry + Tagine

#1 VERATI'S HOT CHILI POWDER ⬇⬇⬇

1 TEASPOON CAYENNE PEPPER	1 TEASPOON OREGANO
1 TEASPOON PAPRIKA	2 TEASPOONS GARLIC POWDER
2 TEASPOONS GROUND CUMIN	

#2 VERATI'S MEDIUM HEAT CHILI POWDER ⬇⬇⬇

3 TABLESPOONS ANCHO CHILI POWDER	2 TEASPOONS GARLIC POWDER
1 TABLESPOON CUMIN	1 TEASPOON CORIANDER
2 TEASPOONS DRIED OREGANO	SEA SALT & PEPPER TO TASTE

#3 VERATI'S CURRY BLEND ⬇⬇⬇   *SINGLE USE RECIPE, MAKE IT X4 IF YOU WANT TO STORE SOME!*

1/2 TEASPOON CAYENNE PEPPER	1 TEASPOON CORIANDER, GROUND
1 TEASPOON CUMIN, GROUND	1 TEASPOON CURRY, POWDER

#4 VERATI'S TAGINE BLEND ⬇⬇⬇   *SINGLE USE RECIPE, MAKE IT X4 IF YOU WANT TO STORE SOME!*

1 TEASPOON GROUND GINGER	1 TEASPOON GROUND TURMERIC
1 TEASPOON GROUND CUMIN	1 TEASPOON GROUND CINNAMON
1 TEASPOON GROUND CORIANDER	1/4 TEASPOON GROUND ALLSPICE

#5 VERATI'S TAGINE BLEND ⬇⬇⬇   *SINGLE USE RECIPE, MAKE IT X4 IF YOU WANT TO STORE SOME!*

1 TEASPOON GARLIC POWDER	2 TABLESPOONS GROUND CORIANDER
1 TEASPOON GROUND GINGER	1 TEASPOON FENUGREEK POWDER
1 TEASPOON CLOVES POWDER	1 TEASPOON GROUND CINNAMON
1/2 TEASPOON GRATED NUTMEG	1 TEASPOON FRESH GROUND BLACK PEPPER
1 TEASPOON MACE POWDER	1 TEASPOON GROUND BROWN CARDAMOM SEEDS
11/2 TABLESPOONS CUMIN POWDER	

READY TO COOK

1. **COMBINE** ALL SPICES IN A SMALL BOWL 2. **MIX** WELL 3. **PUT** IN RECIPE OR JAR. 4. **STORE** JAR IN A DARK CUPBOARD.

I LIKE TO PREPARE MINE IN ADVANCE! TO MAKE IT EASY, PUT THE INGREDIENTS IN A JAR WITH A LID, SHAKE AND STORE!
-CHEF VERATI

CARBS

 FAT

best at dinner time

FACT #4

CARBS

ARE THE MAIN FUEL FOR YOUR BODY. THEY PROVIDE ENERGY FOR THE BODY'S CELLS AND TISSUES. THE CARB INTAKE IN YOUR DAILY DIET ENERGIZES YOUR BRAIN.

Freedom

TURKEY BURGER

a Real One

24 OUNCES GROUND TURKEY

1 TEASPOON CUMIN

1 TEASPOON CORIANDER

1 TEASPOON OIL

4 CUPS MUSHROOMS, SLICED

1/4 CUP FRESH PARSLEY, CHOPPED

4 TEASPOONS LOW FAT MAYONNAISE

4 BUNS, TOASTED

1 TOMATO, SLICED

4 DILL PICKLES, SLICED

4 CUPS MIXED GREEN SALAD

4 OUNCES LOW FAT LOW CARB HOUSE DRESSING (*SEE PAGE 95*)

SEA SALT & PEPPER TO TASTE

READY TO COOK

1. IN A BOWL, MIX THE GROUND CHICKEN WITH THE CUMIN, CORIANDER, SEA SALT AND PEPPER UNTIL THE MIXTURE IS WELL BLENDED. 2. SHAPE INTO FOUR PATTIES. 3. COOK SLOWLY IN ONE TEASPOON OF THE OIL UNTIL BROWNED, TURNING ONCE HALF WAY THROUGH, UNTIL THE CHICKEN IS COOKED (ABOUT 10-12 MINUTES). 4. SAUTÉ THE MUSHROOMS IN THE REMAINING TEASPOON OF OIL FOR 3-4 MINUTES, UNTIL SOFT. 5. SPOON THE MUSHROOMS OVER THE CHICKEN BURGERS BEFORE SERVING, ADDING A LITTLE OF THE CHOPPED PARSLEY TO EACH. 6. SPOON 1 TEASPOON OF MAYONNAISE ON ONE SIDE OF TOASTED BUN. 7. TOP WITH SLICED TOMATO AND PICKLE. 8. SERVE WITH A GREEN SALAD AND LOW FAT LOW CARB HOUSE DRESSING.

▶YOU'VE EARNED YOUR BREAD
BURGER BUNS, BAGUETTES, CIABATTAS, CROISSANTS, PANCAKES, SCONES. SWEET AND SAVORY; THAT'S *Freedom*
PRIORITIZE WHOLEGRAIN FOODS; AS THEY ARE HIGHER IN FIBER.

PER SERVING: 572 CALORIES // 46G CARBOHYDRATE // 55G PROTEIN // 13G FAT

SPLASH OF WINE
Coq au Vin

24 **OUNCES** CHICKEN PIECES

4 PEARS HALVES (CANNED OR FRESH), CHOPPED

1 **TABLESPOON** GRAPE SEED OIL

2 **CUPS** WHOLE PEARL ONIONS OR **2 CUPS** ONIONS, CHOPPED

2 **CUPS** FRESH MUSHROOMS, WHOLE

4 **CLOVES** GARLIC, CHOPPED

1 **CUP** RED WINE

1 **CUP** CHICKEN BROTH

1 **TABLESPOON** TOMATO PASTE

2 BAY LEAVES

1 **TABLESPOON** FRESH MARJORAM

1 **TABLESPOON** FRESH THYME

2 **TEASPOONS** CORN STARCH

1/4 **CUP** WATER

4 **CUPS** SPINACH, BLANCHED (*SEE PAGE 129*)

SEA SALT & PEPPER TO TASTE

READY TO COOK

1. **IN** A LARGE POT, COOK THE PEARS IN A SMALL AMOUNT OF THE OIL UNTIL LIGHTLY BROWNED.

2. **ADD** THE ONIONS AND STIR UNTIL LIGHTLY BROWNED.

3. **ADD** GARLIC AND COOK 1 MINUTE. REMOVE EVERYTHING FROM THE PAN.

4. **PUT** THE CHICKEN PIECES IN THE PAN WITH A LITTLE MORE OIL AND BROWN ON ALL SIDES.

5. **ADD** THE ONIONS, PEARS AND GARLIC BACK INTO THE PAN ALONG WITH THE WINE, TOMATO PASTE, BAY LEAVES, MARJORAM, THYME, SEA SALT AND PEPPER AND SIMMER, COVERED, FOR 50 MINUTES.

6. **ADD** THE WHOLE FRESH MUSHROOMS AND CORN STARCH DISSOLVED IN THE WATER AND SIMMER FOR ANOTHER 10 MINUTES.

7. **BLANCH** THE SPINACH.

Serve with spinach.

DISCOVER THE JOYS OF FREEDOM IN YOUR DAY TO DAY COOKING...

PER SERVING: 492 CALORIES // 22G CARBOHYDRATE // 56G PROTEIN // 11G FAT

HERBED CHICKEN
with Vegetables

24 OUNCES CHICKEN (4 BREASTS), BONELESS & SKINLESS

1 TEASPOON GRAPE SEED OIL

1 TEASPOON PAPRIKA

1 TEASPOON MARJORAM

2 SPRIGS FRESH PARSLEY

2 SPRIGS FRESH THYME

1/4 CUP FLOUR

2 CUPS CHICKEN BROTH

2 CUPS BUTTERNUT SQUASH, PEELED & CUBED

2 CUPS SMALL MUSHROOMS, WHOLE

4 CUPS SPINACH

4 OUNCES LOW FAT LOW CARB HOUSE DRESSING (*SEE PAGE 95*)

SEA SALT & PEPPER TO TASTE

READY TO COOK ⬇⬇⬇

1. IN A BOWL, MIX TOGETHER THE SEA SALT, PEPPER, PAPRIKA, MARJORAM AND FLOUR. **2. COAT** THE CHICKEN PIECES, SHAKING OFF EXCESS. **3. HEAT** OIL IN A LARGE FRYING PAN AND BROWN THE CHICKEN ON ALL SIDES. **4. ADD** THE CHICKEN BROTH, SQUASH, SPRIGS OF FRESH PARSLEY AND THYME. **5. COVER** AND SIMMER 45 MINUTES. **6. ADD** THE MUSHROOMS AND COOK, UNCOVERED UNTIL THE LIQUID IS REDUCED TO HALF.

Serve on a small bed of spinach.

PER SERVING: 410 CALORIES // 28G CARBOHYDRATE // 58G PROTEIN // 10G FAT

SPICY SLOPPY JOES
with Green Salad

24 OUNCES GROUND CHICKEN OR TURKEY

1 TEASPOON GRAPE SEED OIL

1 CUP ONIONS, FINELY CHOPPED

1 CLOVE GARLIC, FINELY CHOPPED

1 CUP GREEN PEPPERS, FINELY CHOPPED

1 CUP SWEET RED PEPPERS, FINELY CHOPPED

1/2 TEASPOON CINNAMON

1/2 TEASPOON CHILI POWDER (*SEE PAGE 173*)

2 CUPS PREPARED SPICY TOMATO SAUCE

2 WHOLE WHEAT ROLLS, HALVED

5 CUPS MIXED GREEN SALAD

4 OUNCES LOW FAT LOW CARB HOUSE DRESSING (*SEE PAGE 95*)

SEA SALT & PEPPER TO TASTE

READY TO COOK ⬇⬇⬇

1. HEAT OIL IN A PAN AND COOK THE ONIONS UNTIL JUST SOFT. **2. ADD** THE GARLIC, RED AND GREEN PEPPERS, SEA SALT PEPPER, CINNAMON AND CHILI POWDER. **3. ADD** THE GROUND CHICKEN OR TURKEY AND COOK UNTIL IT IS NO LONGER PINK, STIRRING OCCASIONALLY. **4. ADD** THE SPICY TOMATO SAUCE AND SIMMER FOR 20 MINUTES. **5. SPOON** 1/4 OF THE MIXTURE ON EACH OF THE WHOLE WHEAT ROLL HALVES.

Serve with fresh green salad.

PER SERVING: 468 CALORIES // 28G CARBOHYDRATE // 51G PROTEIN // 15G FAT

TURKEY À L'ORANGE
with Zucchini

24 OUNCES TURKEY, BONELESS & SKINLESS	
2 TEASPOONS PAPRIKA	
1 CUP CHICKEN BROTH	
2 TEASPOONS FLOUR	
2 TEASPOONS VINEGAR	
2 TEASPOONS SUGAR	
1 TABLESPOON LEMON JUICE	
1/2 CUP FROZEN ORANGE JUICE CONCENTRATE	
8 CUPS ZUCCHINI, SLICED	
SEA SALT & PEPPER TO TASTE	

READY TO COOK ⬇ ⬇ ⬇

1. SEASON TURKEY WITH SEA SALT AND PEPPER TO TASTE AND PAPRIKA. **2. BAKE** ON A RACK OVER A ROASTING PAN IN A PRE-HEATED **350⁰ F** OVEN. **3. PUT** THE ROASTING PAN ON THE STOVE TOP AND, OVER **LOW HEAT**, STIR THE FLOUR INTO THE PAN JUICES. **4. ADD** CHICKEN BROTH, VINEGAR, SUGAR, LEMON JUICE AND ORANGE JUICE AND CONTINUE TO STIR UNTIL THE DRIPPINGS FROM THE BOTTOM OF THE PAN ARE AMALGAMATED AND THE SAUCE IS THICKENED SLIGHTLY. **5. PLACE** THE TURKEY ON A LARGE SERVING PLATTER AND POUR THE ORANGE SAUCE OVER TOP.

Serve with steamed zucchini.

PER SERVING: 429 CALORIES // 35G CARBOHYDRATE // 35G PROTEIN // 7G FAT

MOUNT CHICKEN
with *Simmered Apricots*

24 OUNCES CHICKEN (4 BREASTS), BONES IN & SKIN ON	1/2 TEASPOON ALLSPICE
1/2 CUP APRICOTS, DRIED	1 TABLESPOON HONEY
1 TEASPOON CUMIN	1 TEASPOON GRAPE SEED OIL
1 TEASPOON DRIED CORIANDER	2 CUPS RICE, COOKED
1 CUP ONIONS, FINELY CHOPPED	7 CUPS SPINACH
2 CLOVES GARLIC, FINELY CHOPPED	SEA SALT & PEPPER TO TASTE
1/2 TEASPOON CINNAMON	

READY TO COOK

1. SEASON THE CHICKEN BREASTS WITH SEA SALT AND PEPPER, CUMIN, CORIANDER, CINNAMON AND ALLSPICE.

2. HEAT THE OIL IN A PAN AND BROWN THE CHICKEN ON BOTH SIDES.

3. ADD THE CHOPPED ONIONS AND GARLIC AND COOK FOR ANOTHER 4-5 MINUTES ON MEDIUM HEAT.

4. CHOP THE DRIED APRICOTS INTO SMALL PIECES. ADD TO THE PAN.

5. COVER AND SIMMER FOR 25-30 MINUTES UNTIL THE CHICKEN IS COOKED.

6. COOK THE RICE IN WATER ON THE STOVE TOP OR IN THE MICROWAVE UNTIL THE RICE IS SOFT, ADDING A LITTLE MORE WATER IF NECESSARY.

7. SAUTÉ THE SPINACH.

SERVE WITH A DRIZZLE OF HONEY ON TOP OF THE CHICKEN, STEAMED RICE AND SPINACH.

ENJOY YOUR MEAL ...
TAKE YOUR TIME TO CHEW YOUR FOOD!

PER SERVING: 614 CALORIES // 63G CARBOHYDRATE // 62G PROTEIN // 9G FAT

CHICKEN & SWISS CHARD
Romano Bean Casserole

20 OUNCES CHICKEN (4 BREASTS), BONELESS, SKINLESS & CUBED	**2 CUPS** SWISS CHARD, CHOPPED
1 CUP COOKED ROMANO BEANS	**2 CUPS** CHICKEN BROTH
2 CUPS ONIONS, CHOPPED	**1 TEASPOON** THYME
1 CUP CELERY, CHOPPED	**1 TEASPOON** OREGANO
1 CUP CARROTS, SLICED	**1 TEASPOON** BASIL
1 CUP RUTABAGA	**1 TEASPOON** GRAPE SEED OIL
1 CUP SWEET POTATOES, CUBED	SEA SALT & PEPPER TO TASTE

READY TO COOK

1. **SEASON** THE CHICKEN WITH SEA SALT AND PEPPER.

2. **HEAT** THE OIL IN A FRYING PAN AND BROWN THE CHICKEN ON ALL SIDES.

3. **REMOVE** THE CHICKEN AND SAUTÉ THE ONIONS UNTIL SOFT.

4. **PLACE** THE BROWNED CHICKEN AND ONIONS IN AN OVEN-PROOF CASSEROLE DISH.

5. **ADD** THE ROMANO BEANS, CELERY, CARROTS, SWEET POTATOES, SWISS CHARD, CHICKEN BROTH, THYME, OREGANO AND BASIL.

6. **COVER** AND BAKE IN THE OVEN FOR 45-50 MINUTES AT **350°F**.

Serve with garnish on the side.

MEXICAN TURKEY
Tabbouleh

24 OUNCES TURKEY (4 BREASTS), BONELESS & SKINLESS	**1 CUP** GREEN ONIONS, FINELY CHOPPED
1 CUP BULGAR	**1/4 CUP** LEMON JUICE
3 CUPS BOILING WATER	**2 TEASPOONS** CUMIN
2 TEASPOONS GRAPE SEED OIL	**1 TEASPOON** CORIANDER
2 CUPS FRESH TOMATOES, CUBED	**1/4 TEASPOON** ALLSPICE
2 CUPS CUCUMBERS, PEELED AND CUBED	**1/2 CUP** FRESH CILANTRO, CHOPPED
1 CUP GREEN PEPPERS, FINELY CHOPPED	**1/2 CUP** FRESH MINT LEAVES, CHOPPED
1 CUP SWEET RED PEPPERS, FINELY CHOPPED	**1 TABLESPOON** FRESH OREGANO, CHOPPED
1 CUP KERNEL CORN, CANNED OR FROZEN	SEA SALT & PEPPER TO TASTE

READY TO COOK

1. **POUR** THE BOILING WATER OVER THE BULGAR AND ALLOW TO STAND FOR 40 MINUTES.

2. **DRAIN** WELL, PRESSING TO RELEASE ANY WATER.

3. **SEASON** THE TURKEY BREASTS WITH 1 TEASPOON OF CUMIN AND CORIANDER AND BROWN IN 1 TEASPOON OF OIL.

4. **PLACE** THE BREASTS IN THE OVEN AND COOK AT **350° F** FOR 20-25 MINUTES OR UNTIL DONE.

5. **IN** A LARGE BOWL, WHISK THE REMAINING TEASPOON OF OIL WITH THE LEMON JUICE, SEA SALT AND PEPPER, 1 TEASPOON OF CUMIN AND ALLSPICE.

6. **ADD** THE BULGAR AND TOSS WELL.

7. **ADD** THE TOMATOES, CUCUMBERS, RED AND GREEN PEPPERS, CORN AND GREEN ONIONS AND TOSS AGAIN.

8. **JUST** BEFORE SERVING, MIX IN THE CILANTRO, MINT LEAVES AND OREGANO.

Serve with fresh herbs on top.

PER SERVING: 582 CALORIES // 54G CARBOHYDRATE // 59G PROTEIN // 13G FAT

GRANDMA'S CHICKEN
and White Bean Casserole

20 OUNCES CHICKEN (4 BREASTS), BONELESS & SKIN ON	**2 CUPS** COOKED WHITE KIDNEY BEANS
1 CUP ONIONS, CHOPPED	**2 TEASPOONS** OREGANO
4 CLOVES GARLIC, FINELY CHOPPED	**1 TEASPOON** MARJORAM
1 CUP DICED TOMATOES	**1 TABLESPOON** GRAPE SEED OIL
1 CUP TOMATO SAUCE	**1/2 CUP** WATER OR CHICKEN BROTH (OPTIONAL)
1 CUP CARROTS, DICED	**2 TEASPOONS** LEMON ZEST
1 CUP FRESH SPINACH, SHREDDED	**4 TEASPOONS** FRESH PARSLEY, CHOPPED
1 CUP BLACK OLIVES	SEA SALT & PEPPER TO TASTE

READY TO COOK

1. **HEAT** THE OIL IN A PAN AND SAUTÉ THE ONIONS AND GARLIC UNTIL SOFT, BUT NOT BROWNED.
2. **SEASON** THE CHICKEN PIECES WITH SEA SALT AND PEPPER TO TASTE AND BROWN EVENLY.
3. **ADD** THE CARROTS, KIDNEY BEANS, TOMATO SAUCE, TOMATOES, OREGANO, MARJORAM AND BLACK OLIVES.
4. **THERE** SHOULD BE ABOUT 1" OF LIQUID ON THE BOTTOM OF THE PAN.
5. **IF** NECESSARY, ADD 1/2 CUP WATER OR CHICKEN BROTH.
6. **COVER** AND COOK FOR 25 MINUTES OR UNTIL THE CHICKEN IS COOKED.

Serve with parsley, spinach and lemon zest on top.

VERATI *Twist*

WHEN YOU DON'T HAVE TIME TO COOK YOUR WHITE KIDNEY BEANS, USE CANNED!

PER SERVING: 629 CALORIES // 47G CARBOHYDRATE // 67G PROTEIN // 12G FAT

CHICKEN PENNE
with Vegetables

2 **CUPS** WHOLE-WHEAT PENNE

24 **OUNCES** CHICKEN BREASTS, BONELESS & SKINLESS

6 **CUPS** FROZEN MIXED VEGETABLES

2 **CUPS** BROCCOLI FRESH OR FROZEN, FLORETS

1/2 **CUP** GREEN ONIONS, FINELY CHOPPED

1 1/2 **CUPS** LOW FAT MILK

1 **TABLESPOON** CORN STARCH

1 **TEASPOON** BUTTER

1/8 **TEASPOON** NUTMEG

SEA SALT & PEPPER TO TASTE

READY TO COOK ⬇ ⬇ ⬇

1. **COOK** THE PASTA IN BOILING WATER UNTIL AL DENTE, ADDING THE FROZEN VEGETABLES FOR THE LAST 7 MINUTES. 2. **BROWN** AND COOK THE CHICKEN CUBES IN THE OIL. 3. **DRAIN** PASTA AND VEGETABLES. 4. **ADD** THE COOKED CHICKEN. 5. **PUT** THE TEASPOON OF BUTTER IN ANOTHER PAN AND MELT. 6. **IN** A MEASURING CUP, MIX CORN STARCH AND MILK AND STIR UNTIL THE CORN STARCH IS DISSOLVED. 7. **ADD** TO THE BUTTER IN THE PAN AND STIR CONSTANTLY UNTIL THE MIXTURE IS THICKENED AND SMOOTH. 8. **ADD** SEA SALT, PEPPER, NUTMEG AND FINELY CHOPPED GREEN ONION. 9. **POUR** THE SAUCE OVER THE PASTA MIXTURE.

Toss well and serve.

PER SERVING: 535 CALORIES // 46G CARBOHYDRATE // 64G PROTEIN // 8G FAT

BROWN RICE & CHICKPEA
Chicken Casserole

20 **OUNCES** CHICKEN (4 BREAST), BONELESS & SKINLESS

1 **CUP** CHICKPEAS, COOKED OR CANNED

1 **CUP** MUSHROOMS, SLICED

1/2 **CUP** LOW FAT SOUR CREAM

1 **CUP** BROWN RICE, COOKED

2 **CUPS** WATER

1 **CUP** CELERY, FINELY CHOPPED

1 **CUP** CARROTS, FINELY CHOPPED

1 **CUP** ONIONS, FINELY CHOPPED

1 **TEASPOON** GRAPE SEED OIL

1/4 **CUP** FRESH PARSLEY, CHOPPED

4 **CUPS** MIXED GREEN SALAD

4 **OUNCES** LOW FAT LOW CARB HOUSE DRESSING (*SEE PAGE 95*)

READY TO COOK ⬇ ⬇ ⬇

1. **COOK** THE RICE IN WATER ON THE STOVE TOP OR IN THE MICROWAVE UNTIL THE RICE IS SOFT, ADDING A LITTLE MORE WATER IF NECESSARY. 2. **BROWN** THE CHICKEN PIECES IN THE OIL. 3. **ADD** THE ONIONS AND MUSHROOMS AND COOK 2-3 MINUTES, UNTIL THE ONIONS AND MUSHROOMS ARE SOFT BUT NOT BROWN. SET THE CHICKEN AND ONIONS ASIDE. 4. **IN** THE 2 CUPS OF WATER, COOK THE CELERY AND CARROTS UNTIL JUST TENDER. 5. **DRAIN**, KEEPING THE WATER THEY WERE COOKED IN. 6. **MIX** THE RICE, ONIONS, CELERY, CARROTS, SEA SALT AND PEPPER, AND STIR IN THE CHICKPEAS. 7. **LAY** THE CHICKEN PIECES ON TOP. 8. **COVER** AND BAKE AT **350° F** FOR 45 MINUTES OR UNTIL THE CHICKEN IS DONE.

Serve with a sprinkle of parsley and a mixed green salad.

PER SERVING: 599 CALORIES // 47G CARBOHYDRATE // 52G PROTEIN // 15G FAT

SESAME CHICKEN
with Snow Peas

24 **OUNCES** CHICKEN (4 BREASTS), BONELESS & SKINLESS

2 **TABLESPOONS** LEMON JUICE

1 **CUP** LOW FAT BUTTERMILK

1/4 **CUP** SESAME SEEDS

1/2 **CUP** BREAD CRUMBS OR PANKO

6 **CUPS** SNOW PEAS

2 **CUPS** RED PEPPERS, SLICED

SEA SALT & PEPPER TO TASTE

READY TO COOK ⬇⬇⬇

1. IN A BOWL, COMBINE THE LEMON JUICE, SEA SALT AND PEPPER AND BUTTERMILK. COAT THE CHICKEN BREASTS WITH THE MIXTURE AND LEAVE TO MARINATE FOR 1 HOUR (OR OVERNIGHT IN THE REFRIGERATOR). **2. COMBINE** THE SESAME SEEDS AND BREAD CRUMBS OR PANKO IN A SHALLOW DISH. REMOVE EACH CHICKEN BREAST FROM THE MARINADE AND COAT LIBERALLY WITH THE SESAME AND BREAD CRUMB MIXTURE. **3. PLACE** THE CHICKEN ON AN OVEN PAN AND BAKE 45-50 MINUTES UNTIL THE CHICKEN IS DONE AND THE COATING IS CRISP AND GOLDEN BROWN.

Serve with steamed snow peas and red peppers.

PER SERVING: 570 CALORIES // 31G CARBOHYDRATE // 63G PROTEIN // 12G FAT

CHICKEN, MUSHROOM
and Leek Pie

20 **OUNCES** CHICKEN (4 BREASTS), BONELESS, SKINLESS & CUBED

3 **CUPS** LEEKS, WHITE SECTIONS ONLY

5 **CUPS** MUSHROOMS, FINELY SLICED

1/2 **CUP** SKIM MILK

1 BAY LEAF

1/2 **CUP** CHICKEN BROTH

2 **TEASPOONS** CORN STARCH

2 **TEASPOONS** CURRY POWDER

1 PIE SHELL (*SEE PAGE 397*)

1 **TEASPOON** GRAPE SEED OIL

2 **TABLESPOONS** PARMESAN CHEESE, LOW FAT, GRATED

4 **CUPS** MIXED GREEN SALAD

4 **OUNCES** LOW FAT LOW CARB HOUSE DRESSING (*SEE PAGE 95*)

READY TO COOK ⬇⬇⬇

1. POACH CHICKEN CUBES IN THE BROTH. **2. ADD** THE LEEKS AND MUSHROOMS AND COOK UNTIL SOFT. **3. ADD** THE MILK AND BAY LEAF. **4. STIR** THE CORN STARCH INTO THE MILK AND ADD TO THE PAN. **5. ADD** THE CURRY POWDER, SEA SALT AND PEPPER AND STIR WELL. **6. REDUCE** THE HEAT AND SIMMER UNTIL THE SAUCE IS THICKENED. **7. POUR** THE MIXTURE INTO THE PIE SHELL. **8. SPRINKLE** PARMESAN CHEESE OVER TOP AND BAKE IN A **350⁰ F** OVEN FOR 45-50 MINUTES.

Serve with a green salad.

PER SERVING: 517 CALORIES // 37G CARBOHYDRATE // 52G PROTEIN // 17G FAT

SPICY CHICKEN STRIPS
and Brussel Sprouts

24 OUNCES CHICKEN (4 BREASTS), BONELESS, SKINLESS & SLICED	4 CUPS BRUSSEL SPROUTS, WHOLE
2 EGG WHITES	1 TABLESPOON WALNUT, PIECES
1 TEASPOON CAYENNE PEPPER	4 TABLESPOONS LOW FAT SOUR CREAM
4 TEASPOON VERATI'S MEDIUM HEAT CHILI (*SEE PAGE 173*)	1 TEASPOON GRAPE SEED OIL
1 TEASPOON ONION SALT	SEA SALT & PEPPER TO TASTE
4 CUPS BABY ONIONS, WHOLE	

READY TO COOK

1. BEAT THE EGG WHITES UNTIL FLUFFY IN A SHALLOW BOWL.
2. COMBINE THE CUMIN, CORIANDER, PAPRIKA, CAYENNE PEPPER, ONION SALT AND GARLIC POWDER.
3. DIP THE CHICKEN STRIPS FIRST INTO THE EGG WHITES, THEN INTO THE HERB MIXTURE.
4. PLACE THE STRIPS ON AN OILED OVEN SHEET AND BAKE AT 350°F FOR 10-15 MINUTES EACH SIDE, TURNING THE STRIPS OVER HALF-WAY THROUGH THE COOKING TIME.
5. BOIL THE ONIONS AND BRUSSEL SPROUTS UNTIL TENDER. DRAIN.
6. ARRANGE ON PLATES WITH THE CHICKEN STRIPS AND DRIZZLE THE SOUR CREAM OVER TOP.

SERVE WITH A SPRINKLE OF WALNUT PIECES.

PER SERVING: 444 CALORIES // 21G CARBOHYDRATE // 58G PROTEIN // 10G FAT

CREAMY CHICKEN
and Vegetable Stew

20 OUNCES CHICKEN (4 BREASTS), BONELESS & SKINLESS	**4 CLOVES** GARLIC, FINELY CHOPPED
1 CUP ONIONS, COARSELY CHOPPED	**1 CUP** LOW FAT SOUR CREAM
1 CUP TURNIP, CUBED	**2 TEASPOONS** GRAPE SEED OIL
1 CUP CELERY, COARSELY CHOPPED	**2 TABLESPOONS** DRIED PARSLEY
2 CUPS SMALL MUSHROOMS, WHOLE	**1 TEASPOON** ONION POWDER
1 CUP CAULIFLOWER, COARSELY CHOPPED	**1 CUP** ORZO
2 CUPS FRESH OR FROZEN GREEN BEANS	SEA SALT & PEPPER TO TASTE
4 CUPS LOW FAT CHICKEN OR VEGETABLE BROTH	

READY TO COOK

1. **SEASON** THE CHICKEN WITH SEA SALT, PEPPER AND ONION POWDER AND BROWN WITH ONE TEASPOON OF OIL IN A PAN.

2. **REMOVE** FROM THE PAN AND SET ASIDE.

3. **COOK** ONIONS IN THE PAN UNTIL THEY BECOME TRANSPARENT (DO NOT BROWN).

4. **ADD** THE GARLIC AND COOK FOR ONE MINUTE.

5. **REMOVE** BOTH FROM THE PAN.

6. **IN** A LARGE OVEN-PROOF CASSEROLE, PLACE THE ONIONS, GARLIC, TURNIP, CELERY, CAULIFLOWER AND GREEN BEANS.

7. **PLACE** THE CHICKEN PIECES ON TOP OF THE VEGETABLES. POUR CHICKEN OR VEGETABLE BROTH OVER TOP.

8. **COOK,** COVERED, FOR ONE HOUR OR UNTIL THE CHICKEN JUICES ARE CLEAR.

9. **SAUTÉ** THE MUSHROOMS IN THE REMAINING TEASPOON OF OIL FOR ONE MINUTE.

10. **REMOVE** THE PAN FROM THE OVEN.

11. **STIR** IN THE CUP OF LOW FAT SOUR CREAM, THE MUSHROOMS AND PARSLEY.

12. **RETURN** THE PAN TO THE OVEN AND COOK, UNCOVERED, ANOTHER 15 MINUTES.

Serve the beans on top of the chicken breasts.

PER SERVING: 711 CALORIES // 48G CARBOHYDRATE // 72G PROTEIN // 18G FAT

CHICKEN WRAPS
with Brown Rice and Lentils

20 OUNCES CHICKEN (4 BREASTS), BONELESS & SKINLESS	**1 TEASPOON** LEMON JUICE
1/2 CUP BROWN RICE, COOKED	**1 TEASPOON** CHILI SAUCE
1 CUP LENTILS, COOKED OR CANNED	**1 CUP** FRESH CILANTRO, CHOPPED
1 CUP RED ONIONS, THINLY SLICED	**1 TEASPOON** GRAPE SEED OIL
1 CUP GREEN ONIONS, FINELY CHOPPED	**1 TEASPOON** CUMIN
1 CUP SWEET RED PEPPERS, SLICED	**1 TEASPOON** CORIANDER
1 CUP LETTUCE, SLICED	**8-12 LEAVES** OF ICEBERG OR BOSTON LETTUCE
2 CUPS FRESH TOMATOES, CUBED	SEA SALT & PEPPER TO TASTE
1 CUP AVOCADO, MASHED	

READY TO COOK

1. **STIR FRY** THE CHICKEN IN OIL UNTIL COOKED.
2. **USING** A FORK, MASH THE AVOCADO WITH THE TEASPOON OF LEMON JUICE.
3. **SPREAD** THE AVOCADO MIXTURE AND CHILI SAUCE ON EACH OF THE LETTUCE WRAPS.
4. **DIVIDE** THE RED ONIONS, RED AND GREEN PEPPERS, LETTUCE AND HALF THE TOMATOES AMONG THE WRAPS AND ROLL UP.
5. **PLACE** ON PLATE SEAM SIDE DOWN.
6. **COOK** THE RICE IN WATER ON THE STOVE TOP OR IN THE MICROWAVE UNTIL THE RICE IS SOFT, ADDING A LITTLE MORE WATER IF NECESSARY.
7. **HEAT** THE LENTILS.
8. **WHEN** THE RICE IS COOKED, ADD CUMIN, CORIANDER AND SEA SALT.
9. **STIR** IN REMAINING TOMATOES AND ADD THE CHOPPED GREEN ONIONS AND THE HEATED LENTILS AND TOSS WELL.

Serve with the lettuce wraps.

VERATI TIPS
BROWN RICE WILL TAKE ABOUT 15 MINUTES TO COOK IN THE MICROWAVE - ADD DOUBLE THE AMOUNT OF WATER TO THE RICE AND COOK IN 3 MINUTE INCREMENTS, ADDING ADDITIONAL WATER IF NECESSARY.

PER SERVING: 629 CALORIES // 49G CARBOHYDRATE // 57G PROTEIN // 15G FAT

OPEN-FACED CHICKEN

What a Sandwich!

20 OUNCES CHICKEN (4 BREASTS), BONELESS & SKINLESS

1 TABLESPOON LOW FAT MAYONNAISE

1 TEASPOON OIL

1 TABLESPOON LEMON JUICE

1/4 CUP FRESH CILANTRO, FINELY CHOPPED

1 TEASPOON CUMIN

2 CIABATTA ROLLS

1 TOMATO, SLICED

4 LEAVES BOSTON LETTUCE

8 CUPS MIXED GREEN SALAD

4 OUNCES LOW FAT LOW CARB HOUSE DRESSING (*SEE PAGE 95*)

SEA SALT & PEPPER TO TASTE

READY TO COOK ⬇ ⬇ ⬇

1. COMBINE THE MAYONNAISE, LEMON JUICE AND CILANTRO IN A BLENDER AND BLEND FOR 1 MINUTE. 2. CUT THE CHICKEN BREASTS IN HALF AND POUND OUT WITH A MALLET OR ROLLING PIN UNTIL QUITE THIN. 3. SEASON WITH SEA SALT AND PEPPER TO TASTE AND CUMIN AND COOK UNTIL DONE, ABOUT 10-12 MINUTES, OR UNTIL THE JUICES RUN CLEAR. 4. CUT EACH OF THE CIABATTA ROLLS IN HALF AND TOAST THE INSIDE OF EACH PIECE. 5. PUT ONE QUARTER OF THE MAYONNAISE MIXTURE ON EACH ROLL. 6. TOP WITH A SLICE OF TOMATO AND A SLICE OF LETTUCE AND ONE OF THE COOKED CHICKEN BREASTS.

SERVE WITH MIXED GREEN SALAD.

PER SERVING: 333 CALORIES // 28G CARBOHYDRATE // 45G PROTEIN // 6G FAT

DIJON CHICKEN
with Butternut Squash

24 OUNCES CHICKEN (4 BREASTS), BONELESS & SKINLESS

1 TABLESPOON LEMON JUICE

2 TABLESPOONS DIJON MUSTARD

4 CUPS MUSHROOMS, SLICED

4 CUPS (1 LARGE) BUTTERNUT SQUASH, SEEDS REMOVED, QUARTERED

1 TEASPOON BUTTER

1 TEASPOON DRIED THYME

1 TEASPOON OIL

1/2 CUP SKIM MILK

1 TEASPOON CORN STARCH

1 1/2 POUNDS POTATOES, QUARTERED

SEA SALT & PEPPER TO TASTE

READY TO COOK ↓↓↓

1. PUT THE SQUASH PIECES AND POTATOES ON AN OILED OVEN PAN, BRUSH WITH THE BUTTER AND SPRINKLE EACH PIECE WITH THE THYME. **2. COOK** IN 350 F OVEN UNTIL SOFT, (ABOUT 40 MINUTES). **3. ADD** SEA SALT AND PEPPER TO THE CHICKEN PIECES AND BROWN IN OIL IN A LARGE FRYING PAN. COOK 10-15 MINUTES UNTIL THE CHICKEN IS COOKED THROUGH. **4. REMOVE** FROM THE PAN. **5. ADD** THE MUSHROOMS TO THE PAN AND SAUTÉ 2-3 MINUTES. **6. ADD** WATER WITH THE CORN STARCH DISSOLVED IN IT. **7. STIR** IN LEMON JUICE AND DIJON MUSTARD. **8. CONTINUE** STIRRING UNTIL THE SAUCE IS SMOOTH. **9. PUT** THE CHICKEN PIECES BACK IN AND HEAT OVER LOW HEAT FOR 7-10 MINUTES. STIRRING OCCASIONALLY AND ADD THE BUTTERNUT SQUASH.

Serve with boiled or roasted potatoes

PER SERVING: 558 CALORIES // 48G CARBOHYDRATE // 57G PROTEIN // 14G FAT

LEMON GINGER
Chicken with Rapini

24 OUNCES CHICKEN (4 BREASTS), BONELESS & SKINLESS

1/4 CUP LEMON JUICE

1 TEASPOON LEMON ZEST

1 TEASPOON GROUND GINGER

1 TEASPOON CINNAMON

1/2 CUP WHITE GRAPE JUICE

2 CUPS SWEET POTATOES, SLICED

2 CUPS ONIONS, SLICED

4 CUPS RAPINI

1 TEASPOON GRAPE SEED OIL

SEA SALT & PEPPER TO TASTE

READY TO COOK ↓↓↓

1. HEAT THE OIL IN AN OVEN-PROOF PAN. **2. SEASON** THE CHICKEN BREASTS WITH SEA SALT, PEPPER, CINNAMON AND GINGER. **3. BROWN** THE BREASTS ON EACH SIDE. **4. REMOVE** THE BREASTS FROM THE PAN WHILE YOU PUT A LAYER OF SWEET POTATOES AND SLICED ONIONS ON THE BOTTOM. **5. PUT** THE BREASTS BACK IN AND ADD THE BALANCE OF THE SWEET POTATOES OVER TOP. **6. ADD** THE LEMON JUICE, LEMON ZEST AND GRAPE JUICE. COVER AND BAKE IN A 350º F OVEN FOR 45-50 MINUTES.

Serve with steamed rapini.

PER SERVING: 525 CALORIES // 36G CARBOHYDRATE // 51G PROTEIN // 13G FAT

YOGURT CHICKEN
Drumsticks

VERATI **TIPS**
MARINATE OVERNIGHT,
COVERED, IN REFRIGERATOR
FOR BEST RESULTS!

32 OUNCES	CHICKEN DRUMSTICKS, SKINLESS
1/2 TEASPOON	CHILI POWDER (*SEE PAGE 173*)
1/2 TEASPOON	ONION POWDER
1/2 TEASPOON	GARLIC POWDER
1 TEASPOON	PAPRIKA
1/2 CUP	COARSE CORN MEAL
1 CUP	PLAIN LOW FAT YOGURT
1 TABLESPOON	GRAPE SEED OIL
6 CUPS	RAPINI
1 CUP	RED PEPPERS, CHOPPED
1 CUP	GREEN ONIONS, SLICED
SEA SALT & PEPPER TO TASTE	

READY TO COOK ⬇ ⬇ ⬇

1. MARINATE THE CHICKEN IN THE YOGURT FOR 30-40 MINUTES. **2. COMBINE** THE SEA SALT, PEPPER, CHILI POWDER, PAPRIKA AND CORN MEAL IN A BOWL. **3. REMOVE** THE CHICKEN FROM THE YOGURT PIECE BY PIECE AND DREDGE WITH THE CORN MEAL MIXTURE. **4. HEAT** THE OIL IN A LARGE PAN AND COOK THE CHICKEN, TURNING TO BROWN EACH SIDE. DO NOT CROWD THE PAN. **5. COOK** IN BATCHES IF NECESSARY, KEEPING THE ALREADY BROWNED PIECES IN A WARM OVEN. **6. COOK** UNTIL THE CHICKEN IS DONE, ABOUT 15-18 MINUTES, OR UNTIL THE JUICES RUN CLEAR.

Serve with steamed rapini, red peppers and onions.

PER SERVING: 566 CALORIES // 29G CARBOHYDRATE // 66G PROTEIN // 14G FAT

SATAY CHICKEN
with Peanut Sauce

24 OUNCES CHICKEN (4 BREASTS), BONELESS, SKINLESS & CUBED	**2 CUPS** RICE, COOKED
1 TEASPOON DRIED CORIANDER	**1/2 CUP** CHICKEN BROTH
1 TEASPOON DRIED CUMIN	**2 TABLESPOONS** LIME JUICE
1 CUP RED PEPPERS, CUBED	**1 TABLESPOON** PEANUT BUTTER
1 CUP GREEN PEPPERS, CUBED	**1/2 CUP** FRESH CILANTRO, CHOPPED
6 CUPS CUCUMBERS, CUBED	**1 TABLESPOON** GARLIC, FINELY CHOPPED
4 OUNCES LOW FAT LOW CARB HOUSE DRESSING (*SEE PAGE 95*)	SEA SALT & PEPPER TO TASTE

READY TO COOK

1. **COOK** THE RICE IN WATER ON THE STOVE TOP OR IN THE MICROWAVE UNTIL THE RICE IS SOFT, ADDING A LITTLE MORE WATER IF NECESSARY.

2. **IN** A BOWL, TOSS THE CHICKEN CUBES WITH CORIANDER, CUMIN, SEA SALT AND PEPPER TO TASTE.

3. **THREAD** THE PIECES ON SKEWERS ALTERNATELY WITH THE RED AND GREEN PEPPERS.

4. **PUT** ALL THE INGREDIENTS FOR THE PEANUT SAUCE IN A BLENDER OR FOOD PROCESSOR AND BLEND FOR 1 MINUTE.

5. **DIVIDE** THE SAUCE IN HALF.

6. **BRUSH** THE CHICKEN PIECES WITH HALF THE SAUCE UNTIL WELL COATED AND GRILL UNDER THE **OVEN BROILER**, TURNING ONCE, FOR 5-6 MINUTES OR UNTIL THE CHICKEN IS COOKED THROUGH.

7. **POUR** THE BALANCE OF THE SAUCE OVER THE CHICKEN WHEN SERVING.

Serve with cucumber salad and rice.

PER SERVING: 455 CALORIES // 33G CARBOHYDRATE // 58G PROTEIN // 8G FAT

TURKEY SCALLOPINI
with Cauliflower

24 OUNCES TURKEY (4 BREASTS), BONELESS & SKINLESS	**7 CUPS** CAULIFLOWER, FLORETS
1 TEASPOON GRAPE SEED OIL	**4 CLOVES** GARLIC, FINELY CHOPPED
2 TABLESPOONS LOW FAT BUTTERMILK	**1 CUP** GREEN ONIONS, CHOPPED
1/2 CUP FINE BREAD CRUMBS	**1/4 CUP** LOW FAT MILK
1 TEASPOON LEMON JUICE	**1 TEASPOON** BUTTER
1 TEASPOON LEMON ZEST	SEA SALT & PEPPER TO TASTE
1 TEASPOON PARSLEY	

READY TO COOK

1. **COOK** THE CAULIFLOWER AND GARLIC UNTIL SOFT AND DRAIN.

2. **ADD** THE MILK AND BUTTER, SEA SALT AND PEPPER AND BLEND OR MASH UNTIL SMOOTH.

3. **ADD** GREEN ONIONS AND MIX WELL.

4. **PLACE** EACH TURKEY BREAST BETWEEN LAYERS OF WAXED PAPER AND POUND OUT UNTIL THIN (ABOUT 1/4 INCH).

5. **IN** A BOWL, COMBINE THE BUTTERMILK AND LEMON JUICE.

6. **IN** ANOTHER BOWL, COMBINE THE BREAD CRUMBS, SEA SALT, PEPPER, LEMON ZEST AND PARSLEY.

7. **COAT** THE TURKEY PIECES FIRST WITH THE BUTTERMILK, THEN WITH THE BREAD CRUMBS.

8. **HEAT** THE GRAPE SEED OIL IN A FRYING PAN AND BROWN THE TURKEY ON EACH SIDE. DO NOT OVERCROWD IN THE PAN. DO SEPARATELY IF NECESSARY.

9. **WHEN** ALL THE TURKEY PIECES ARE BROWNED, PLACE THEM ON AN OVEN PAN IN A PRE-HEATED **350° F** OVEN AND BAKE FOR 10-15 MINUTES.

Serve with the mashed cauliflower.

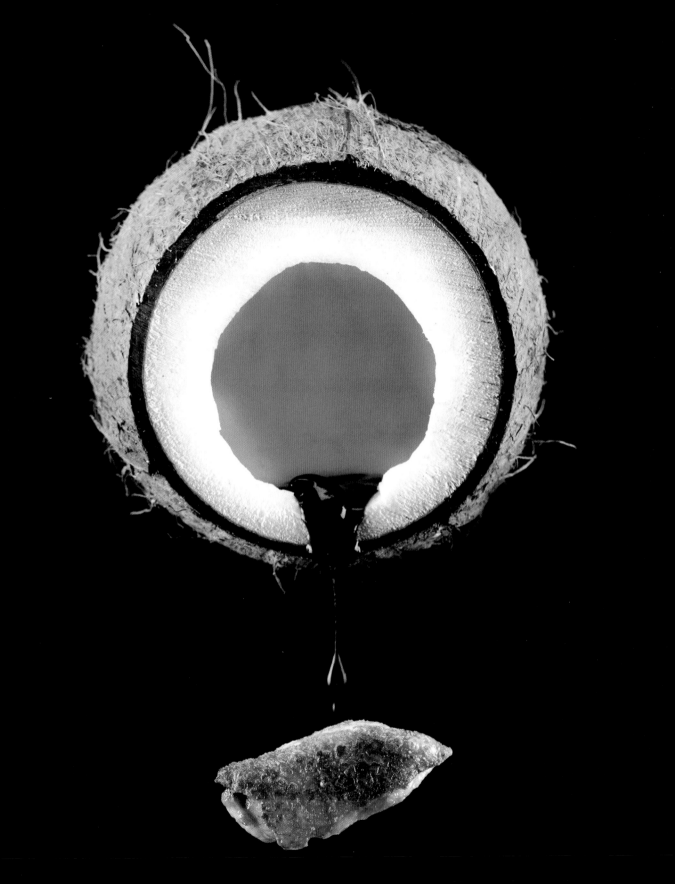

HOISIN CHICKEN
with Coconut Sauce

24 OUNCES CHICKEN (4 BREASTS), BONELESS & SKINLESS

2 CUPS RICE, COOKED

4 TABLESPOONS HOISIN SAUCE

1" PIECE FRESH GINGER, PEELED & CHOPPED

1 CUP ONIONS, FINELY CHOPPED

1/4 CUP GREEN ONIONS, FINELY CHOPPED

1/2 CUP COCONUT MILK

1/2 CUP FAT FREE CHICKEN BROTH

1 TEASPOON FRESH CILANTRO

1 TEASPOON DRIED CUMIN

2 CUPS SWEET RED PEPPERS, SLICED

2 CUPS FROZEN GREEN PEAS

1 CUP EGGPLANTS, CUBED

1 CUP SWEET POTATOES, CUBED

1 TEASPOON CHILI GARLIC SAUCE

2 TEASPOONS CURRY PASTE

1 CUP TOMATOES, DICED

SEA SALT & PEPPER TO TASTE

READY TO COOK

1. COOK THE RICE IN WATER ON THE STOVE TOP OR IN THE MICROWAVE UNTIL THE RICE IS SOFT, ADDING A LITTLE MORE WATER IF NECESSARY.

2. HEAT THE OIL IN A LARGE FRYING PAN.

3. COAT THE CHICKEN PIECES WITH THE HOISIN SAUCE AND BROWN ON ALL SIDES IN THE PAN.

4. ADD THE GARLIC AND COOK FOR 2-3 MINUTES.

5. ADD THE GINGER, CUMIN, RED PEPPERS, GREEN PEAS, EGGPLANTS AND CHILI GARLIC SAUCE AND CONTINUE TO HEAT.

6. STIR IN THE CURRY PASTE AND DICED TOMATOES.

7. ADD THE COCONUT MILK, CHICKEN BROTH AND SIMMER FOR 45 MINUTES UNTIL THE CHICKEN IS COOKED.

8. SPRINKLE WITH GREEN ONIONS AND CILANTRO BEFORE SERVING.

SERVE WITH RICE.

GET IN THE KITCHEN
AND BE CREATIVE WITH FOOD

PER SERVING: **556** CALORIES // **40G** CARBOHYDRATE // **61G** PROTEIN // **14G** FAT

LEMON ROASTED
Whole Chicken

64 OUNCES WHOLE CHICKEN

1 TABLESPOON GRAPE SEED OIL

1 CUP CHICKEN BROTH

2 WHOLE LEMONS, ZESTS + WHOLE

2 CLOVES GARLIC, FINELY CHOPPED

2 CLOVES GARLIC, WHOLE

4 SAGE LEAVES, WHOLE

4 SPRIGS FRESH SAVORY

4 SPRIGS FRESH ROSEMARY

2 SMALL ONIONS, WHOLE

2 CUPS ONIONS, QUARTERED

2 CUPS FRESH GREEN BEANS, WHOLE

2 CUPS CAULIFLOWER, FLORETS

2 CUPS BRUSSEL SPROUTS, WHOLE

SEA SALT & PEPPER TO TASTE

READY TO COOK

1. **PLACE** THE CHICKEN ON AN OVEN RACK AND RUB THE OUTSIDE WITH THE OIL.

2. **SEASON** WITH SEA SALT AND PEPPER.

3. **PIERCE** THE SKIN OF THE LEMONS WITH A FORK AND PLACE THEM INSIDE THE CHICKEN CAVITY.

4. **ADD** THE WHOLE GARLIC CLOVES, 2 OF THE SAGE LEAVES, 2 SPRIGS OF FRESH SAVORY, 2 SPRIGS OF FRESH ROSEMARY AND THE 2 WHOLE ONIONS.

5. **LIFT** THE SKIN FROM THE CHICKEN BREAST AND INSERT THE REMAINING SAGE, SAVORY AND ROSEMARY UNDERNEATH.

6. **PLACE** THE OVEN RACK WITH THE CHICKEN OVER A ROASTING PAN AND ARRANGE THE QUARTERED ONIONS, GREEN BEANS, CAULIFLOWER AND BRUSSEL SPROUTS AROUND THE CHICKEN.

7. **POUR** THE CHICKEN BROTH INTO THE ROASTING PAN AND BAKE AT **350° F** FOR 1 HOUR TO 1 1/2 HOURS OR UNTIL THE CHICKEN AND VEGETABLES ARE DONE.

8. **REMOVE** FROM THE OVEN AND ALLOW THE CHICKEN TO REST FOR 10 MINUTES BEFORE SERVING.

Serve with lemon zests on top.

PER SERVING: 524 CALORIES // 28G CARBOHYDRATE // 68G PROTEIN // 12G FAT

CRISPY CHICKEN SAUTÉ
with Walnuts and Brown Rice

24 OUNCES CHICKEN (4 BREASTS), BONELESS, SKINLESS & CUBED

1 EGG WHITE

1 TABLESPOON CORN STARCH

3 TABLESPOONS WATER

1/2 CUP WALNUTS, WHOLE

1" PIECE FRESH GINGER, PEELED & CHOPPED

1 CUP GREEN ONIONS, LENGTHS SLICED

1 CUP SWEET RED PEPPERS, SLICED

1 CUP GREEN PEPPERS, SLICED

1 TEASPOON HOT SAUCE (*OPTIONAL*)

1 TEASPOON GRAPE SEED OIL

5 CUPS ICEBURG LETTUCE

4 OUNCES LOW FAT LOW CARB HOUSE DRESSING (*SEE PAGE 95*)

2 TABLESPOONS SOY SAUCE

1/4 CUP KETCHUP

1 TABLESPOON VINEGAR

1 TEASPOON CORN STARCH

2 TABLESPOONS WATER

2 CUPS BROWN RICE, COOKED

SEA SALT & PEPPER TO TASTE

READY TO COOK

1. **COOK** THE RICE IN WATER ON THE STOVE TOP OR IN THE MICROWAVE UNTIL THE RICE IS SOFT, ADDING A LITTLE MORE WATER IF NECESSARY.

2. **DISSOLVE** THE CORN STARCH IN THE WATER.

3. **ADD** EGG WHITE AND MIX WELL.

4. **ADD** THE CUBED CHICKEN AND TOSS UNTIL COATED AND SET ASIDE.

5. **COMBINE** THE CORN STARCH AND WATER, ADD KETCHUP, SOY SAUCE, VINEGAR AND MIX WELL. SET ASIDE.

6. **ADD** OIL TO PAN AND COOK THE CHICKEN PIECES.

7. **ADD** THE WALNUTS AND GINGER AND SAUTÉ FOR 1 MINUTE.

8. **ADD** THE GREEN ONIONS, RED AND GREEN PEPPERS AND COOK FOR ANOTHER 2-3 MINUTES.

9. **ADD** THE SAUCE, STIRRING TO COAT THE CHICKEN AND VEGETABLES. IF THERE IS NOT ENOUGH SAUCE, ADD A LITTLE WATER.

10. **ADD** THE HOT PEPPER SAUCE IF DESIRED AND STIR WELL.

Serve with brown rice and side of salad.

VERATI**TIPS**

BROWN RICE WILL TAKE ABOUT 15 MINUTES IN THE MICROWAVE - ADD DOUBLE THE AMOUNT OF WATER TO THE RICE AND COOK IN 3 MINUTES INCREMENTS, ADDING ADDITIONAL WATER IF NECESSARY.

PER SERVING: 761 CALORIES // 61G CARBOHYDRATE // 66G PROTEIN // 18G FAT

MEDITERRANEAN STYLE
Chicken Stew

20 **OUNCES** CHICKEN (4 BREASTS), BONELESS & SKINLESS	1 **TEASPOON** CUMIN
1 **TEASPOON** GRAPE SEED OIL	1 **TEASPOON** CORIANDER
2 **CUPS** ONIONS, CHOPPED	1 **TEASPOON** CINNAMON
2 **CUPS** FRESH GREEN BEANS	1 **TEASPOON** GROUND GINGER
2 **CUPS** CARROTS, CHOPPED	3 **TABLESPOONS** LEMON JUICE
1 **CUP** CHICKPEAS, COOKED	3 **CUPS** CHICKEN BROTH
1 **CUP** CELERY, CHOPPED	2 **CUPS** COUSCOUS, STEAMED
4 **CLOVES** GARLIC, FINELY CHOPPED	SEA SALT & PEPPER TO TASTE

READY TO COOK

1. **PLACE** CHICKEN BREASTS IN AN OVEN-PROOF PAN.
2. **SAUTÉ** THE ONIONS IN OIL UNTIL THEY BEGIN TO SOFTEN.
3. **ADD** THE GARLIC AND COOK 1 MINUTE. STIR IN THE CUMIN, CORIANDER, CINNAMON, GINGER, CHICKEN BROTH AND LEMON JUICE.
4. **ADD** THE GREEN BEANS, CARROTS AND CHICKPEAS. PLACE ON TOP OF CHICKEN, COVER AND BAKE AT **350°F** FOR 35-40 MINUTES.
5. **REMOVE** THE CHICKEN AND VEGETABLES FROM THE PAN AND BOIL THE BROTH UNTIL REDUCED BY HALF.
6. **ADD** THE CHOPPED CILANTRO AND POUR THE SAUCE OVER THE CHICKEN AND VEGETABLES.

Serve with couscous.

PER SERVING: 650 CALORIES // 59G CARBOHYDRATE // 63G PROTEIN // 10G FAT

SPICY BUTTERMILK
Marinated Chicken with Cole Slaw

32 OUNCES CHICKEN DRUMSTICKS WITH SKIN REMOVED

1 CUP LOW FAT BUTTERMILK

1/2 TEASPOON CAYENNE PEPPER

2 TABLESPOONS FLOUR

1/2 CUP COARSE BREAD CRUMBS

5 CUPS CABBAGE, FINELY SHREDDED

2 CUPS CARROTS, GRATED

1/2 CUP GREEN ONIONS, CHOPPED

1/2 CUP CELERY, CHOPPED

3 TABLESPOONS VINEGAR OR WHITE BALSAMIC VINEGAR

1 TABLESPOON OLIVE OIL

1 TEASPOON SUGAR

SEA SALT & PEPPER TO TASTE

READY TO COOK

1. **MARINATE** THE CHICKEN IN A BOWL WITH THE BUTTERMILK, SEA SALT AND PEPPER TO TASTE AND CAYENNE FOR 30 MINUTES.

2. **REMOVE** THE DRUMSTICKS FROM THE MARINADE AND PUT THEM IN A PLASTIC BAG WITH THE FLOUR AND BREAD CRUMBS.

3. **SHAKE** UNTIL THE CHICKEN IS COATED.

4. **PLACE** THE PIECES ON A RACK SUSPENDED OVER A COOKIE SHEET AND BAKE IN THE OVEN AT **375ºF** FOR 35-40 MINUTES OR UNTIL COOKED THROUGH, TURNING THE PIECES OVER HALF WAY THROUGH THE COOKING TIME.

Serve with coleslaw.

VERATI TIPS
MARINATE OVERNIGHT, COVERED, IN REFRIGERATOR FOR BEST RESULTS!

PER SERVING: 520 CALORIES // 29G CARBOHYDRATE // 68G PROTEIN // 12G FAT

OVEN FRESH
Chicken Pizza

2 PIZZA PRE-MADE DOUGH OR HOMEMADE, THINLY ROLLED (*SEE PAGE 215*)

20 OUNCES CHICKEN (4 BREASTS), BONELESS, SKINLESS & SLICED

1 TEASPOON GRAPE SEED OIL

1 TEASPOON OREGANO

1 TEASPOON MARJORAM

1 TEASPOON ROSEMARY

2 CUPS ONIONS, SLICED

1 CUP GREEN PEPPERS, SLICED

1 CUP SWEET RED PEPPERS, SLICED

2 CUPS TOMATOES, DICED

1 CUP OLIVES, WHOLE

1 CUP MUSHROOMS, SLICED

3 TABLESPOONS LOW FAT PARMESAN CHEESE, GRATED

8 CUPS MIXED GREEN SALAD

4 OUNCES LOW FAT LOW CARB HOUSE DRESSING (*SEE PAGE 95*)

SEA SALT & PEPPER TO TASTE

READY TO COOK

1. **SEASON** THE CHICKEN WITH OREGANO AND MARJORAM, SEA SALT AND PEPPER TO TASTE AND COOK IN THE OIL UNTIL BROWNED ON ALL SIDES.

2. **REMOVE** THE CHICKEN FROM THE PAN AND COOK THE ONIONS UNTIL SOFT BUT NOT BROWNED. SET ASIDE.

3. **PUT** THE PIZZA DOUGH ON A ROUND PAN AND SPREAD THE TOMATOES EVENLY OVER THE SURFACE OF THE DOUGH.

4. **DISTRIBUTE** THE CHICKEN PIECES, THEN THE ONIONS EVENLY OVER THE TOP.

5. **ADD** THE RED AND GREEN PEPPERS, MUSHROOMS AND OLIVES.

6. **SPRINKLE** WITH THE ROSEMARY AND PARMESAN CHEESE.

7. **BAKE** FOR 10 MINUTES AT **450° F**.

8. **REDUCE** THE HEAT TO **350° F** AND COOK FOR AN ADDITIONAL 20 MINUTES OR UNTIL THE BOTTOM OF THE PIZZA CRUST IS GOLDEN, AND THE TOP IS BUBBLY

Serve with mixed green salad on the side.

TURKEY TETRAZZINI
with Low Fat Parmesan Cheese

24 OUNCES TURKEY (4 BREASTS), SKINLESS, BONELESS & CUBED

1/2 CUP LOW FAT PARMESAN CHEESE, GRATED

4 CLOVES GARLIC, FINELY CHOPPED

1 TEASPOON OIL

2 CUPS MUSHROOMS, SLICED

2 CUPS FAT FREE CHICKEN OR VEGETABLE BROTH

1 1/2 TABLESPOONS CORN STARCH

1 CUP SKIM MILK

1/8 TEASPOON NUTMEG

1/4 TEASPOON CHILI POWDER (*SEE PAGE 173*)

1/2 CUP FRESH PARSLEY, CHOPPED

2 CUPS WHOLE WHEAT PASTA (*SEE PAGE 215*)

6 CUPS MIXED GREEN SALAD

4 OUNCES LOW FAT LOW CARB HOUSE DRESSING (*SEE PAGE 95*)

SEA SALT & PEPPER TO TASTE

READY TO COOK

1. **COOK** THE WHOLE WHEAT PASTA UNTIL JUST TENDER AND DRAIN.

2. **BROWN** THE TURKEY PIECES IN OIL AND COOK FOR 3-4 MINUTES.

3. **ADD** THE BROTH AND THE CORN STARCH, WHICH HAS BEEN DISSOLVED IN THE MILK.

4. **ADD** THE SEA SALT AND PEPPER TO TASTE AND NUTMEG.

5. **STIR** CONSTANTLY TO PREVENT LUMPS FROM FORMING.

6. **ADD** THE MUSHROOMS AND COOK ANOTHER 2 MINUTES.

7. **ADD** THE CHEESE AND COOK AT **LOW HEAT** UNTIL THE CHEESE HAS MELTED.

8. **IN** AN OVEN CASSEROLE, COMBINE THE TURKEY AND SAUCE MIXTURES WITH THE PASTA AND TOSS WELL.

9. **BAKE** IN A **350°F** OVEN FOR 35-40 MINUTES.

10. **SPRINKLE** WITH PARSLEY BEFORE SERVING.

Serve with green salad.

PER SERVING: 723 CALORIES // 46G CARBOHYDRATE // 63G PROTEIN // 21G FAT

CITRUS CHICKEN
with Whole Wheat Couscous

24 OUNCES CHICKEN (4 BREASTS), BONELESS, SKINLESS & SLICED

4 CUPS CHINESE EGGPLANTS, CUBED

2 CUPS GREEN PEPPERS, CUBED

2 CUPS TOMATOES, CHOPPED

1 ORANGE, PEELED & CUBED

2 TEASPOONS GROUND CUMIN

2 TEASPOONS GROUND CORIANDER

2 TABLESPOONS FLOUR

1 TEASPOON GRAPE SEED OIL

1/4 CUP WATER

1/4 CUP SKIM MILK

1 TABLESPOON LEMON JUICE

2 CUPS COUSCOUS, WHOLE WHEAT

BOILING WATER TO JUST COVER

1 TEASPOON CUMIN

1 TEASPOON CORIANDER

2 TEASPOONS LEMON ZEST

1/4 CUP RAISINS (*OPTIONAL*)

SEA SALT & PEPPER TO TASTE

READY TO COOK

1. **PLACE** CHICKEN IN A BOWL AND ADD FLOUR, CUMIN, CORIANDER, SEA SALT AND PEPPER TO TASTE.

2. **TOSS** UNTIL THE CHICKEN IS COMPLETELY COATED.

3. **HEAT** OIL IN A FRYING PAN AND COOK CHICKEN, TOSSING CONSTANTLY UNTIL IT IS NO LONGER PINK.

4. **ADD** THE CUBES OF EGGPLANTS AND GREEN PEPPERS.

5. **ADD** WATER, **LOWER** HEAT AND SIMMER UNTIL THE EGGPLANTS ARE SOFT.

7. **ADD** ORANGES TO THE CHICKEN MIXTURE.

8. **ADD** MILK AND LEMON JUICE AND HEAT UNTIL BUBBLY.

9. **PUT** THE LEMON ZEST, CUMIN, CORIANDER AND SEA SALT IN A BOWL.

10. **ADD** THE COUSCOUS AND COVER WITH BOILING WATER. THE COUSCOUS WILL ABSORB THE WATER WITHOUT STIRRING.

11. **IF** USING RAISINS, BOIL THEM FOR 1 MINUTE IN WATER AND DRAIN.

12. **WHEN** THE COUSCOUS HAS ABSORBED ALL THE WATER, STIR IN THE RAISINS BEFORE SERVING.

Serve with lemon zests on top.

PER SERVING: 621 CALORIES // 62G CARBOHYDRATE // 66G PROTEIN // 14G FAT

MAKE IT POP!
Grilled Chicken Breasts with Corn on the Cob

24 OUNCES CHICKEN BREASTS, BONELESS & SKINLESS	4 COBS CORN
1 TEASPOON OLIVE OIL	4 CUPS MIXED GREEN SALAD
2 TABLESPOONS DIJON MUSTARD	4 OUNCES LOW FAT LOW CARB HOUSE DRESSING (*SEE PAGE 95*)
1 TEASPOON DRIED ROSEMARY	SEA SALT & PEPPER TO TASTE
2 TEASPOONS BUTTER	

READY TO COOK

1. BRUSH THE CHICKEN BREASTS WITH OIL AND DIJON MUSTARD.
2. SEASON WITH SEA SALT AND PEPPER TO TASTE AND ROSEMARY.
3. GRILL UNDER THE OVEN GRILL FOR 3-4 MINUTES ON EACH SIDE.
4. TURN THE OVEN TO BAKE AND CONTINUE TO COOK AT 350° F UNTIL THE CHICKEN IS DONE, ABOUT 20 MINUTES, OR UNTIL THE JUICES RUN CLEAR.
5. BREAK THE CORN COBS INTO 3" PIECES AND BOIL 5-7 MINUTES.
6. SPRINKLE WITH DRIED SAGE AND BUTTER.

SERVE WITH GRILLED CHICKEN AND A GREEN SALAD AND LOW FAT LOW CARB HOUSE DRESSING.

TRY THIS RECIPE ON THE BARBECUE!

PER SERVING: **499 CALORIES // 37G CARBOHYDRATE // 54G PROTEIN // 14G FAT**

THE DAY AFTER...
Thanksgiving

24 OUNCES TURKEY, COOKED & COOKED	**1/2 TEASPOON** DRIED SAVOURY
1 CUP ONIONS, DICED	**2 CUPS** TURKEY OR VEGETABLE BROTH
2 CUPS CELERY, DICED	**2 CUPS** SKIM MILK
2 CUPS CARROTS, DICED	**3 TABLESPOONS** CORN STARCH
2 CUPS POTATOES, DICED	**1 TEASPOON** GRAPE SEED OIL
1 CUP TURNIP, DICED	**1/2 CUP** FRESH PARSLEY, CHOPPED
1 TEASPOON THYME	SEA SALT & PEPPER TO TASTE
1 TEASPOON FRESH SAGE	

READY TO COOK

1. **IN** A LARGE POT, HEAT OIL AND COOK ONIONS, CARROTS, CELERY, POTATOES AND TURNIP UNTIL VEGETABLES BEGIN TO SOFTEN (ABOUT 10 MINUTES), STIRRING OCCASIONALLY.
2. **ADD** THE THYME, SAGE AND SAVORY AND THE BROTH.
3. **MIX** THE CORN STARCH INTO THE MILK AND STIR UNTIL THE CORN STARCH IS COMPLETELY DISSOLVED.
4. **ADD** TO THE POT, STIRRING WELL.
5. **ADD** THE TURKEY, SEA SALT AND PEPPER. BRING TO BOIL AND IMMEDIATELY REDUCE HEAT TO SIMMER.
6. **WATCH** FOR APPROXIMATELY 15 MINUTES OR UNTIL THE VEGETABLES ARE DONE.

Serve in soup bowls and sprinkle with fresh parsley before serving.

PER SERVING: 680 CALORIES // 30G CARBOHYDRATE // 73G PROTEIN // 16G FAT

LEFTOVER TURKEY
Shepherd's Pie

24 OUNCES GROUND TURKEY, COOKED

2 CUPS ONIONS, CHOPPED

1 CUP FROZEN GREEN PEAS

1 CUP FROZEN KERNEL CORN

2 CUPS MASHED POTATOES

1 CUP GREEN ONIONS, SLICED

1 CUP COOKED CUBED TURNIP

14 OUNCES TURKEY GRAVY

1/4 CUP SKIM MILK

2 TABLESPOONS GROUND PARSLEY

2 TABLESPOONS GROUND SAGE OR SAVORY

1 TABLESPOON DRIED BREAD CRUMBS

SEA SALT & PEPPER TO TASTE

READY TO COOK

1. **PUT** THE TURKEY THROUGH A MEAT GRINDER, OR CHOP VERY FINE.

2. **ADD** SEA SALT AND PEPPER, SAGE OR SAVORY AND TURKEY GRAVY AND SET ASIDE.

3. **IN** A FRYING PAN, COOK THE ONIONS UNTIL SOFT, BUT NOT BROWNED.

4. **PUT** THE FROZEN PEAS AND CORN IN THE PAN WITH THE ONIONS; ADD 1/4 CUP WATER AND HEAT UP TO BOILING POINT.

5. **POUR** THE ONIONS, PEAS AND CORN MIXTURE INTO THE BOWL WITH THE TURKEY.

6. **MIX** WELL (IT SHOULD BE MOIST BUT NOT WET). IF THE MIXTURE IS TOO DRY, ADD MORE GRAVY OR MORE WATER.

7. **PLACE** IN A CASSEROLE DISH AND SMOOTH THE TOP.

8. **PUT** THE LEFTOVER MASHED POTATOES AND TURNIP IN A SAUCEPAN.

9. **ADD** 1/4 CUP WATER OR 1/4 CUP SKIM MILK AND HEAT, STIRRING TO KEEP FROM STICKING.

10. **REMOVE** FROM THE HEAT. USING A HAND MIXER, BLEND THE POTATOES AND TURNIP UNTIL SMOOTH.

11. **MIX** IN THE GREEN ONIONS AND SCOOP THE MIXTURE OVER THE TURKEY.

12. **SPRINKLE** THE PARSLEY AND BREAD CRUMBS OVER TOP.

13. **BAKE** IN A **350° F** OVEN FOR 45-50 MINUTES OR UNTIL IT IS BUBBLING.

Serve really hot in a family dish.

ROLL IT!
Individual Spinach Lasagna

20 OUNCES CHICKEN (4 BREASTS), BONELESS, SKINLESS & SLICED	**1 CUP** CHEESE LOW FAT MOZZARELLA
8 LASAGNA NOODLES	**1 TEASPOON** BASIL
1 CUP ONIONS, FINELY CHOPPED	**1 TEASPOON** THYME
2 CUPS MUSHROOMS, SLICED	**1 TEASPOON** GRAPE SEED OIL
3 CUPS FRESH SPINACH, CHOPPED	**6 CUPS** MIXED GREEN SALAD
1 CUP TOMATO SAUCE	**4 OUNCES** LOW FAT LOW CARB HOUSE DRESSING (*SEE PAGE 95*)
1 CUP FRESH TOMATOES, CHOPPED	SEA SALT & PEPPER TO TASTE

READY TO COOK

1. **HEAT** HALF THE OIL IN A PAN AND SAUTÉ THE ONIONS AND GARLIC UNTIL SOFT, BUT NOT BROWNED.

2. **ADD** THE CHOPPED SPINACH AND COOK 1–2 MINUTES OR UNTIL THE SPINACH IS COMPLETELY WILTED.

3. **ADD** SEA SALT AND PEPPER TO TASTE, BASIL AND THYME AND STIR INTO MIX.

4. **IN** A SEPARATE PAN, HEAT THE REMAINDER OF THE OIL AND QUICKLY SAUTÉ THE CHICKEN STRIPS.

5. **REMOVE** THE CHICKEN AND COOK THE MUSHROOMS FOR 1–2 MINUTES.

6. **ADD** THE CHICKEN TO THE PAN WITH THE ONIONS, GARLIC AND SPINACH.

7. **COOK** THE LASAGNA NOODLES UNTIL SOFT. REMOVE AND REFRESH IN COLD WATER FOR 1 MINUTE.

8. **WHEN** THE NOODLES ARE COOL ENOUGH TO HANDLE, SPREAD EACH ONE WITH A PORTION OF THE ONION, GARLIC, SPINACH AND CHICKEN MIXTURE.

9. **ROLL** UP THE LASAGNA NOODLES AND STAND THEM UP ON THEIR ENDS IN AN OVEN-PROOF PAN.

10. **USE** A PAN SMALL ENOUGH TO CONTAIN THE NOODLES SO THAT THEY JUST TOUCH ONE ANOTHER.

11. **SPREAD** THE MUSHROOMS OVER TOP.

12. **ADD** THE FRESH CHOPPED TOMATOES AND POUR THE TOMATO SAUCE EVENLY OVER THE NOODLES.

13. **TOP** WITH THE CHEESE AND BAKE, UNCOVERED, IN A **350ºF** OVEN FOR 45 MINUTES UNTIL BUBBLY AND THE CHEESE IS MELTED.

Serve with green salad.

PER SERVING: 556 CALORIES // 47G CARBOHYDRATE // 60G PROTEIN // 12G FAT

PIZZA CRUST
Basic

#1 BASIC & EASY ⬇⬇⬇

2 CUPS WHOLE WHEAT FLOUR	**1** EGG
1 TEASPOON SEA SALT	**1/2 CUP** 1% MILK
1/2 TABLESPOON DRY YEAST	**2 TABLESPOONS** OLIVE OIL

READY TO COOK

1. MIX ALL INGREDIENTS (BY HAND OR IN A MIXER) FOR ABOUT 15 MINUTES OR UNTIL THE DOUGH IS SMOOTH AND ELASTIC. **2. MAKE** A BALL AND LET IT SIT IN A WARM PLACE FOR ABOUT 45 MINUTES. **3. ROLL** OUT YOUR PIZZA DOUGH. **4. COOK** UNTIL READY.

*Here are quick and easy recipes.
Don't be shy to add herbs or garlic to them!
-Chef Verati*

FRESH PASTA
Basic

#1 BASIC & EASY ⬇⬇⬇

1 1/4 CUPS FLOUR	**1 OUNCE** OLIVE OIL
4 EGGS	**1 PINCH** SEA SALT

READY TO COOK

1. MIX TOGETHER AND LET REST FOR ONE HOUR. **2. ROLL** OUT YOUR PASTA WITH A MACHINE OR BY HAND.

*Don't work the dough too much
or it will become elastic.
-Chef Verati*

Ideal
MEAT
FREEDOM OF PROTEIN

TIPS

TRICKS

WRITE TO **CHEFVERATI@IDEALPROTEIN.COM**

FIND US ON **CHEF VERATI'S FACEBOOK PAGE**

VISIT **LOWFATLOWCARB.COM**

EAT

Best at lunch time

FACT # 5 225

BEEF STEAK WITH HERB BUTTER ···················· 227
BEEF CURRY WITH CAULIFLOWER & ZUCCHINI ······· 229
BEEF SATAY WITH PEANUT SAUCE ···················· 230
T-BONE STEAK WITH BLUE CHEESE DRESSING ······· 231
BEEF LETTUCE WRAPS BURRITO STYLE ·············· 233
KORMA & CURRY PORK & VEGETABLES ··············· 234
PORK CHOPS CACCIATORE ··························· 235
PORTERHOUSE STEAKS WITH ANCHOVY BUTTER & SPINACH 239
PORK CHOPS WITH DIJON MUSTARD SAUCE ··········· 241
HOT ITALIAN SAUSAGE TOMATO CASSEROLE ········· 243
BEEF & BACON STEW ITALIAN STYLE ················ 244
CURRIED PORK CHOPS WITH RED CABBAGE ··········· 245
LAMB CHOPS WITH TOMATO & CUCUMBER SALSA ···· 247
BEEF ROLL-UPS WITH DILL PICKLES ················· 248
CALF'S LIVER & BACON, WITH MUSHROOMS ··········· 248

BEEF STROGANOFF WITH ASPARAGUS ················ 249
HOT POT LAMB, PEPPER & KALAMATA ·············· 251
MINTY LAMB CHOPS WITH BROCCOLI ················ 252
BEEF, SAUSAGE & PARMESAN BALLS ················· 252
PEPPER STEAK WITH BELGIAN ENDIVES ············· 253
PORK GOULASH WITH SAUERKRAUT ················· 253
QUICK VEAL PICCATA WITH ASPARAGUS ············· 254
BEEF & VEGETABLES STIR-FRY ····················· 254
VEAL & SAUSAGE PATTIES ························· 255
VEAL MARENGO WITH RAPINI & MUSHROOMS ········ 258
RIB EYE STEAK WITH ASPARAGUS ·················· 259
TOMATO & LAMB MUSHROOM STEW ················· 260
TANDOORI MASALA LAMB CHOPS ···················· 261
MILK SIMMERED & PORK SHOULDER ················· 262
SALSA // EASY + TWIST + FUNKY ················· 263

"CARBS"

Best at dinner time

FACT # 6 ·· 265

BEEF BRAISED IN BEER WITH SNOW PEAS ············ 267

EGGPLANT MOUSSAKA WITH CHEESE SAUCE ·········· 271

YANKEE POT ROAST WITH POTAOES & LEEKS ······· 272

VEAL CUTLETS WITH TOMATOES ···················· 273

CIABATTA STEAK SANDWICH WITH BBQ SAUCE ······· 275

SWEET & SOUR PORK WITH A PINEAPPLE TWIST ···· 277

BEEF TACOS WITH AVOCADO ························ 278

SWISS STEAK IN TOMATO SAUCE ···················· 278

BAKED TOMATOES WITH BEEF ······················ 279

LAMB STEW IRISH STYLE ·························· 279

THANKSGIVING HAM WITH BAKED AUTUMN VEGETABLES 280

BEEF & PEPPER STIR FRY WITH RICE ··············· 281

LAMB BURGERS WITH TOMATO & BASIL SALAD ······· 283

QUICK BEEF FAJITAS WITH A MIXED GREEN SALAD ··· 284

LAMB & LEMON HOT POT ·························· 285

PORK TENDERLOIN WITH ROASTED VEGETABLES ······ 286

SPAGHETTI BOLOGNESE WITH MIXED GREEN SALAD ··· 287

EASY STUFFED PORK TENDERLOIN ··················· 289

CRISPY BEEF WITH BOK CHOY ····················· 290

EASY PORK STEW WITH BEER SAUCE ··············· 291

STUFFED CABBAGE ROLLS WITH TOMATO SAUCE ····· 292

BEEF & MUSHROOM STEW WITH GREEN BEANS ······· 293

OSSO BUCCO WITH GREMOLATA ····················· 295

SHEPHERD'S PIE WITH MACEDOINE ·················· 296

CREOLE BEEF ···································· 297

SPICY MEXICAN PORK ····························· 299

MOCK DUCK WITH BROCCOLI ······················· 300

SAUSAGE & BEAN STEW ··························· 301

LAMB & LENTIL CASSEROLE ························ 304

LAMB MOUSSAKA WITH LOW FAT CREAM SAUCE ····· 305

CHILI CON CARNE ································· 306

SAUCES // EASY + TWIST + FUNKY ·············· 307

Each recipe serves four.

FAT

CARBS

best at lunch time

FACT #5

MOST FATS

THAT HAVE A HIGH PERCENTAGE OF SATURATED FAT OR TRANS FAT ARE SOLID AT ROOM TEMPERATURE. THESE FATS CAN INCREASE YOUR RISK OF CARDIOVASCULAR DISEASE AND TYPE 2 DIABETES. READ THE NUTRITION FACTS LABEL AND CHOOSE YOUR FOOD WISELY.

BEWARE

Freedom

BEEF STEAK
with Herb Butter

32 OUNCES BEEF STEAKS

1 TEASPOON GRAPE SEED OIL

4 LEMON SLICES

8 CUPS GREEN BEANS, COOKED

3 OUNCES BUTTER, AT ROOM TEMPERATURE

1 TABLESPOON FRESH PARSLEY, CHOPPED

1 TABLESPOON FRESH CHIVES, CHOPPED

1 TABLESPOON FRESH CHERVIL, CHOPPED

1 TABLESPOON FRESH TARRAGON, CHOPPED

1 TABLESPOON GREEN ONIONS, CHOPPED

SEA SALT & PEPPER TO TASTE

READY TO COOK

1. IN A MIXING BOWL, COMBINE BUTTER, PARSLEY, CHIVES, CHERVIL, TARRAGON, GREEN ONIONS, SEA SALT AND PEPPER. 2. PLACE MIXTURE ON WAXED PAPER OR PLASTIC WRAP AND FORM INTO A ROLL. 3. REFRIGERATE WHILE STEAKS ARE COOKING. 4. BRUSH THE STEAKS WITH OIL AND BROIL ON EACH SIDE AT 350°F FOR ABOUT 5 MINUTES OR UNTIL DESIRED DONENESS. 5. PLACE MEAT ON PLATES AND ADD A SLICE OF LEMON AND A SLICE OF HERB BUTTER OVER EACH PIECE. 6. SERVE STEAKS WITH FRESH COOKED GREEN BEANS.

▶ BUTTER UP!
BUTTER WILL ALWAYS
BE BUTTER.SIMPLE *Freedom*
BE MINDFUL OF THOSE SATURATED FATS. MODERATION HAS MUCH BETTER TASTE.

PER SERVING: 614 CALORIES // 32G FAT // 70G PROTEIN // 15G CARBOHYDRATE.

BEEF CURRY
with Cauliflower and Zucchini

24 OUNCES GROUND BEEF

2 CUPS ONIONS, CHOPPED

1 CLOVE GARLIC, CHOPPED

1 1/2" PIECE FRESH GINGER, FINELY SLICED

2 CUBES BEEF STOCK, DISSOLVED IN WATER

2 TEASPOONS GROUND CORIANDER

1 TEASPOON GROUND CUMIN

1/2 TEASPOON GROUND CLOVES

3 TABLESPOONS GROUND CURRY POWDER

1 BAY LEAF

2 TEASPOONS GRAPE SEED OIL

2 GREEN CHILIES, FINELY CHOPPED

3 CUPS CAULIFLOWER, PARBOILED

3 CUPS FRESH ZUCCHINI, PARBOILED

1 CUP 35% COOKING CREAM OR SOUR CREAM OR PLAIN YOGURT

1/2 CUP FRESH CORIANDER, CHOPPED

SEA SALT & PEPPER TO TASTE

READY TO COOK

1. IN THE OIL, COOK GROUND BEEF, ONIONS, GARLIC, GINGER AND BEEF STOCK CUBES UNTIL BEEF IS BROWNED.

2. DRAIN EXCESS FAT IF NECESSARY.

3. ADD CORIANDER, CUMIN, CLOVES, CURRY POWDER, GREEN CHILIES AND BAY LEAF AND SIMMER 15 MINUTES.

4. ADD CAULIFLOWER, ZUCCHINI AND 1/2 CUP CREAM AND SIMMER ANOTHER 5 MINUTES.

SERVE WITH FRESH CORIANDER ON TOP.

MIND YOUR FINGERS
WHILE CHOPPING GREEN CHILIES.

PER SERVING: 451 CALORIES // 24G FAT // 58G PROTEIN // 13G CARBOHYDRATE

BEEF SATAY
with Peanut Sauce

24 OUNCES SIRLOIN (4 STEAKS), SLICED	**1 CUP** SWEET RED PEPPERS, CUBED
2 TABLESPOONS PEANUT BUTTER	**1 CUP** CELERY OR CELERY ROOT, CHOPPED
3 TABLESPOONS SOY SAUCE	**1 CUP** ENGLISH CUCUMBERS, CUBED
2 TABLESPOONS LIME JUICE	**2 CUPS** FRESH ZUCCHINI, CUBED
2 TABLESPOONS HOISIN SAUCE	**1/4 CUP** VINEGAR OR WHITE BALSAMIC VINEGAR
2 TABLESPOONS COCONUT MILK	**2 TABLESPOONS** GRAPE SEED OIL
1 CUP CAULIFLOWER, CUBED	**1/4 CUP** FRESH CHIVES, CHOPPED
1 CUP VIDALIA ONIONS, SLICED	**1/4 CUT** FRESH OREGANO, CHOPPED
1 CUP GREEN PEPPERS, CUBED	SEA SALT & PEPPER TO TASTE

READY TO COOK

1. **IN** A BOWL, COMBINE PEANUT BUTTER, SOY SAUCE, LIME JUICE, HOISIN SAUCE AND COCONUT MILK AND WHISK UNTIL SMOOTH.

2. **PLACE** THE BEEF STRIPS IN THE BOWL AND COAT WELL.

3. **COVER** AND REFRIGERATE FOR 30 MINUTES OR OVERNIGHT.

4. **IN** A SAUCEPAN OF BOILING WATER, COOK CAULIFLOWER, CELERY OR CELERY ROOT AND ZUCCHINI FOR ABOUT 8 MINUTES.

5. **DRAIN** AND RUN UNDER COLD WATER.

6. **DRAIN** AND PLACE IN A BOWL WITH ONIONS, RED AND GREEN PEPPERS AND CUCUMBERS.

7. **IN** A SEPARATE BOWL, COMBINE VINEGAR OR WHITE BALSAMIC VINEGAR, GRAPE SEED OIL, CHIVES AND OREGANO AND WHISK UNTIL WELL MIXED.

8. **POUR** OVER THE VEGETABLE MIXTURE.

9. **REFRIGERATE** FOR 30 MINUTES OR OVERNIGHT.

10. **AT** THE SAME TIME, PUT 8 WOODEN SKEWERS IN WATER AND ALLOW TO SOAK.

11. **WHEN** READY TO COOK, REMOVE THE BEEF FROM THE MARINADE AND THREAD THE BEEF STRIPS ONTO THE SKEWERS.

12. **GRILL** IN OVEN FOR 10 MINUTES, TURNING ONCE.

Serve beef satay with marinated vegetables on the side.

PER SERVING: 534 CALORIES // 25G FAT // 56G PROTEIN // 13G CARBOHYDRATE

T-BONE STEAK
with Blue Cheese Dressing

32 OUNCES T-BONE STEAKS

1 CUP RED ONIONS, SLICED

1/2 CUP BLUE CHEESE, CRUMBLED

4 TABLESPOONS 35% COOKING CREAM

2 CUPS MUSHROOMS, SLICED

1 TABLESPOON GRAPE SEED OIL

4 CUPS ASPARAGUS, SPEARS & BLANCHED (*SEE PAGE 129*)

1/2 CUP RED ONIONS, SLICED

1/2 CUP SWEET RED PEPPERS, SLICED

1 TEASPOON FRESH CHIVES, FINELY CHOPPED

1 TEASPOON FRESH SAGE, FINELY CHOPPED

1 TABLESPOON LEMON JUICE

4 TABLESPOONS FRESH CORIANDER, CHOPPED

SEA SALT & PEPPER TO TASTE

READY TO COOK

1. **BLANCH** THE ASPARAGUS.

2. **IN** A BOWL, COMBINE THE ASPARAGUS, FRESH HERBS, RED ONIONS AND RED PEPPERS.

3. **TOSS** WITH LEMON JUICE AND LEAVE AT ROOM TEMPERATURE UNTIL THE STEAKS ARE COOKED.

4. **HEAT** THE OIL IN A LARGE FRYING PAN AND SAUTÉ THE ONIONS AND MUSHROOMS FOR 3-4 MINUTES UNTIL THE ONIONS ARE JUST SOFT.

5. **REMOVE** FROM THE PAN AND KEEP WARM.

6. **SEASON** THE STEAKS WITH SEA SALT AND PEPPER AND COOK FOR ABOUT 3 MINUTES ON EACH SIDE OR UNTIL DESIRED DONENESS.

7. **RETURN** THE ONIONS AND MUSHROOMS TO THE PAN.

8. **ADD** THE CRUMBLED BLUE CHEESE AND CREAM AND STIR UNTIL EVERYTHING IS AMALGAMATED.

Serve steaks topped with blue cheese dressing, asparagus salad on the side.

BEEF LETTUCE WRAPS

Burrito Style

24 OUNCES LEAN GROUND BEEF

4 CLOVES GARLIC, CHOPPED

1 CUP ONIONS, FINELY CHOPPED

3 CUPS TOMATOES, CHOPPED

1/2 CUP GREEN PEPPERS, CHOPPED

1/2 CUP CHILI PEPPERS, FINELY CHOPPED

1 CUP CHEESE, GRATED

1 TEASPOON FRESH OREGANO, CHOPPED

4 TABLESPOONS SOUR CREAM

1 HEAD ICEBERG LETTUCE

2 CUPS AVOCADOS

1 CUP GREENS ONIONS, FINELY CHOPPED

1 TEASPOON OLIVE OIL

2 LIMES, JUICED

1/2 JALEPENO PEPPER, FINELY CHOPPED

1/4 CUP FRESH CORIANDER, CHOPPED

SEA SALT & PEPPER TO TASTE

READY TO COOK

1. COOK ONIONS, GARLIC, SEA SALT, PEPPER, OREGANO AND BEEF UNTIL THE BEEF IS BROWNED.

2. ADD GREEN PEPPERS AND CHILI PEPPERS AND COOK ANOTHER 10 MINUTES.

3. MIX THE AVOCADOS WITH 1 CUP OF THE TOMATOES, GREEN ONIONS, THE OLIVE OIL, LIME JUICE, JALAPENOS AND CORIANDER, SET ASIDE.

4. HEAT THE TORTILLAS IN A MICROWAVE OVEN FOR 30 SECONDS OR WRAPPED IN FOIL IN A 350°F OVEN FOR ABOUT 10 MINUTES.

5. DIVIDE THE 2 CUPS OF TOMATOES, GRATED CHEESE, AND MEAT MIXTURE INTO 8 EQUAL PORTIONS AND PLACE SOME ON A LETTUCE LEAF.

6. TOP EACH WITH 1 TABLESPOON OF SOUR CREAM AND 1 TABLESPOON OF GUACAMOLE.

7. TUCK IN ENDS OF THE LETTUCE AND ROLL UP.

SERVE 2 PER PERSON WITH ADDITIONAL GUACAMOLE AND TOMATOES.

PER SERVING: 525 CALORIES // 25G FAT // 61G PROTEIN // 13G CARBOHYDRATE

KORMA & CURRY
Pork and Vegetables

24 OUNCES PORK SHOULDER, CUBES	**1 TEASPOON** GROUND CUMIN
1 CUP ONIONS, COARSELY CHOPPED	**2 TEASPOONS** DRIED CORIANDER
1 CUP MUSHROOMS, SLICED	**4 TEASPOONS** CURRY POWDER
1 CUP GREEN PEPPERS, CHOPPED	**1 TEASPOON** GROUND GINGER
1 CUP RED PEPPERS, CHOPPED	**4 TABLESPOONS** KORMA SAUCE
4 CLOVES GARLIC, FINELY CHOPPED	**1 CUP** COCONUT MILK
2 CUPS CAULIFLOWER, FLORETS	**1 TEASPOON** GRAPE SEED OIL
2 CUPS BROCCOLI, FLORETS	SEA SALT & PEPPER TO TASTE

READY TO COOK

1. **BROWN** PORK CUBES IN GRAPE SEED OIL UNTIL EACH SIDE IS SLIGHTLY COLORED.

2. **ADD** ONIONS AND GARLIC AND COOK FOR 2-3 MINUTES.

3. **ADD** RED AND GREEN PEPPERS, CAULIFLOWER, BROCCOLI AND MUSHROOMS AND MIX WELL.

4. **ADD** SEA SALT, PEPPER, CUMIN, CORIANDER, GINGER AND CURRY POWDER.

5. **STIR** AND COOK FOR ANOTHER 3 MINUTES.

6. **ADD** THE COCONUT MILK AND THE KORMA SAUCE AND STIR WELL.

7. **SIMMER** FOR 30 MINUTES.

8. **IF** THE CURRY BECOMES TOO DRY, ADD MORE COCONUT MILK.

9. **TASTE** AND ADJUST SEASONING, ADDING MORE CURRY POWDER OR KORMA SAUCE IF NECESSARY.

Serve pork and vegetable curry over rice if desired.

VERATITIPS

KORMA SAUCE IS A MILD, CREAMY CURRY SAUCE FROM NORTHERN INDIA.
YOU WILL FIND IT AT YOUR LOCAL SUPERMARKET OR INDIAN GROCERY STORE.

PER SERVING: 628 CALORIES // 50G FAT // 45G PROTEIN // 19G CARBOHYDRATE

PORK CHOPS
Cacciatore

24 OUNCES PORK (4 CHOPS)	**2 CUPS** GREEN PEPPERS, SLICED
1 TEASPOON GRAPE SEED OIL	**2 CUPS** FRESH MUSHROOMS, SLICED
1 CUP ONIONS, CHOPPED	**1 TEASPOON** DRIED OREGANO
4 CLOVES GARLIC, FINELY CHOPPED	**1 TEASPOON** DRIED MARJORAM
3 CUPS FRESH TOMATO SAUCE	**1 TEASPOON** DRIED BASIL
2 CUPS RED PEPPERS, CUT IN STRIPS	SEA SALT & PEPPER TO TASTE

READY TO COOK

1. **IN** A LARGE FRYING PAN, HEAT THE OIL AND BROWN THE PORK CHOPS ON EACH SIDE.

2. **REMOVE** FROM THE PAN AND SET ASIDE.

3. **ADD** ONIONS AND GARLIC TO THE PAN AND COOK UNTIL ONIONS BEGIN TO SOFTEN.

4. **ADD** THE MUSHROOMS, STIR AND COOK ABOUT 2-3 MINUTES.

5. **ADD** THE RED AND GREEN PEPPERS, TOMATO SAUCE AND ALL THE SEASONINGS.

6. **RETURN** THE PORK CHOPS TO THE PAN, COVER AND SIMMER FOR 1 HOUR OR UNTIL THE PORK CHOPS ARE DONE.

Serve pork chops topped with tomato and vegetable sauce.

VERATI *Twist*
TRY THIS RECIPE WITH CHICKEN, YOUR TASTES BUDS WILL LOVE IT!

PER SERVING: 611 CALORIES // 45G FAT // 42G PROTEIN // 14G CARBOHYDRATE

CHEF
VERATi.

We had fun cooking with OB and we have
it on tape. Thanks to Arnaud and Sylvain!
-Chef Verati

PORTERHOUSE STEAKS
with Anchovy Butter and Spinach

32 OUNCES PORTERHOUSE (4 STEAKS)	**1/2 CUP** CHIVES
4 TABLESPOONS BUTTER	**1 TEASPOON** LEMON JUICE
2 ANCHOVY FILLETS	**2 TABLESPOONS** GRAPE SEED OIL
6 CUPS SPINACH	**4 OUNCES** LOW FAT LOW CARB HOUSE DRESSING (*SEE PAGE 95*)
1/2 CUP RED ONIONS, CHOPPED	SEA SALT & PEPPER TO TASTE
1 CUP CHERRY TOMATOES	

READY TO COOK

1. **MASH** THE ANCHOVY FILLETS WITH A FORK AND COMBINE WITH THE BUTTER UNTIL WELL MIXED.

2. **FORM** INTO 4 SMALL BALLS AND REFRIGERATE.

3. **IN** A LARGE BOWL, COMBINE THE CHERRY TOMATOES, ONIONS, CHIVES AND LEMON JUICE.

4. **ADD** THE SPINACH AND TOSS WELL TO COAT.

5. **HEAT** THE GRAPE SEED OIL IN A PAN.

6. **SEASON** THE PORTERHOUSE STEAKS WITH SEA SALT AND PEPPER AND COOK FOR ABOUT 3-4 MINUTES ON EACH SIDE.

Serve steaks topped with a ball of anchovy butter next to some spinach and cherry tomato salad with low carbohydrate house dressing.

PER SERVING: 716 CALORIES // 43G FAT // 45G PROTEIN // 12G CARBOHYDRATE

PORK CHOPS
with Dijon Mustard Sauce

24 OUNCES PORK TENDERLOIN, SLICED

1 TEASPOON GRAPE SEED OIL

1 CUP PLAIN YOGURT

3 TABLESPOONS DIJON MUSTARD

1 TEASPOON LEMON JUICE

8 CUPS CAULIFLOWER, FLORETS

SEA SALT & PEPPER TO TASTE

READY TO COOK

1. STEAM THE CAULIFLOWER FLORETS UNTIL JUST TENDER.

2. REMOVE FROM HEAT AND KEEP WARM.

3. POUND THE PORK CHOPS UNTIL FLATTENED TO ABOUT 1/4 INCH THICK.

4. HEAT THE OIL IN A FRYING PAN AND SAUTÉ THE PORK FOR ABOUT 3 MINUTES ON EACH SIDE.

5. REMOVE FROM THE PAN AND KEEP WARM.

6. PUT THE YOGURT, DIJON MUSTARD AND LEMON JUICE IN THE PAN AND STIR TO MIX.

7. ADD SEA SALT AND PEPPER AND STIR 1 MINUTE.

SERVE PORK CHOPS TOPPED WITH A SPOONFUL
OF DIJON MUSTARD SAUCE AND STEAMED CAULIFLOWER ON THE SIDE.

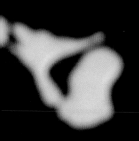

HOT ITALIAN SAUSAGE
Tomato Casserole

24 OUNCES HOT ITALIAN SAUSAGES	**1 TEASPOON** DRIED BASIL
4 CUPS FRESH TOMATOES, DICED	**1 TEASPOON** DRIED THYME
2 CUPS ONIONS, CHOPPED	**1 TEASPOON** FRESH SAGE, CHOPPED
4 CLOVES GARLIC, FINELY CHOPPED	**1 BAY LEAF**
1 CUP SWEET RED PEPPERS, CHOPPED	**1 TEASPOON** GRAPE SEED OIL
1 CUP GREEN BELL PEPPERS, CHOPPED	SEA SALT & PEPPER TO TASTE

READY TO COOK

1. **HEAT** THE OIL IN A FRYING PAN AND COOK THE SAUSAGES UNTIL DONE, PRICKING THE SKIN TO ALLOW SOME OF THE FAT TO ESCAPE.

2. **REMOVE** THE SAUSAGES FROM THE PAN AND SAUTÉ THE ONIONS AND GARLIC FOR A FEW MINUTES.

3. **PLACE** THE TOMATOES, RED AND GREEN PEPPERS, SAUSAGES, ONIONS AND GARLIC IN AN OVEN PROOF PAN.

4. **ADD** THE BASIL, THYME, SAGE AND BAY LEAF.

5. **THERE** SHOULD BE ENOUGH LIQUID JUST TO COVER THE INGREDIENTS; IF NOT ADD A SMALL AMOUNT OF WATER.

6. **BAKE,** COVERED, AT **350⁰F** FOR 45 MINUTES.

Serve sausages with a spoonful of vegetables on the side.

VERATI *Twist*
TO SAVE TIME, USE CANNED DICED TOMATOES INSTEAD OF FRESH ONES.

PER SERVING: 642 CALORIES // 42G FAT // 36G PROTEIN // 12G CARBOHYDRATE

BEEF & BACON STEW
Italian Style

24 OUNCES LEAN BEEF, CUBED	**2 CUPS** MUSHROOMS, SLICED
6 OUNCES BACON, FINELY CHOPPED	**2 SPRIGS** PARSLEY, FINELY CHOPPED
1 TEASPOON GRAPE SEED OIL	**2 CUPS** FRESH TOMATOES, DICED
1 CUP GREEN ONIONS, FINELY CHOPPED	**1 BAY LEAVES**
4 CLOVES GARLIC, FINELY CHOPPED	**1 TEASPOON** DRIED OREGANO
1 CUP CELERY, FINELY CHOPPED	**1 TEASPOON** DRIED BASIL
2 CUPS CELERY ROOT, FINELY CHOPPED	SEA SALT & PEPPER TO TASTE

READY TO COOK

1. **PLACE** THE BACON, GREEN ONIONS, CELERY, CELERY ROOT, GARLIC AND PARSLEY IN A LARGE PAN OR DUTCH OVEN.

2. **ADD** GRAPE SEED OIL AND SAUTÉ UNTIL BACON IS BROWNED AND VEGETABLES ARE SLIGHTLY SOFT.

3. **ADD** BEEF CUBES AND BROWN ON ALL SIDES.

4. **DRAIN** OFF ANY EXCESS FAT AND ADD TOMATOES, BAY LEAVES, BASIL, OREGANO, SEA SALT AND PEPPER.

5. **SIMMER** 2 HOURS OR UNTIL THE BEEF IS VERY TENDER.

Serve with parsley on top.

PER SERVING: 500 CALORIES // 26G FAT // 57G PROTEIN // 13G CARBOHYDRATE

CURRIED PORK CHOPS
with Red Cabbage

24 OUNCES PORK (4 CHOPS)

4 TABLESPOONS CURRY POWDER

2 TEASPOONS GRAPE SEED OIL

1 1/2 CUPS COCONUT MILK

1 TABLESPOON FRESH CORIANDER, CHOPPED

1 TEASPOON GROUND CUMIN

2 TABLESPOONS CREAMED COCONUT, GRATED

7 CUPS RED CABBAGE, SHREDDED

1 CUP ONIONS, CHOPPED

1 OUNCE WHITE OR RASPBERRY VINEGAR

1 TEASPOON CARAWAY SEEDS

SEA SALT & PEPPER TO TASTE

READY TO COOK

1. **COAT** THE PORK CHOPS LIBERALLY WITH THE CURRY POWDER.

2. **PLACE** IN A LARGE FRYING PAN WITH 1 TEASPOON OF GRAPE SEED OIL AND FRY UNTIL LIGHTLY BROWNED ON BOTH SIDES.

3. **ADD** COCONUT MILK, CORIANDER, CUMIN AND CREAMED COCONUT AND SIMMER FOR 1 HOUR.

4. **ADD** 1 TEASPOON OF GRAPE SEED OIL TO ANOTHER FRYING PAN AND COOK ONIONS UNTIL SOFT BUT NOT BROWNED.

5. **ADD** CABBAGE AND SIMMER GENTLY FOR ABOUT 10 MINUTES OR UNTIL THE CABBAGE IS COOKED.

6. **WATER** SHOULD BE REDUCED BY THE END OF THE COOKING; IF NOT, DRAIN OFF ALL BUT 1/4 CUP.

7. **ADD** VINEGAR AND CARAWAY SEEDS AND CONTINUE COOKING UNTIL THE CABBAGE HAS A GLAZED APPEARANCE AND THE LIDQUID IS ABSORBED.

Serve curried pork chops with red cabbage on the side.

VERATITRICK

WHEN COOKING THE PORK CHOPS, ADD SOME MILK IF THE LIQUID LEVEL IS TOO LOW. YOU WANT TO END UP WITH A CREAMY SAUCE THAT COVERS THE MEAT WHILE IT SIMMERS.

PER SERVING: 622 CALORIES // 44G FAT // 40G PROTEIN // 10G CARBOHYDRATE

LAMB CHOPS
with Tomato and Cucumber Salsa

32 OUNCES LAMB (4 CHOPS)

2 TEASPOONS FRESH MINT, CHOPPED

4 TABLESPOONS FRESH CORIANDER, CHOPPED

2 TABLESPOONS LEMON JUICE

3 CUPS FRESH TOMATOES, SEEDS REMOVED & CHOPPED

3 CUPS SEEDLESS CUCUMBERS, FINELY CHOPPED

1 CUP SWEET YELLOW PEPPERS, SLICED

1 CUP SWEET RED PEPPERS, SLICED

2 TABLESPOONS GRAPE SEED OIL

SEA SALT & PEPPER TO TASTE

READY TO COOK

1. IN A BOWL, COMBINE THE TOMATOES, CUCUMBERS, YELLOW AND RED PEPPERS, CORIANDER AND MINT.

2. DRIZZLE WITH LEMON JUICE AND TOSS THE SALSA UNTIL WELL COMBINED.

3. ALLOW TO MARINATE AT ROOM TEMPERATURE FOR ABOUT 30 MINUTES.

4. SEASON THE LAMB CHOPS WITH SEA SALT AND PEPPER.

5. HEAT THE OIL IN A FRYING PAN AND COOK THE LAMB CHOPS UNTIL DESIRED DONENESS, ABOUT 2-3 MINUTES PER SIDE.

SERVE THE LAMB CHOPS WITH A GENEROUS PORTION OF THE SALSA OVER TOP.

MARINATE OVERNIGHT, COVERED, IN REFRIGERATOR FOR BEST RESULTS!

PER SERVING: 559 CALORIES // 23G FAT // 49G PROTEIN // 8G CARBOHYDRATE

BEEF ROLL-UPS
with Dill Pickles

24 OUNCES	BEEF LOIN (4 STEAKS)
8 STRIPS	BACON
2	DILL PICKLES, SLICED
1 TEASPOON	GRAPE SEED OIL
1 TABLESPOON	DIJON MUSTARD
8 CUPS	MIXED GREENS
4 OUNCES	LOW FAT LOW CARB HOUSE DRESSING (*SEE PAGE 95*)
STRING	
SEA SALT & PEPPER TO TASTE	

READY TO COOK ⬇⬇⬇

1. POUND OUT EACH OF THE 4 STEAKS ON A FLAT SURFACE. **2. SPRINKLE** WITH SEA SALT AND PEPPER. **3. SPREAD** SOME OF THE DIJON MUSTARD OVER EACH STEAK. **4. LAY** 2 BACON STRIPS ON TOP OF THE MUSTARD. **5. LAY** SLICES OF DILL PICKLES ON TOP OF THE BACON. **6. ROLL** EACH PIECE OF MEAT UP. **7. SECURE** WITH STRING. **8. HEAT** OIL IN A OVEN PROOF PAN AND BROWN EACH ROLL-UP. **9. TURN** CAREFULLY TO BROWN EVERY SIDE. **10. REMOVE** FROM THE PAN. **11. PLACE** IN OVEN-PROOF PAN AND POUR IN THE BEEF BROTH, FINELY CHOPPED ONIONS, CARROTS, CELERY AND BAY LEAVES. **12. COVER** AND BAKE AT **350⁰F** FOR 1 1/2 HOURS. **13. REMOVE** FROM THE OVEN. **14. REMOVE** THE STRING AND PLACE THE MEAT ON A CUTTING BOARD **15. STIR** CORN STARCH INTO THE WATER AND ADD TO THE OVENPAN, STIRRING CONSTANTLY AS THE MIXTURE IS ADDED. **16. WHEN** THE SAUCE HAS THICKENED AND IS BUBBLY, POUR OVER THE MEAT.

Serve beef roll-ups with a green salad drizzled with low carbohydrate house dressing.

PER SERVING: 562 CALORIES // 30G FAT // 66G PROTEIN // 9G CARBOHYDRATE.

CALF'S LIVER & BACON
with Mushrooms

20 OUNCES	CALF'S LIVER, SLICED
8 OUNCES	BACON
2 CUPS	ONIONS, CHOPPED
2 CUPS	MUSHROOMS, SLICED
2 TABLESPOONS	FLOUR
2 TABLESPOONS	GRAPE SEED OIL
4 CUPS	SPINACH
1 TABLESPOON	BUTTER
SEA SALT & PEPPER TO TASTE	

READY TO COOK ⬇⬇⬇

1. COMBINE THE FLOUR, SEA SALT AND PEPPER IN A SHALLOW BOWL. **2. DREDGE** THE LIVER IN THE FLOUR MIXTURE AND SHAKE OFF THE EXCESS. **3. IN** A FRYING PAN, GENTLY SAUTÉ THE BACON, ONIONS AND MUSHROOMS FOR 3-4 MINUTES. **4. ADD** THE SPINACH AND COOK FOR 1 MINUTE AND SET ASIDE. **5. HEAT** THE OIL AND BUTTER AND COOK THE LIVER TURNING ONCE.

Serve calf liver with the mixture of bacon, onions, mushrooms and spinach on top.

PER SERVING: 610 CALORIES // 42G FAT // 55G PROTEIN // 11G CARBOHYDRATE

BEEF STROGANOFF
with Asparagus

24 OUNCES LEAN BEEF (4 FILLETS), SLICED

1/2 CUP GREEN ONIONS, FINELY CHOPPED

2 TEASPOONS GRAPE SEED OIL

2 TABLESPOONS BUTTER

2 CUPS MUSHROOMS, SLICED

1 1/2 CUPS SOUR CREAM OR PLAIN YOGURT

DASH GROUND NUTMEG

6 CUPS ASPARAGUS, SPEARS

2 TABLESPOONS FRESH PARSLEY, CHOPPED

SEA SALT & PEPPER TO TASTE

WHEN PARING A FOOD HIGH ON THE GLYCEMIC INDEX WITH A FOOD LOW ON THE GLYCEMIC INDEX, THE RESULT IS THE AVERAGE OF THE TWO.

READY TO COOK ⬇ ⬇ ⬇

1. COOK ONIONS IN A PAN FOR ABOUT 3 MINUTES, UNTIL THEY BEGIN TO SOFTEN. **2. ADD** THE BEEF AND COOK UNTIL JUST BROWNED. **3. REMOVE** ONIONS AND BEEF AND KEEP WARM. **4. ADD** BUTTER AND MUSHROOMS TO PAN AND COOK FOR ABOUT 2 MINUTES. **5. RETURN** ONIONS AND BEEF TO PAN. **6. ADD** SEA SALT, PEPPER AND SOUR CREAM OR YOGURT. **7. TOSS** UNTIL WELL AMALGAMATED AND ADD A DASH OF NUTMEG. **8. POUR** ALL ONTO A SERVING PLATTER.

Serve with a sprinkle of chopped fresh parsley and steamed asparagus.

PER SERVING: 604 CALORIES // 37G FAT // 57G PROTEIN // 12G CARBOHYDRATE

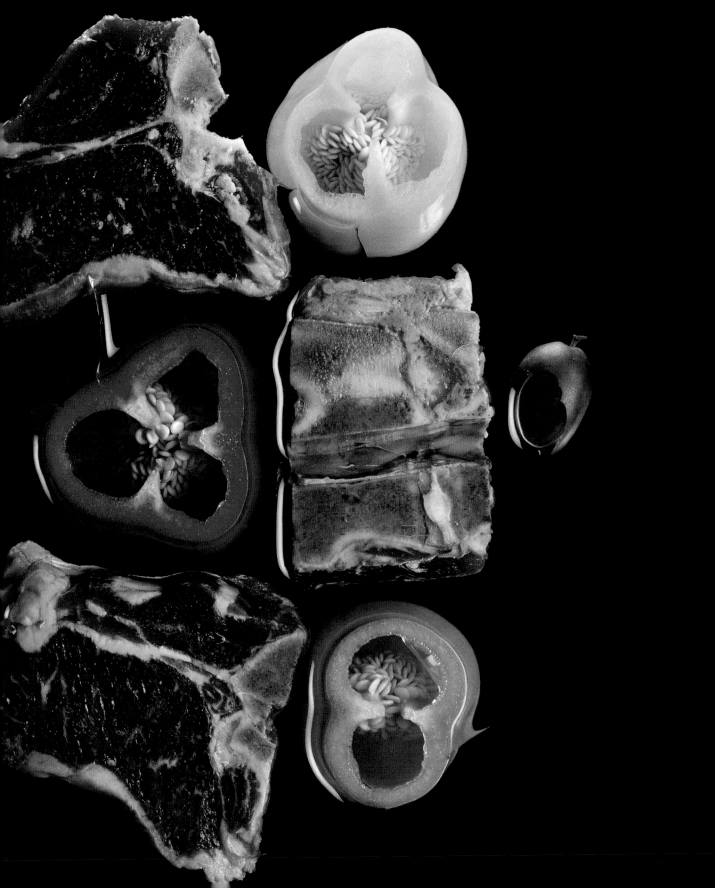

HOT POT
Lamb, Pepper and Kalamata

32 OUNCES LAMB (4 CHOPS)	3 TABLESPOONS CAPERS
4 CLOVES GARLIC, FINELY CHOPPED	1 CUP KALAMATA OLIVES, PITTED
1 CUP ONIONS, SLICED	1/4 CUP FRESH PARSLEY, CHOPPED
2 CUPS SWEET RED PEPPERS, SLICED	2 TEASPOONS LEMON JUICE
2 CUPS GREEN BELL PEPPERS, SLICED	1 TABLESPOON GRAPE SEED OIL
2 CUPS YELLOW BELL PEPPERS, SLICED	SEA SALT & PEPPER TO TASTE

READY TO COOK

1. SEASON THE LAMB CHOPS WITH SEA SALT AND PEPPER.

2. HEAT THE GRAPE SEED OIL IN A PAN AND BROWN THE CHOPS LIGHTLY ON EACH SIDE.

3. REMOVE FROM THE PAN AND SET ASIDE.

4. ADD THE ONIONS AND GARLIC TO THE PAN AND SAUTÉ UNTIL THE ONIONS BEGIN TO SOFTEN.

5. ADD THE RED, GREEN AND YELLOW PEPPERS.

6. PUT THE LAMB CHOPS BACK INTO THE PAN, COVER AND SIMMER FOR 35-40 MINUTES, STIRRING OCCASIONALLY.

7. ADD THE CAPERS, OLIVES, PARSLEY AND LEMON JUICE AND CONTINUE TO HEAT FOR 2-3 MINUTES.

SERVE LAMB CHOPS WITH GREEN, RED AND YELLOW PEPPERS ON THE SIDE.

PER SERVING: 577 CALORIES // 26G FAT // 50G PROTEIN // 12G CARBOHYDRATE

MINTY LAMB CHOPS
with Broccoli

32 **OUNCES** LAMB (4 CHOPS)

1 **TEASPOON** DRIED OREGANO

1/2 **TEASPOON** GARLIC POWDER

1 **TEASPOON** LEMON JUICE

1 **TEASPOON** GRAPE SEED OIL

8 **CUPS** BROCCOLI, FLORETS & BLANCHED (*SEE PAGE 129*)

4 **TEASPOONS** MINT SAUCE

SEA SALT & PEPPER TO TASTE

READY TO COOK ↓↓↓

1. BLANCH THE BROCCOLI. **2. COMBINE** OREGANO, SEA SALT, PEPPER, GARLIC POWDER, GRAPE SEED OIL AND LEMON JUICE IN A SMALL BOWL AND MIX WELL. **3. COAT** EACH SIDE OF THE LAMB CHOPS WITH THE MIXTURE. **4. PLACE** THE MEAT ON A RACK AND GRILL AT 350°F FOR 4 MINUTES ON EACH SIDE.

Serve pork chops with a hint of mint sauce and broccoli on the side.

PER SERVING: 509 CALORIES // 27G FAT // 52G PROTEIN // 12G CARBOHYDRATE

BEEF, SAUSAGE
and Parmesan Balls

16 **OUNCES** LEAN GROUND BEEF

2 HOT ITALIAN SAUSAGES

1 **CUP** ONIONS, FINELY CHOPPED

2 **CLOVES** GARLIC, FINELY CHOPPED

1 **TEASPOON** DRIED OREGANO

1 **TEASPOON** DRIED MARJORAM

1/4 **CUP** PARMESAN CHEESE

1 EGG

2 **TEASPOONS** GRAPE SEED OIL

2 **CUPS** TOMATO SAUCE

8 **CUPS** MIXED GREENS

4 **OUNCES** LOW FAT LOW CARB HOUSE DRESSING (*SEE PAGE 95*)

SEA SALT & PEPPER TO TASTE

READY TO COOK ↓↓↓

1. REMOVE SKIN CASES FROM THE ITALIAN SAUSAGES AND BREAK INTO PIECES. **2. IN** A MIXING BOWL, COMBINE THE SAUSAGES WITH THE GROUND BEEF. **3. ADD** ONIONS, GARLIC, OREGANO, MARJORAM, PARMESAN CHEESE, SEA SALT, PEPPER AND EGG TO THE BOWL AND MIX WELL. **4. FORM** THE MIXTURE INTO BALLS OF DESIRED SIZE. **5. PUT** THE OIL IN A FRYING PAN AND COOK THE MEATBALLS ON **MEDIUM HEAT** UNTIL BROWNED ON ALL SIDES.

Serve meat balls with a spoonful of tomato sauce over top and green salad on the side.

PER SERVING: 660 CALORIES // 38G FAT // 60 G PROTEIN // 11G CARBOHYDRATE

PEPPER STEAK
with Belgian Endives

24 **OUNCES** BEEF (4 FILETS MIGNON STEAKS)

1/4 **CUP** PEPPERCORNS, CRUSHED

2 **TEASPOONS** GRAPE SEED OIL

1/4 **CUP** BUTTER

5 **TABLESPOONS** LEMON JUICE

6 **CUPS** MIXED GREENS SALAD

2 **CUPS** BELGIAN ENDIVES, BLANCHED (*SEE PAGE 129*)

1/2 **CUP** VEGETABLE STOCK

4 **OUNCES** LOW FAT LOW CARB HOUSE DRESSING (*SEE PAGE 95*)

SEA SALT & PEPPER TO TASTE

READY TO COOK ⬇ ⬇ ⬇

1. CRUSH PEPPERCORN UNTIL PIECES ARE WELL CRACKED. **2. PRESS** THE CRUSHED PEPPERCORNS INTO BOTH SIDES OF THE STEAK AND COOK IN A HOT RIBBED PAN UNTIL THE DESIRED LEVEL OF RARENESS. **3. REMOVE** FROM HEAT. **4. IN** ANOTHER PAN, MELT THE BUTTER AND ADD 2 TABLESPOONS OF LEMON JUICE. **5. POUR** THIS MIXTURE OVER THE STEAKS. **6. BLANCH** THE ENDIVES. **7. GREASE** AN OVEN DISH WITH GRAPE SEED OIL. **8. PLACE** THE ENDIVES IN THE OVEN DISH. **9. POUR** IN VEGETABLE STOCK AND 3 TABLESPOONS OF LEMON JUICE. **10. COVER** AND BAKE AT **350ºF** FOR 20 MINUTES.

Serve steaks with belgian endives and green salad with low carbohydrate house dressing.

PER SERVING: 462 CALORIES // 25G FAT // 47G PROTEIN // 9G CARBOHYDRATE

PORK GOULASH
with Sauerkraut

24 **OUNCES** LEAN PORK, CUBED

1 **CUP** ONIONS, CHOPPED

1 **CUP** RED PEPPERS, SLICED

4 **CUPS** SAUERKRAUT, DRAINED

1 **CUP** TOMATOES, DICED

1 **CUP** GREEN CABBAGE, SLICED

2 **TEASPOONS** CARAWAY SEEDS

3 **TEASPOONS** SMOKED PAPRIKA

1 **CUP** SOUR CREAM OR LOW FAT YOGURT

1 **TEASPOON** GRAPE SEED OIL

SEA SALT & PEPPER TO TASTE

READY TO COOK ⬇ ⬇ ⬇

1. SAUTÉ THE ONIONS IN GRAPE SEED OIL UNTIL SOFT. **2. ADD** THE PORK CUBES AND SAUTÉ UNTIL BROWNED ON ALL SIDES. **3. ADD** THE CABBAGE, SAUERKRAUT, RED PEPPERS, TOMATOES, CARAWAY SEED AND PAPRIKA. **4. HEAT** TO BOIL TURN DOWN HEAT AND SIMMER FOR 1 HOUR. **5. ADD** SOUR CREAM OR YOGURT, SEA SALT AND PEPPER.

Serve with sour cream on the side.

PER SERVING: 536 CALORIES // 30G FAT // 53G PROTEIN // 13G CARBOHYDRATE

QUICK VEAL PICCATA
with Asparagus

24 OUNCES VEAL (4 CUTLETS)

1/8 CUP FLOUR

1 TEASPOON GRAPE SEED OIL

2 TEASPOONS BUTTER

4 TABLESPOONS LEMON JUICE

2 CLOVES GARLIC, FINELY CHOPPED

4 CUPS FRESH MUSHROOMS, SLICED

2 TABLESPOONS CAPERS

1/4 CUP FRESH PARSLEY, CHOPPED

1/2 CUP VEGETABLE OR CHICKEN STOCK

4 CUPS ASPARAGUS, SPEARS & BLANCHED (*SEE PAGE 129*)

SEA SALT & PEPPER TO TASTE

READY TO COOK ↓↓↓

1. BLANCH ASPARAGUS. **2. POUND** THE VEAL CUTLETS USING A MALLET OR A ROLLING PIN UNTIL AS THIN AS POSSIBLE. **3. HEAT** THE OIL AND THE BUTTER IN A FRYING PAN. **4. IN** A MIXING BOWL, COMBINE SEA SALT AND PEPPER WITH THE FLOUR AND DREDGE THE VEAL, SHAKING OFF ANY EXCESS FLOUR. **5. SAUTÉ** VEAL IN THE OIL/BUTTER MIXTURE FOR 2-3 MINUTES, BROWNING EACH SIDE. **6. MOVE** THE VEAL TO A PLATE. **7. SAUTÉ** MUSHROOMS AND GARLIC FOR 2-3 MINUTES. **8. RETURN** THE VEAL TO THE PAN. **9. ADD** LEMON JUICE AND VEGETABLE OR CHICKEN STOCK AND HEAT TO BOILING POINT. **10. REMOVE** FROM HEAT IMMEDIATELY.

Serve veal with fresh parsley and capers over top and asparagus on the side.

PER SERVING: 475 CALORIES // 25G FAT // 56G PROTEIN // 12G CARBOHYDRATE

BEEF & VEGETABLES
Stir-Fry

24 OUNCES BEEF (4 STEAKS), SLICED

1 CUP GREEN ONIONS, CHOPPED

4 CLOVES GARLIC, FINELY CHOPPED

2 CUPS RED BELL PEPPERS, CHOPPED

2 CUPS GREEN BELL PEPPERS, CHOPPED

1 1/2 CUPS BEEF BROTH OR WATER

3 CUPS ASPARAGUS, SPEARS

2 TEASPOONS GRAPE SEED OIL

4 TABLESPOONS SOY SAUCE

2 TABLESPOONS RICE WINE VINEGAR

2 TABLESPOONS FRESH GINGER, PEELED & FINELY CHOPPED

2 TABLESPOONS SUSHI GINGER

SEA SALT & PEPPER TO TASTE

READY TO COOK ↓↓↓

1. HEAT OIL IN LARGE FRYING PAN. **2. ADD** STRIPS OF STEAK SEASONED WITH SEA SALT AND PEPPER AND COOK 2-3 MINUTES. **3. REMOVE** FROM PAN. **4. ADD** GREEN ONIONS, GARLIC, GINGER, RED AND GREEN PEPPERS AND COOK UNTIL THE ONIONS AND GARLIC ARE SOFT BUT NOT BROWNED. **5. ADD** MEAT BACK INTO THE MIXTURE. **6. TURN** HEAT TO **LOW**, ADD BEEF BROTH OR WATER, SOY SAUCE, RICE WINE VINEGAR AND ASPARAGUS SPEARS. **7. SIMMER** 5-10 MINUTES UNTIL THE ASPARAGUS ARE JUST TENDER.

Serve with some sushi ginger on top.

PER SERVING: 420 CALORIES // 28G FAT // 51G PROTEIN // 13G CARBOHYDRATE

VEAL &
SAUSAGE
Patties

12 OUNCES LEAN VEAL, GROUND

12 OUNCES LEAN PORK, GROUND

1 EGG, WHOLE

1/2 TEASPOON GROUND SAVOURY OR SAGE

1/2 TEASPOON DRIED MARJORAM

DASH NUTMEG

1 TEASPOON GRAPE SEED OIL

8 CUPS MIXED GREEN SALAD

4 OUNCES LOW FAT LOW CARB HOUSE DRESSING (*SEE PAGE 95*)

SEA SALT & PEPPER TO TASTE

READY TO COOK ↓↓↓

1. COMBINE ALL INGREDIENTS TOGETHER IN A BOWL, EXCEPT THE OIL
AND MIXED GREENS. **2. MIX** VERY WELL. **3. MAKE** INTO 4 LARGE OR
8 SMALL PATTIES AND COOK IN OIL UNTIL MEAT IS NO LONGER PINK.

*Serve meat next to green salad with
low carbohydrate house dressing.*

PER SERVING: 452 CALORIES // 24G FAT // 46G PROTEIN // 8G CARBOHYDRATE

CONSULT
NUTRITION
FACTS TABLES
TO STAY
AWAY FROM
FOODS HIGH
IN SUGARS.

CHEF
VERATi.

*I love adding smoked paprika.
It gives a nice light smoked flavor to
foods and adds color to your plate.*
—Chef Verati

VEAL MARENGO
with Rapini and Mushrooms

24 OUNCES VEAL (4 CUTLETS)	**2 TABLESPOONS** GRAPE SEED OIL
1 TEASPOON DRIED TARRAGON	**4 CUPS** RAPINI, BLANCHED (*SEE PAGE 129*)
1 TABLESPOON FLOUR	**1 TABLESPOON** BUTTER
1 CUP BEEF BROTH	**4 TABLESPOONS** ALMONDS, SLIVERED & ROASTED
2 CUPS FRESH TOMATOES, DICED	SEA SALT & PEPPER TO TASTE
4 CLOVES GARLIC, FINELY CHOPPED	WAXED PAPER
2 CUPS MUSHROOMS, SLICED	

READY TO COOK

1. **ROAST** THE ALMONDS IN THE OVEN.

2. **ADD** RAPINI TILL HOT.

3. **PLACE** THE VEAL CUTLETS BETWEEN SHEETS OF WAXED PAPER AND POUND OUT AS THIN AS POSSIBLE.

4. **IN** A BOWL, COMBINE THE TARRAGON, SEA SALT, PEPPER AND FLOUR.

5. **DREDGE** THE CUTLETS IN THE FLOUR, SHAKE OFF EXCESS AND KEEP THE REMAINING FLOUR MIXTURE.

6. **HEAT** THE OIL IN A LARGE FRYING PAN AND BROWN THE CUTLETS ON EACH SIDE.

7. **ADD** A LITTLE OF THE BROTH AND STIR IN THE REMAINING FLOUR MIXTURE.

8. **STIRRING** CONSTANTLY, ADD THE REMAINING BROTH, AS WELL AS THE TOMATOES, GARLIC AND MUSHROOMS.

9. **COVER** AND SIMMER FOR 45 MINUTES.

Serve veal with rapini seasoned with butter and roasted slivered almonds.

PER SERVING: 556 CALORIES // 29G FAT // 58G PROTEIN // 12G CARBOHYDRATE

RIB EYE STEAK
with Asparagus

32 OUNCES PORTERHOUSE (4 STEAKS)	**4 CUPS** ASPARAGUS, SPEARS
1 TABLESPOON GRAPE SEED OIL	**4 CUPS** MIXED GREEN SALAD
1-2 TABLESPOONS GARLIC, MINCED	**2 OUNCES** LOW FAT LOW CARB HOUSE DRESSING (*SEE PAGE 95*)
4 LEMON WEDGES	SEA SALT & PEPPER TO TASTE

READY TO COOK

1. **RUB** THE STEAKS WITH OIL, SEA SALT, PEPPER AND GARLIC.

2. **LET** STAND FOR 1 HOUR IN THE REFRIGERATOR, COVERED.

3. **REMOVE** FROM REFRIGERATOR AND LET STAND AT ROOM TEMPERATURE FOR 20 MINUTES BEFORE COOKING.

4. **IF** GRILLING OUTDOORS, PLACE OAK CHIPS IN FOIL IN BOTTOM OF THE BARBECUE.

5. **IF** GRILLING INDOORS, PLACE ON RACK IN THE MIDDLE OF A **450⁰F** OVEN.

6. **GRILL** FOR 3-4 MINUTES ON EACH SIDE OR TO JUST A LITTLE LESS THAN THAN DESIRED DONENESS.

7. **REMOVE** FROM OVEN OR BARBECUE AND LET REST FOR 8-10 MINUTES.

8. **BLANCH** ASPARAGUS .

Serve steaks next to asparagus topped with lemon wedges and green salad with low carbohydrate house dressing.

VERATITRICK

THE MOST COMPLICATED PART OF THIS RECIPE IS TO FIND 4 PORTERHOUSE STEAKS OF AT LEAST 8 OUNCES EACH AND CUT AS THICK AS POSSIBLE. IT IS BEST TO SEE YOUR LOCAL BUTCHER.

PER SERVING: 638 CALORIES // 34G FAT // 72G PROTEIN // 11G CARBOHYDRATE

TOMATO & LAMB
Mushroom Stew

32 OUNCES LAMB, CUBED

1 CUP PEARL ONIONS, CHOPPED

3 CUPS FRESH TOMATOES, DICED

1 CUP TOMATO JUICE

2 CUPS TURNIP, PEELED & CUBED

2 CUPS BUTTON MUSHROOMS

2 TEASPOONS GROUND THYME

2 TEASPOONS GROUND CORIANDER

2 TABLESPOONS GRAPE SEED OIL

2 TABLESPOONS FRESH MINT, CHOPPED

SEA SALT & PEPPER TO TASTE

READY TO COOK

1. **HEAT** GRAPE SEED OIL IN A LARGE PAN AND BROWN THE LAMB LIGHTLY.

2. **ADD** THE ONIONS, TOMATOES, TOMATO JUICE AND TURNIP TO THE PAN.

3. **STIR** IN THE THYME, CORIANDER AND MUSHROOMS.

4. **COVER** AND BAKE AT **350⁰F** FOR 1 1/2 HOURS.

5. **REMOVE** THE COVER AND ALLOW TO BAKE FOR ANOTHER 30 MINUTES.

Serve with fresh mint on top.

VERATI *Twist*
TO SAVE TIME, USE CANNED DICED TOMATOES INSTEAD OF FRESH ONES.

PER SERVING: 527 CALORIES // 23G FAT // 49G PROTEIN // 11G CARBOHYDRATE

TANDOORI MASALA
Lamb Chops

32 OUNCES LAMB (4 CHOPS)

1/4 CUP TANDOORI MASALA SPICE BLEND (*SEE RECIPE PAGE 169*)

1/4 CUP PLAIN YOGURT

4 TABLESPOONS LEMON JUICE

1 TEASPOON GRAPE SEED OIL

8 CUPS MIXED GREENS

4 OUNCES LOW FAT LOW CARB HOUSE DRESSING (*SEE PAGE 95*)

SEA SALT & PEPPER TO TASTE

READY TO COOK

1. **IN** A BOWL, MIX THE TANDOORI MASALA WITH LEMON JUICE, SEA SALT, PEPPER AND YOGURT.

2. **COAT** THE LAMB CHOPS WELL WITH THE MIXTURE AND LEAVE TO MARINATE FOR ABOUT 1 HOUR OR OVERNIGHT.

3. **HEAT** THE OIL IN A FRYING PAN AND COOK GENTLY, BASTING WITH ANY REMAINING MARINADE UNTIL THE LAMB CHOPS ARE COOKED.

Serve lamb chops alongside green salad drizzled with low carbohydrate house dressing.

VERATI **TIPS**

TANDOORI MASALA IS A MIXTURE OF SPICES USED IN TRADITIONAL INDIAN, PAKISTANI AND AFGHAN COOKING. YOU CAN EASILY FIND IT AT YOUR LOCAL SUPERMARKET OR INDIAN GROCERY STORE. YOU CAN ALSO MIX YOUR OWN. (*SEE RECIPE PAGE 173*)

PER SERVING: 567 CALORIES // 22G FAT // 64G PROTEIN // 6G CARBOHYDRATE

MILK SIMMERED
Pork Shoulder

24 OUNCES LEAN PORK SHOULDER

1 LITER WHOLE MILK

2 TABLESPOONS BUTTER

1/2 CUP BACON, CHOPPED

2 CUPS ONIONS, FINELY CHOPPED

4 CLOVES GARLIC, CHOPPED

2 TEASPOONS DRIED MARJORAM

6 CUPS ZUCCHINI, SLICED & BLANCHED (*SEE PAGE 129*)

SEA SALT & PEPPER TO TASTE

READY TO COOK

1. **MELT** THE BUTTER IN A FRYING PAN, BROWN THE ONIONS THEN REMOVE FROM PAN AND SET ASIDE.

2. **BROWN** THE BACON, REMOVE FROM PAN AND SET ASIDE.

3. **MAKE** CUTS IN THE PORK WITH A SHARP KNIFE AND INSERT ONE HALF OF THE GARLIC SLICES INTO THE SLOTS.

4. **RUB** 1 TEASPOON OF MARJORAM, SEA SALT AND PEPPER INTO THE SURFACE OF THE PORK.

5. **BROWN** THE PORK IN THE FRYING PAN IN WHICH ONIONS AND BACON WERE COOKED, REMOVE FROM PAN AND SET ASIDE.

6. **HEAT** THE MILK IN A SEPARATE PAN UNTIL IT COMES TO A BOIL.

7. **IN** A PAN LARGE ENOUGH TO JUST FIT THE INGREDIENTS, PLACE PORK SHOULDER, BACON, ONIONS, 1 TEASPOON OF MARJORAM AND REMAINING GARLIC.

8. **POUR** THE MILK IN, MAKING SURE IT COVERS ALL THE INGREDIENTS AND SIMMER FOR 2 HOURS, UNCOVERED. REMOVE THE PORK AND KEEP WARM.

9. **COOK** THE ZUCCHINIS.

10. **TURN UP** THE HEAT TO REDUCE THE MIXTURE UNTIL THE MILK, ONIONS, BACON AND HERBS MAKE A THICK SAUCE. ADJUST SALT IF NECESSARY.

Serve the porc with a generous amount of the milk sauce and zuccinis.

VERATI **TIPS**

DO NOT STIR THE SIMMERING PORK, YOU DON'T WANT TO DISTURB THE MILK CRUST FORMING OVER THE MEAT.

PER SERVING: 642 CALORIES // 37G FAT // 55G PROTEIN // 18G CARBOHYDRATE

SALSA
Easy + Twist + Funky

#1 EASY & BASIC ↓↓↓

4 **CUPS** FRESH TOMATOES, DICED

1 **CUP** GREEN ONIONS, FINELY CHOPPED

1 **CUP** FRESH CILANTRO, CHOPPED

1 **TEASPOON** LIME JUICE

1 **TEASPOON** GARLIC SALT

1 **TEASPOON** ONION POWDER

1 **TEASPOON** OLIVE OIL

· ·

#2 ADD A SPICY TWIST ↓↓↓

4 **CUPS** FRESH TOMATOES, DICED

1 **CUP** GREEN ONIONS, FINELY CHOPPED

1 **CUP** SWEET RED PEPPERS, CHOPPED

1 **CUP** GREEN PEPPERS, CHOPPED

1 **CUP** CUCUMBERS, DICED

1 **CUP** FRESH CILANTRO, CHOPPED

1 **TEASPOON** GROUND CORIANDER

1 **TEASPOON** LIME JUICE

2 **TEASPOONS** LEMON JUICE

1/2 **TEASPOON** CAYENNE PEPPER OR CHILI POWDER (SEE PAGE 173)

1 **TEASPOON** GARLIC SALT

1 **TEASPOON** ONION POWDER

1 **TEASPOON** OLIVE OIL

· ·

#3 FUNKY & TROPICAL ↓↓↓

2 **CUPS** FRESH MANGO, CUBED

2 **CUPS** CUCUMBERS, CUBED

1 **CUP** RED ONIONS, VERY FINELY SLICED

1/2 **CUP** FRESH MINT, CHOPPED

1/2 **CUP** FRESH CORIANDER, CHOPPED

1 **CUP** SWEET RED PEPPERS, CHOPPED

2 **TABLESPOONS** LIME JUICE

· ·

#4 FUNKY & FRUITY ↓↓↓

2 **CUPS** STRAWBERRIES, CUBED

2 **CUPS** SEEDLESS CUCUMBERS, CUBED

1 **CUP** SWEET RED PEPPERS, CHOPPED

1 **CUP** GREEN BELL PEPPERS, CHOPPED

1 **TABLESPOON** LIME JUICE

3 **TEASPOONS** FRESH MINT, CHOPPED

1/2 **TEASPOON** HOT PEPPER SAUCE

READY TO COOK

1. IN A LARGE BOWL, COMBINE ALL INGREDIENTS. **2. MIX** WELL **3. MARINATE** FOR 30 MINUTES AT ROOM TEMPERATURE.

You can even salsa your salads on the fun day!!
-Chef Verati

CARBS

↓ ↓ ↓ ↓ ↓ ↓ ↓ ↓ ↓

FAT

— best at dinner time —

FACT #6

FRUITS ARE EASY

TO DIGEST AND RELEASE IMMEDIATE ENERGY; THESE ARE SIMPLE CARBS. WHOLE GRAINS ARE DIGESTED SLOWLY AND THEREFORE PROVIDE LONG-LASTING ENERGY; THESE ARE COMPLEX CARBS. MAKE SURE YOU ADD A SOURCE OF ENERGY TO YOUR DIET BY INCLUDING CARBS!

ENERGY

Freedom

BEEF BRAISED IN BEER

with Snow Peas

24 OUNCES BEEF SHOULDER, CUBED

4 CUPS ONIONS, THINLY SLICED

2 CLOVES GARLIC, CHOPPED

1 BAY LEAF

6 OUNCES TOMATO PASTE

1/2 TEASPOON THYME

1/4 CUP CHOPPED PARSLEY

2 TEASPOONS GRAPE SEED OIL

1/2 CUP FLOUR

1 CUP BEEF BROTH

12 OUNCES DARK BEER

8 CUPS SNOW PEAS, STEAMED

SEA SALT & PEPPER TO TASTE

READY TO COOK

1. IN A BOWL, MIX FLOUR, SEA SALT AND PEPPER. 2. DREDGE BEEF CUBES WITH FLOUR MIXTURE. 3. HEAT OIL IN A LARGE OVEN PAN WHICH HAS A TIGHT-FITTING LID AND BROWN THE BEEF ON ALL SIDES. 4. ADD ALL THE REMAINING INGREDIENTS, EXCEPT THE PARSLEY, AND HEAT THOROUGHLY. 5. REMOVE FROM HEAT, COVER, AND BAKE IN A PREHEATED 325°F OVEN FOR 2 HOURS. 6. REMOVE BAY LEAF, STIR IN THE CHOPPED PARSLEY AND COOK FOR AN ADDITIONAL 10 MINUTES. 7. STEAM THE SNOW PEAS. 8. SERVE BRAISED BEEF WITH SNOW PEAS ON THE SIDE.

▶ GLOU GLOU GLOUK!
BEER WILL ALWAYS
BE BEER. SIMPLE *Freedom*
BEER CONTAINS MALTOSE: THAT'S A DOUBLE DOSE OF SUGAR! MODERATION HAS MUCH BETTER TASTE.

PER SERVING: 625 CALORIES // 48G CARBOHYDRATE // 61G PROTEIN // 12G FAT

CHEF

VERATi.

WORKING IS MUCH MORE FUN WITH
LAUGHTER! LIFE IS GREAT WHEN YOU GO
THROUGH IT WITH A SMILE... AND GOOD FOOD!
-CHEF VERATI

EGGPLANT MOUSSAKA
with Cheese Sauce

4 EGGPLANTS, THICKLY SLICED

20 OUNCES LEAN GROUND BEEF

1 TEASPOON GRAPE SEED OIL

1 CUP ONIONS, CHOPPED

4 CLOVES GARLIC, FINELY CHOPPED

2 CUPS FRESH TOMATOES, DICED

1 TEASPOON DRIED OREGANO

1/2 TEASPOON GROUND CINNAMON

1 CUP BREAD CRUMBS

4 EGG WHITES, BEATEN

3 TABLESPOONS CORN STARCH

2 CUPS 1% MILK

4 SLICES 1% SKIM MILK CHEESE

PINCH GROUND NUTMEG

SEA SALT & PEPPER TO TASTE

READY TO COOK

1. SEASON WITH SEA SALT AND PEPPER TO TASTE AND LEAVE FOR 30 MINUTES.
2. DRY EGGPLANTS WITH PAPER TOWELS AND DIP FIRST IN EGG WHITES, THEN IN BREAD CRUMBS, COATING EACH SIDE.
3. PLACE ON BAKING SHEETS AND COOK AT 350°F FOR 30 MINUTES, TURNING ONCE. REMOVE FROM OVEN.
4. IN A PAN, COOK ONIONS IN OIL UNTIL LIGHTLY BROWNED. STIR IN MEAT AND COOK FOR 5 MINUTES.
5. ADD TOMATOES, GARLIC, OREGANO, CINNAMON, SEA SALT AND PEPPER. COOK ANOTHER 10 MINUTES, STIRRING OCCASIONALLY.
6. IN A 9" X 13" PAN, PUT A LAYER OF THE TOMATO SAUCE THEN A LAYER OF THE EGGPLANT AND REPEAT UNTIL ABOUT 1 ' FROM THE TOP OF THE PAN.
7. BAKE AT 350°F AND REHEAT WHILE YOU MAKE THE BÉCHAMEL SAUCE.
8. DISSOLVE CORN STARCH IN SKIM MILK AND STIR UNTIL SMOOTH.
9. HEAT MIXTURE IN A SAUCEPAN AND STIR CONTINUOUSLY TO PREVENT LUMPING.
10. ADD CHEESE SLICES AND STIR UNTIL MELTED. REMOVE FROM HEAT.
11. REMOVE THE EGGPLANT DISH FROM THE OVEN. POUR THE BÉCHAMEL SAUCE EVENLY OVER THE TOP AND RETURN TO THE OVEN.
12. COOK 30 MINUTES OR UNTIL THE MIXTURE IS BUBBLY.

SERVE REALLY HOT! IF YOU CAN, WAIT A DAY...IT TASTES BETTER!

PER SERVING: **594 CALORIES // 63G CARBOHYDRATE // 53G PROTEIN // 12G FAT**

YANKEE POT ROAST
with Potaoes and Leeks

24 OUNCES BEEF SIRLOIN ROAST	**1 TEASPOON** DRIED BASIL
3 CUPS ONIONS, CHOPPED	**1 TEASPOON** DRIED ROSEMARY
2 1/2 CUPS CELERY, CHOPPED	**1 TEASPOON** GRAPE SEED OIL
1/2 CUP CARROTS, CHOPPED	**2 CUPS** FRESH GREEN BEANS, WHOLE
4 CLOVES GARLIC, CHOPPED	**2 CUPS** LEEKS, CHOPPED
2 BAY LEAVES	**2 CUPS** POTATOES, CUBED
6 OUNCES TOMATO PASTE	**1 TABLESPOON** CORN STARCH
2 CUPS BEEF STOCK	**1 CUP** WATER
1 TEASPOON DRIED PARSLEY	SEA SALT & PEPPER TO TASTE
1 TEASPOON DRIED THYME	

READY TO COOK

1. **IN** A ROASTING PAN, SEAR THE ROAST IN OIL ON ALL SIDES.
2. **REMOVE** TO A PLATTER.
3. **ADD** 1 CUP OF ONIONS, 1/2 CUP OF CELERY, CARROTS AND GARLIC TO THE PAN AND COOK FOR ABOUT 5 MINUTES.
4. **STIR** IN THE TOMATO PASTE AND BEEF STOCK.
5. **ADD** PARSLEY, THYME, BASIL AND ROSEMARY.
6. **ADD** ROAST BACK INTO THE PAN, COVER AND BAKE AT **325°F** FOR 2 HOURS.
7. **AFTER** 2 HOURS, REMOVE THE ROAST FROM THE OVEN PAN AND STRAIN THE STOCK, DISCARDING THE VEGETABLES.
8. **SAUTÉ** 2 CUPS OF ONIONS, 2 CUPS OF CELERY, GREEN BEANS, LEEKS AND POTATOES IN ANOTHER PAN ON STOVE TOP.
9. **PUT** THE STRAINED STOCK, SAUTÉED VEGETABLES AND THE ROAST BACK IN THE OVEN PAN.
10. **DISSOLVE** CORN STARCH IN WATER AND ADD TO POT.
11. **HEAT**, STIRRING OCCASIONALLY, UNTIL THE SAUCE IS SLIGHTLY THICKENED.
12. **CONTINUE** COOKING UNTIL VEGETABLES ARE TENDER.

Serve the roast alongside a serving of vegetables.

VERATI Twist
YOU CAN USE THE LEFTOVERS TO MAKE THE RECIPE PAGE 441.

PER SERVING: 567 CALORIES // 47G CARBOHYDRATE // 67G PROTEIN // 11G FAT

VEAL CUTLETS
with Tomatoes

24 OUNCES VEAL, SLICED	**2 CUPS** TOMATO SAUCE
1 EGG WHITE, BEATEN	**1 TEASPOON** GRAPE SEED OIL
4 TABLESPOONS SKIM MILK	**2 CUPS** SPAGHETTI, COOKED
4 TABLESPOONS FLOUR	**8 CUPS** MIXED GREEN SALAD
1/4 CUP FINE BREAD CRUMBS	**4 OUNCES** LOW FAT LOW CARB HOUSE DRESSING (*SEE PAGE 95*)
4-8 FRESH BASIL LEAVES	SEA SALT & PEPPER TO TASTE

READY TO COOK

1. **COOK** THE PASTA IN BOILING WATER UNTIL AL DENTE. DRAIN AND SET ASIDE.

2. **PUT** THE FLOUR, SEA SALT AND PEPPER IN A SHALLOW BOWL.

3. **PUT** THE BREAD CRUMBS IN A SECOND BOWL.

4. **COMBINE** THE MILK AND EGG IN A THIRD BOWL.

5. **DUST** THE VEAL SLICES WITH FLOUR, THEN DIP INTO THE EGG AND MILK MIXTURE, THEN INTO THE BREAD CRUMBS.

6. **IN** A FRYING PAN, HEAT THE OIL AND COOK THE VEAL CUTLETS, TURNING IN THE PAN UNTIL THEY ARE COOKED AND BROWNED ON EACH SIDE.

7. **SPOON** TOMATO SAUCE ON TOP OF EACH CUTLET.

Serve veal with pasta and fresh basil and green salad on the side.

VERATI**TIPS**
AL DENTE MEANS "TO THE TOOTH". WHEN PASTA IS COOKED AL DENTE, THERE SHOULD BE A SLIGHT RESISTANCE IN THE CENTER OF THE PASTA WHEN CHEWED.

PER SERVING: 591 CALORIES // 49G CARBOHYDRATE // 52G PROTEIN // 17G FAT

CIABATTA STEAK SANDWICH
with Bbq Sauce

24 **OUNCES** LEAN BEEFSTEAKS (4 STEAKS)

4 **CUPS** ONIONS, SLICED

1 **TEASPOON** OLIVE OIL

1/4 **BUNCH** FRESH OREGANO LEAF

4 **LEAVES** RED OR GREEN LEAFY LETTUCE

4 CIABATTA ROLLS, CUT IN HALF

4 **TEASPOONS** LOW FAT MAYONNAISE

4 **TEASPOONS** BBQ SAUCE (*SEE PAGE 307*)

1 **CLOVE** GARLIC, CHOPPED

4 TOMATOES, SLICED

8 **CUPS** MIXED GREEN SALAD

4 **OUNCES** LOW FAT LOW CARB HOUSE DRESSING (*SEE PAGE 95*)

SEA SALT & PEPPER TO TASTE

READY TO COOK

1. **PLACE** CHOPPED ONIONS IN A PAN WITH 1 TEASPOON OIL .

2. **COOK** UNTIL ONIONS ARE SOFT AND GOLDEN.

3. **KEEP** WARM.

4. **IN** A SMALL BOWL, MASH CHOPPED GARLIC WITH MAYONNAISE.

5. **SEASON** THE STEAKS WITH SEA SALT AND PEPPER AND GRILL TO DESIRED DONENESS ON A HOT BBQ OR AN OVEN GRILL.

6. **GRILL** CIABATTA ROLLS FOR 30 SECONDS.

7. **SPREAD** MAYONNAISE AND BBQ SAUCE ON ROLLS.

8. **PLACE** EACH OF THE STEAKS ON ONE OF THE FOUR ROLL HALVES.

9. **ADD** FRESH CHOPPED OREGANO LEAVES, CARAMELIZED ONIONS AND TOMATO SLICE.

10. **TOP** WITH THE OTHER ROLL HALVES.

Serve sandwiches with mixed green salad on the side.

SWEET & SOUR PORK
with a Pineapple Twist

24 OUNCES LEAN PORK, CUBED

1/2 CUP & 2 TEASPOONS CORN STARCH

1 TABLESPOON & 2 TEASPOONS SOY SAUCE

1 CUP PINEAPPLES, DICED

1 1/2 CUPS GREEN ONIONS, CHOPPED

1 TEASPOON GRAPE SEED OIL

3 TABLESPOONS VINEGAR

4 TABLESPOONS KETCHUP

2 TABLESPOONS BROWN SUGAR

1/4 CUP WATER

1 CUP GREEN PEPPERS, DICED

1 CUP CARROTS, SHREDDED

2 CUPS MUSHROOMS, SLICED

2 CUPS BEAN SPROUTS

1 TEASPOON SESAME OIL

SEA SALT & PEPPER TO TASTE

READY TO COOK

1. MARINATE THE PORK IN 1 TABLESPOON OF SOY SAUCE WHILE YOU PREPARE THE REST OF THE INGREDIENTS.

2. DISSOLVE THE CORN STARCH AND WATER IN A SMALL PAN AND STIR.

3. ADD VINEGAR, KETCHUP AND BROWN SUGAR AND STIR OVER LOW HEAT UNTIL THE SAUCE IS THICKENED.

4. STIR CONSTANTLY SO THAT LUMPS DO NOT FORM AND REMOVE FROM THE HEAT.

5. REMOVE THE PORK CUBES FROM THE SOY SAUCE AND DREDGE THE PIECES IN 1/2 CUP CORN STARCH, SHAKING OFF THE EXCESS.

6. HEAT GRAPE SEED OIL IN A FRYING PAN AND BROWN THE PORK ON ALL SIDES UNTIL THE PORK IS CRISPY ON THE OUTSIDE.

7. ADD THE PINEAPPLES AND COOK 3-4 MINUTES.

8. ADD THE SAUCE AND HEAT, TOSSING THE PORK PIECES IN THE SAUCE UNTIL COATED.

9. COOK THE MUSHROOMS IN SESAME OIL FOR 1 MINUTE.

10. ADD THE GREEN PEPPERS, ONIONS, CARROTS AND BEAN SPROUTS AND COOK ANOTHER 2-3 MINUTES, UNTIL HEATED THROUGH.

11. ADD 2 TEASPOONS OF SOY SAUCE AND HEAT 1 MORE MINUTE.

SPRINKLE WITH SESAME OIL AND GREEN ONIONS WHEN SERVING.

PER SERVING: 606 CALORIES // 48G CARBOHYDRATE // 56G PROTEIN // 19G FAT

BEEF TACOS
with avocado

24 OUNCES	LEAN GROUND BEEF
1 CUP	GREEN ONIONS, CHOPPED
1 TABLESPOON	CHILI POWDER (*SEE PAGE 173*)
1 TEASPOON	CUMIN
1 TABLESPOON	FRESH CORIANDER, CHOPPED
1 CUP	AVOCADO, SLICED
2 CUPS	FRESH TOMATOES, DICED
2 CUPS	LETTUCE, SHREDDED
2 CUPS	PREPARED SALSA (*SEE RECIPE PAGE 263*)
8	TACO SHELLS
1/2 CUP	LOW FAT SOUR CREAM (*OPTIONAL*)
	SEA SALT & PEPPER TO TASTE

READY TO COOK ↓↓↓

1. BROWN LEAN GROUND BEEF WITH CHILI POWDER, CUMIN AND CORIANDER. **2. PLACE** SHREDDED LETTUCE ON PLATES, ADD 1/4 MEAT MIXTURE, 3 TABLESPOONS PREPARED SALSA, 1/4 CUP DICED TOMATOES, 1/4 CUP GREEN ONIONS AND 1/4 CUP AVOCADO. WITH TACO SHELLS AND LOW FAT SOUR CREAM.

Serve with taco shells and low fat sour cream (optional).

PER SERVING: 600 CALORIES // 42G CARBOHYDRATE // 50G PROTEIN // 17G FAT

SWISS STEAK
in Tomato Sauce

24 OUNCES	BEEF (4 ROUND STEAKS)
2 CUPS	ONIONS, SLICED
1 CUP	MUSHROOMS, SLICED
1 CUP	CELERY, CHOPPED
2 CUPS	TOMATOES, DICED
6 OUNCES	TOMATO PASTE
1 CUP	BEEF STOCK OR BROTH
1/4 CUP	FRESH PARSLEY, CHOPPED
1 TEASPOON	GRAPE SEED OIL
24 OUNCES	FINGERLING POTATOES, COOKED
	SEA SALT & PEPPER TO TASTE

READY TO COOK ↓↓↓

1. BROWN BOTH SIDES OF STEAKS IN OIL AND REMOVE FROM PAN. **2. PLACE** IN OVEN PROOF DISH. **3. SAUTÉ** ONIONS, MUSHROOMS AND CELERY IN A PAN FOR 10-15 MINUTES. **4. ADD** BEEF STOCK AND STIR UNTIL THICKENED. **5. ADD** TOMATOES, TOMATO PASTE, SEA SALT AND PEPPER AND STIR WELL. **6. POUR** SAUCE OVER THE STEAKS AND BAKE AT **350°F** FOR 2 HOURS. **7. COOK** THE POTATOES IN BOILING WATER.

Serve swiss steaks with a dash of fresh parsley over top and potatoes on the side.

PER SERVING: 525 CALORIES // 46G CARBOHYDRATE // 57G PROTEIN // 11G FAT

BAKED TOMATOES
with Beef

4 TOMATOES, WHOLE

24 **OUNCES** LEAN GROUND BEEF

1 **CUP** GREEN ONIONS, FINELY CHOPPED

1 **CLOVE** GARLIC, FINELY CHOPPED

1 **CUP** BROWN OR WHOLE GRAIN RICE

4 **TABLESPOONS** FINE BREAD CRUMBS

1/4 **CUP** BEEF BROTH OR STOCK

4 **CUPS** SPINACH

2 **OUNCES** LOW FAT LOW CARB HOUSE DRESSING (*SEE PAGE 95*)

SEA SALT & PEPPER TO TASTE

READY TO COOK ↓↓↓

1. SCOOP OUT AND CHOP THE CENTER OF THE TOMATOES. **2. COOK** THE RICE. **3. IN** A FRYING PAN, COOK THE GROUND BEEF, ONIONS AND GARLIC WITH THE CHOPPED TOMATO CENTERS. **4. COMBINE** THE MEAT MIXTURE WITH THE COOKED RICE. **5. ADD** SEA SALT AND PEPPER. **6. SPOON** THE MEAT AND RICE MIXTURE INTO THE EMPTY CENTERS OF THE FRESH TOMATOES UNTIL OVERFULL. **7. SPOON** A LITTLE OF THE BEEF STOCK INTO EACH TOMATO. **8. SPRINKLE** BREAD CRUMBS OVER TOP. **9. PLACE** ON COOKING SHEET IN OVEN AT **250⁰F** FOR ABOUT 30 MINUTES, UNTIL THE TOMATOES SOFTEN BUT DO NOT COLLAPSE.

Serve baked tomatoes with the spinach tossed in low fat house dressing.

PER SERVING: 390 CALORIES // 24G CARBOHYDRATE // 47G PROTEIN // 10G FAT

LAMB STEW
Irish Style

24 **OUNCES** LAMB, CUBED

1/8 **CUP** FLOUR

1 **TEASPOON** GRAPE SEED OIL

1 **CUP** ONIONS, SLICED

1 **CUP** CARROTS, CUBED

1 **CUP** CELERY, CUBED

2 **CUPS** CABBAGE, SLICED

2 **CUPS** POTATOES, PEELED & SLICED

1 **CUP** TURNIPS, CUBED

2 **CUPS** VEGETABLE OR CHICKEN BROTH OR STOCK

1 **TEASPOON** DRIED THYME OR SEVERAL SPRIGS OF FRESH THYME

SEA SALT & PEPPER TO TASTE

READY TO COOK ↓↓↓

1. SEASON LAMB CUBES WITH SEA SALT AND PEPPER. **2. DREDGE** THE MEAT IN SEASONED FLOUR AND BROWN LIGHTLY IN OIL ON EACH SIDE IN A LARGE OVEN-PROOF CASSEROLE. **3. REMOVE** ALL BUT 1/4 OF THE LAMB. **4. COVER** THE REMAINING LAMB WITH A LAYER OF VEGETABLES AND WORK UP TO 4 LAYERS, USING THE OTHER 1/2 OF MEAT. **5. ADD** VEGETABLE STOCK TO COVER. **6. ADD** SEA SALT, PEPPER AND THYME. **7. COVER** THE POT CLOSELY AND BAKE AT **325⁰F** FOR 2 HOURS.

Serve directly in the large oven-proof casserole.

PER SERVING: 447 CALORIES // 26G CARBOHYDRATE // 53G PROTEIN // 13G FAT

THANKSGIVING HAM
with Baked Autumn Vegetables

32 OUNCES TOUPIE OR SPIRAL PRE-COOKED HAM		**1 CUP** ZUCCHINI, CUBED
1 TABLESPOON OLIVE OIL		**1 CUP** SMALL ONIONS, WHOLE
1/8 CUP BROWN SUGAR		**2 CUPS** CARROTS, CUBED
1/2 CUP KETCHUP		**2 CUPS** BRUSSELS SPROUTS
1/4 CUP REGULAR MUSTARD		**2 TABLESPOONS** DRIED ROSEMARY
1/8 TEASPOON GROUND CLOVES		**5 SPRIGS** FRESH THYME
1 CUP TURNIP, CUBED		**5 SPRIGS** FRESH OREGANO
1 CUP BUTTERNUT SQUASH, CUBED		SEA SALT & PEPPER TO TASTE

READY TO COOK

1. **PLACE** ALL VEGETABLES IN A LARGE BOWL.
2. **PUT** 1 TABLESPOON OF OIL, ROSEMARY, SEA SALT AND PEPPER AND TOSS UNTIL COATED.
3. **LAY** ON OVEN PAN IN ONE LAYER.
4. **PUT** A FEW SPRIGS OF FRESH THYME AND OREGANO ON TOP.
5. **SEAL** WITH ALUMINUM FOIL AND BAKE AT **375^{0}F** FOR APPROXIMATELY 30 MINUTES OR UNTIL THE VEGETABLES ARE TENDER.
6. **REMOVE** THE FOIL AND PLACE UNDER BROILER FOR 3-5 MINUTES BEFORE SERVING.
7. **REMOVE** PACKAGING FROM THE HAM, PLACE ON OVEN RACK IN A PAN AND BAKE AT **325^{0}F** FOR 30 MINUTES.
8. **IN** A MIXING BOWL, COMBINE THE BROWN SUGAR, KETCHUP, MUSTARD AND CLOVES.
9. **WITH** A BASTING BRUSH, COAT THE OUTSIDE OF THE HAM COMPLETELY WITH SOME OF THE GLAZE.
10. **RETURN** THE PAN TO THE OVEN AND COOK ANOTHER 30 MINUTES, BASTING WITH MORE OF THE GLAZE EVERY 10 MINUTES.
11. **THE** OVEN CAN BE TURNED UP TO **350^{0}F** AND TURNED TO BROIL FOR THE LAST 5 MINUTES.
12. **WATCH** CAREFULLY SO THAT THE GLAZE DOES NOT BURN.

Serve ham alongside baked autumn vegetables.

PER SERVING: 587 CALORIES // 52G CARBOHYDRATE // 46G PROTEIN // 16G FAT

BEEF & PEPPER STIR FRY
with Rice

24 OUNCES FLANK STEAK, SLICED	**1 TEASPOON** CHILI PASTE
1 CUP ONIONS, SLICED	**1 TEASPOON** CORN STARCH
1 CUP MUSHROOMS, SLICED	**1/4 CUP** WATER
2 CUPS GREEN PEPPERS, SLICED	**1 TEASPOON** GRAPE SEED OIL
2 CUPS RED PEPPERS, SLICED	**2 TABLESPOONS** SOY SAUCE
2 CUPS YELLOW PEPPERS, SLICED	**2 CUPS** RICE, COOKED
4 CLOVES GARLIC, FINELY CHOPPED	SEA SALT & PEPPER TO TASTE

READY TO COOK

1. **COOK** THE RICE IN WATER ON THE STOVE TOP OR IN THE MICROWAVE UNTIL THE RICE IS SOFT.
2. **IN** A LARGE FRYING PAN, PUT THE OIL AND SAUTÉ BEEF UNTIL JUST BROWNED.
3. **ADD** MUSHROOMS AND SAUT 2 MINUTES.
4. **ADD** GARLIC, SOY SAUCE, SLICED PEPPERS AND ONIONS AND COOK UNTIL JUST TENDER.
5. **DISSOLVE** CORN STARCH IN WATER AND ADD TO THE PAN.
6. **STIR** IN CHILI PASTE AND STIR UNTIL SLIGHTLY THICKENED.

Serve the stir fry with steamed rice on the side.

WATER IS THE MAIN INGREDIENT OF DIGESTION. DID YOU DRINK SOME TODAY?

PER SERVING: 641 CALORIES // 63G CARBOHYDRATE // 52G PROTEIN // 12G FAT

LAMB BURGERS
with Tomato and Basil Salad

24 OUNCES GROUND LAMB

4 WHOLE GRAIN ROLLS

1/2 TEASPOON DRIED CUMIN

1/2 TEASPOON DRIED CORIANDER

1/2 TEASPOON GROUND ALLSPICE

1/4 TEASPOON GROUND NUTMEG

2 TABLESPOONS OLIVE OIL

4 TOMATOES, SLICED

4 CUPS CUCUMBERS, SLICED

8 LEAVES FRESH BASIL

SEA SALT & PEPPER TO TASTE

READY TO COOK

1. IN A LARGE BOWL, COMBINE THE LAMB, CUMIN, CORIANDER, ALLSPICE, NUTMEG, SEA SALT AND PEPPER.

2. MIX VERY WELL AND FORM INTO 4 PATTIES.

3. BRUSH BOTH SIDES OF EACH BURGER LIGHTLY WITH OIL AND BROIL UNDER A 425°F GRILL FOR 5 MINUTES ON EACH SIDE.

4. SLICE THE WHOLE GRAIN ROLLS AND TOAST THE INSIDE. PLACE LAMB BURGER ON EACH ROLL.

5. PLACE CHOPPED BASIL ON EACH OF THE TOMATO AND CUCUMBER SLICES. DRIZZLE A LITTLE OF THE SALAD DRESSING OVER TOP.

SERVE LAMB BURGERS WITH TOMATO AND BASIL SALAD ON THE SIDE.

PER SERVING: 517 CALORIES // 76G CARBOHYDRATE // 49G PROTEIN // 12G FAT

QUICK BEEF FAJITAS
with a Mixed Green Salad

24 OUNCES LEAN BEEF, SLICED	**2 CUPS** RED ONIONS, SLICED
1 TABLESPOON FLOUR	**1 TEASPOON** GRAPE SEED OIL
1 TEASPOON GROUND CUMIN	**8** TORTILLA WRAPS
1 TEASPOON DRIED CORIANDER	**2 TABLESPOONS** PREPARED SALSA (SEE PAGE 263)
1 TEASPOON CHILI POWDER (SEE PAGE 173)	**4 TABLESPOONS** LOW FAT SOUR CREAM
1 TEASPOON GARLIC POWDER	**6 CUPS** MIXED GREEN SALAD
1 CUP RED PEPPERS, SLICED	**3 OUNCES** LOW FAT LOW CARB HOUSE DRESSING (SEE PAGE 95)
1 CUP GREEN PEPPERS, SLICED	SEA SALT & PEPPER TO TASTE

READY TO COOK

1. **MIX** FLOUR, CUMIN, CORIANDER, CHILI AND GARLIC IN A SMALL BOWL.
2. **ADD** THE BEEF STRIPS AND COAT WELL ON ALL SIDES.
3. **IN** A FRYING PAN, HEAT OIL.
4. **ADD** BEEF AND COOK UNTIL BROWNED.
5. **ADD** THE ONIONS, RED AND GREEN PEPPERS AND CONTINUE TO COOK FOR ABOUT 5 MINUTES, STIRRING OCCASIONALLY.
6. **REMOVE** FROM HEAT.
7. **HEAT** TORTILLAS ONE AT A TIME IN AN UNOILED FRYING PAN UNTIL JUST BEGINNING TO BROWN.
8. **SPREAD** SOME OF THE LOW FAT SOUR CREAM ON A TORTILLA.
9. **SPOON** SOME OF THE MEAT MIXTURE OVER TOP, THEN SOME OF THE SALSA.
10. **FOLD** THE TORTILLA IN HALF OR ROLL IT UP.

Serve beef fajitas with green salad topped with low fat low carb house dressing.

PER SERVING: 562 CALORIES // 42G CARBOHYDRATE // 58G PROTEIN // 13G FAT

LAMB & LEMON
Hot Pot

24 OUNCES LAMB, CUBED

1 TABLESPOON FLOUR

1 TEASPOON GRAPE SEED OIL

2 CUPS ONIONS, COARSELY CHOPPED

4 CLOVES GARLIC, FINELY CHOPPED

2 CUPS SWEET POTATOES, PEELED & CUBED

2 CUPS BUTTERNUT SQUASH, PEELED & CUBED

1 CUP CELERY, CHOPPED

1 CUP CABBAGE, FINELY SLICED

1 TEASPOON DRIED CORIANDER

1 TEASPOON DRIED CUMIN

1" PIECE FRESH GINGER, PEELED & CHOPPED

2 LEMONS, SLICED & SEEDS REMOVED

3 CUPS VEGETABLE BROTH, VEGETABLE STOCK OR WATER

SEA SALT & PEPPER TO TASTE

READY TO COOK

1. **TOSS** THE LAMB CUBES IN THE FLOUR, SHAKE OFF EXCESS AND BROWN WITH ONIONS IN OIL.

2. **ADD** GARLIC AND COOK ABOUT 1 MINUTE.

3. **PUT** IN A LARGE OVEN-PROOF CASSEROLE WITH ALL THE OTHER INGREDIENTS.

4. **POUR** THE VEGETABLE STOCK OR WATER TO COVER.

5. **BAKE** AT **350°F** FOR 1 1/2 HOURS UNTIL THE LAMB IS TENDER AND THE VEGETABLES ARE COOKED.

Serve oven-proof casserole directly on table.

EATING SMALL MEALS & SNACKS THROUGHOUT THE DAY IS THE BEST WAY TO NEVER FEEL HUNGER.

PER SERVING: 521 CALORIES // 42G CARBOHYDRATE // 55G PROTEIN // 12G FAT

PORK TENDERLOIN
with Roasted Vegetables

24 OUNCES PORK TENDERLOIN	**2 CUPS** SWEET POTATOES, PEELED & CUBED
2 TEASPOONS DRIED ROSEMARY	**1 TABLESPOON** FRESH ROSEMARY
2 TEASPOONS DRIED SAGE	**1 TABLESPOON** FRESH THYME
1 TEASPOON GRAPE SEED OIL	**1 TABLESPOON** FRESH OREGANO
2 CUPS ONIONS, PEELED & QUARTERED	**1 TABLESPOON** OLIVE OIL
2 CUPS TURNIPS, PEELED & CUBED	**3 TABLESPOONS** WATER
2 CUPS PEPPER SQUASH, PEELED & CUBED	SEA SALT & PEPPER TO TASTE

READY TO COOK

1. **MIX** SEA SALT, PEPPER, DRIED ROSEMARY, SAGE AND GRAPE SEED OIL TOGETHER AND RUB INTO OF THE OUTSIDE THE PORK TENDERLOIN.

2. **BAKE** MEAT AT **350⁰F** FOR 30-35 MINUTES OR UNTIL THE INTERNAL TEMPERATURE REACHES **150⁰F**.

3. **REMOVE** FROM OVEN, TENT WITH FOIL AND ALLOW TO REST FOR 15 MINUTES.

4. **IN** A LARGE BOWL, COMBINE ONIONS, TURNIPS, PEPPER SQUASH, POTATOES, FRESH ROSEMARY, THYME, OREGANO AND OLIVE OIL.

5. **TOSS** WELL TO COAT ALL VEGETABLES WITH OIL AND FRESH HERBS.

6. **SPREAD** ONE LAYER OF THE MIXTURE ON A LARGE BAKING SHEET. BAKE AT **350⁰F** FOR 30 MINUTES, TURN THE VEGETABLES.

7. **ADD** 3 TABLESPOONS WATER TO THE PAN AND COOK IN OVEN FOR ANOTHER 15-20 MINUTES OR UNTIL THE VEGETABLES ARE FORK TENDER.

Serve pork tenderloin with roasted vegetables as a side dish.

PER SERVING: 434 CALORIES // 28G CARBOHYDRATE // 46G PROTEIN // 12G FAT

SPAGHETTI BOLOGNESE
with Mixed Green Salad

24 OUNCES LEAN GROUND BEEF	**1 TEASPOON** DRIED PARSLEY
16 OUNCES SPAGHETTI	**2 TEASPOONS** CHILI POWDER (*SEE PAGE 173*)
4 CLOVES GARLIC, CHOPPED	**1 TEASPOON** DRIED SAGE
2 CUPS ONIONS, CHOPPED	**1 TEASPOON** GRAPE SEED OIL
28 OUNCES TOMATO SAUCE	**8 CUPS** MIXED GREEN SALAD
6 OUNCES TOMATO PASTE	**4 OUNCES** LOW FAT LOW CARB HOUSE DRESSING (*SEE PAGE 95*)
1 TEASPOON DRIED MARJORAM	SEA SALT & PEPPER TO TASTE
1 TEASPOON DRIED OREGANO	

READY TO COOK

1. **BROWN** GROUND BEEF AND ONIONS IN A NON-STICK FRYING PAN AND SET ASIDE.
2. **ADD** OIL, GARLIC AND TOMATO PASTE TO THE PAN AND COOK UNTIL THE LIQUID BOILS.
3. **REMOVE** FROM HEAT.
4. **PUT** GROUND BEEF MIXTURE AND CARAMELIZED TOMATO PASTE WITH ALL THE REMAINING INGREDIENTS IN A LARGE SAUCE PAN AND SIMMER FOR 2 HOURS, STIRRING OCCASIONALLY.
5. **COOK** SPAGHETTI IN BOILING WATER UNTIL TENDER AND DRAIN.
6. **DIVIDE** INTO 4 PORTIONS AND TOP WITH A SERVING OF BOLOGNESE SAUCE.

Serve spaghetti with green salad topped with low fat low carb house dressing.

VERATI**TIPS**
DOUBLE UP THE BOLOGNESE SAUCE AND FREEZE IT!
IT WILL BE AN EASY AND QUICK MEAL FOR A BUSY DAY!

PER SERVING: 629 CALORIES // 63G CARBOHYDRATE // 57G PROTEIN // 12G FAT

EASY STUFFED
Pork Tenderloin

24 OUNCES PORK TENDERLOIN	**3/4 TEASPOON** DRIED SAGE
1 TEASPOON GRAPE SEED OIL	**1 TEASPOON** DRIED THYME
1 CUP DRIED BREAD CRUMBS	**2 TABLESPOONS** BUTTER
1 CUP DAY-OLD BREAD, CUBED	**1/4 CUP** VEGETABLE STOCK OR WATER
1 CUP ONIONS, FINELY CHOPPED	**4 CUPS** BROCCOLI FLORETS, BLANCHED (*SEE PAGE 129*)
2 CUPS CELERY, FINELY CHOPPED	SEA SALT & PEPPER TO TASTE
16 OUNCES POTATOES, PEELED & CUBED	STRING
2 CLOVES GARLIC, FINELY CHOPPED	

READY TO COOK

1. **COMBINE** ALL THE INGREDIENTS FOR THE STUFFING, EXCEPT THE STOCK OR WATER, AND WORK THE BUTTER IN WELL.

2. **ADD** STOCK A LITTLE AT A TIME UNTIL THE STUFFING IS MOIST BUT NOT WET.

3. **CUT** THE PORK TENDERLOIN DOWN THE MIDDLE TO WITHIN 1/2 INCH OF THE OTHER SIDE.

4. **DO** NOT CUT THROUGH.

5. **OPEN** THE MEAT OUT AND POUND WITH A MALLET OR ROLLING PIN UNTIL THE PORK IS ABOUT 3/8" THICK.

6. **SPREAD** THE STUFFING ALONG ONE SIDE OF THE PORK AND ROLL UP.

7. **SECURE** WITH STRING.

8. **CAREFULLY** PLACE THE ROLLED PORK IN A FRYING PAN AND BROWN SLIGHTLY ON ALL SIDES.

9. **REMOVE,** PLACE IN A ROASTING PAN AND BAKE AT **350⁰F** FOR 1 HOUR OR UNTIL THE PORK IS NO LONGER PINK.

Serve pork tenderloin in thick slices.

PER SERVING: 545 CALORIES // 50G CARBOHYDRATE // 54G PROTEIN // 12G FAT

CRISPY BEEF
with Bok Choy

1/4 CUP CORN STARCH	**3" PIECE** FRESH GINGER, PEELED & CHOPPED
24 OUNCES FLANK STEAK, THINLY SLICED	**1 TABLESPOON** GRAPE SEED OIL
64 OUNCES OIL FOR FRYING	**4 CLOVES** GARLIC, CHOPPED
4 TABLESPOONS SOY SAUCE	**1 CUP** GREEN ONIONS, SLICED
1 TABLESPOON RICE VINEGAR	**1 CUP** RED BELL PEPPERS, SLICED
1 TABLESPOON RICE WINE	**6 CUPS** BOK CHOY, BLANCHED (*SEE PAGE 129*)
4 TABLESPOONS GRANULATED SUGAR OR XYLITOL	**2 CUPS** RICE, COOKED
1/2 TABLESPOON CHILI PASTE	SEA SALT & PEPPER TO TASTE
1/4 CUP WATER	

READY TO COOK

1. **COOK** THE RICE IN WATER ON THE STOVE TOP OR IN THE MICROWAVE UNTIL THE RICE IS SOFT.

2. **HEAT** OIL IN DEEP-FRYER TO **375°F**.

3. **IN** A BOWL, COMBINE CORN STARCH, SEA SALT AND PEPPER TOGETHER AND MIX THOROUGHLY.

4. **TOSS** THE STEAK SLICES IN THE CORN STARCH MIXTURE AND COAT WELL.

5. **DEEP** FRY THE COATED STEAK SLICES UNTIL GOLDEN BROWN.

6. **CHECK** TO MAKE SURE THEY ARE COOKED THROUGH.

7. **REMOVE** FROM OIL AND SET ASIDE. DRAIN VERY WELL.

8. **IN** ANOTHER MIXING BOWL, COMBINE THE SOY SAUCE, RICE VINEGAR, RICE WINE

9. **ADD** SUGAR, CHILI PASTE, WATER AND GINGER.

10. **MIX** WELL AND SET ASIDE.

11. **IN** A WOK OR DEEP FRYING PAN OVER **HIGH HEAT**, ADD 1 TABLESPOON OF OIL AND QUICKLY SAUTÉ THE GREEN ONIONS, GARLIC AND RED PEPPERS FOR 30 SECONDS.

12. **ADD** THE SAUCE MIXTURE AND COOK ANOTHER 30 SECONDS.

13. **ADD** THE STRIPS OF FRIED STEAK AND TOSS TO HEAT THROUGH AND COAT WITH SAUCE.

Serve crispy beef with rice and bok choy on the side.

PER SERVING: 740 CALORIES // 76G CARBOHYDRATE // 49G PROTEIN // 19G FAT

EASY PORK STEW
with Beer Sauce

24 OUNCES PORK LOIN, CUBED

1 TEASPOON GRAPE SEED OIL

1 CUP ONIONS, CHOPPED

2 CLOVES GARLIC, FINELY CHOPPED

1 CUP CELERY, CHOPPED

1 CUP RED PEPPERS, CUBED

1 CUP GREEN PEPPERS, CUBED

2 CUPS MUSHROOMS, SLICED

2 CUPS POTATOES, PEELED & CUBED

1 TEASPOON DRY BASIL

1 TEASPOON CARAWAY SEEDS

22 OUNCES DARK BEER OR **2 CUPS** VEGETABLE BROTH

1 CUP TOMATOES, DICED

SEA SALT & PEPPER TO TASTE

READY TO COOK

1. **BROWN** THE CUBED PORK IN THE OIL.

2. **STIR** IN THE ONIONS, GARLIC AND CELERY AND COOK FOR 2-3 MINUTES.

3. **ADD** THE RED AND GREEN PEPPERS, MUSHROOMS AND POTATOES WITH ALL THE SPICES.

4. **MIX** AND STIR FOR ANOTHER MINUTE.

5. **ADD** THE BEER OR BROTH AND THE DICED TOMATOES.

6. **BRING** TO A BOIL.

7. **REDUCE** HEAT AND SIMMER, COVERED, FOR 1 HOUR OR UNTIL THE PORK IS TENDER.

Serve in a soup bowl.

PER SERVING: 548 CALORIES // 24G CARBOHYDRATE // 51G PROTEIN // 13G FAT

STUFFED CABBAGE ROLLS
with Tomato Sauce

24 OUNCES LEAN GROUND BEEF	**2 CUPS** TOMATO SAUCE
1 CUP ONIONS, CHOPPED	**PINCH** CAYENNE PEPPER (*OPTIONAL*)
2 CLOVES GARLIC, FINELY CHOPPED	**1/4 CUP** LOW FAT SOUR CREAM OR PLAIN YOGURT
1 CABBAGE HEAD, BLANCHED (*SEE PAGE 129*)	**1/2 TEASPOON** CARAWAY SEEDS (*OPTIONAL*)
1/2 CUP FRESH PARSLEY, CHOPPED	SEA SALT & PEPPER TO TASTE
1 CUP WHITE OR BROWN RICE, COOKED	TOOTHPICKS

READY TO COOK

1. **BLANCH** CABBAGE LEAVES .
2. **BROWN** GROUND BEEF, ONIONS AND GARLIC UNTIL THE MEAT IS COOKED.
3. **ADD** SEA SALT, PEPPER AND CHOPPED PARSLEY.
4. **ADD** COOKED RICE AND MIX WELL.
5. **PUT** 2 TO 3 TABLESPOONS OF FILLING ON EACH CABBAGE LEAF.
6. **FOLD** SIDES OF CABBAGE LEAVES TO THE CENTRE AND ROLL UP.
7. **SECURE** WITH TOOTHPICKS IF NECESSARY.
8. **LAY** THE STUFFED LEAVES SIDE BY SIDE IN A 9" X 13" ROASTING PAN AND POUR TOMATO SAUCE OVER TOP UNTIL JUST COVERED.
9. **BAKE** AT **350⁰F** FOR APPROXIMATELY 45 MINUTES.
10. **CUT** REMAINING CABBAGE PIECES IN STRIPS.
11. **PUT** IN A SAUCEPAN WITH 1/2 CUP ONIONS, 1/2 TEASPOON SEA SALT, 1/2 TEASPOON CARAWAY SEEDS AND SIMMER UNTIL THE CABBAGE IS SOFT.

Serve each cabbage roll topped with a tablespoon of sour cream or plain yogurt and left over cabbage.

PER SERVING: 549 CALORIES // 54G CARBOHYDRATE // 53G PROTEIN // 12G FAT

BEEF & MUSHROOM STEW
with Green Beans

24 OUNCES LEAN TOPSIDE BEEF	**1 TABLESPOON** FLOUR
1 CUP SMALL ONIONS, WHOLE	**2 CUPS** BUTTON MUSHROOMS
1/2 CUP ONIONS, SLICED	**8 OUNCES** MEAT STOCK OR BROTH
2 TEASPOONS THYME	**4 CLOVES** GARLIC
2 TEASPOONS PARSLEY	**2 CUPS** POTATOES, CUBED
2 BAY LEAVES	**4 CUPS** GREEN BEANS, BLANCHED (*SEE PAGE 129*)
1 TEASPOON GRAPE SEED OIL	SEA SALT & PEPPER TO TASTE
8 OUNCES RED WINE	

READY TO COOK

1. **SLICE** MEAT INTO 2 1/2" BY 1/4" PIECES AND PLACE INTO EARTHENWARE DISH WITH SEA SALT AND PEPPER.

2. **COVER** WITH THE SLICED ONIONS, HALF OF THE HERBS AND RED WINE.

3. **MARINATE** FOR 3 TO 6 HOURS OR OVERNIGHT.

4. **HEAT** A LARGE HEAVY STEWING PAN WITH A 4 PINT CAPACITY.

5. **ADD** GRAPE SEED OIL AND THE WHOLE, PEELED SMALL ONIONS AND LET THEM BROWN, TURNING FREQUENTLY AND REMOVE FROM PAN.

6. **SAUTÉ** THE MUSHROOMS IN PAN AND REMOVE.

7. **DRAIN** AND DRY THE PIECES OF MEAT AND BROWN THEM ON EACH SIDE.

8. **SPRINKLE** THE MEAT WITH THE FLOUR, STIRRING TO KEEP FROM STICKING. STRAIN THE MARINADE AND POUR OVER MEAT.

9. **ADD** THE STOCK, GARLIC CLOVES, THE REMAINING HERBS, THYME, PARSLEY AND BAY LEAVES.

10. **COVER** WITH A CLOSE-FITTING LID AND SIMMER ON TOP OF STOVE FOR 1 1/2 HOURS.

11. **ADD** WHOLE ONIONS AND MUSHROOMS BACK INTO THE MIXTURE.

12. **ADD** CUBED POTATOES, STIR WELL AND COOK FOR ANOTHER 1/2 HOUR OR UNTIL THE POTATOES ARE DONE.

13. **BLANCH** THE GREEN BEANS.

Serve stew with green beans.

OSSO BUCCO
with Gremolata

24 OUNCES VEAL SHANKS	**1 TEASPOON** DRIED THYME
3 CUPS ONIONS, CHOPPED	**1 TEASPOON** DRIED OREGANO
1 CUP CELERY, CHOPPED	**1 TEASPOON** GRAPE SEED OIL
2 CUPS CARROTS, CHOPPED	**2 CUPS** COUSCOUS, COOKED
6 CLOVES GARLIC, FINELY CHOPPED	**2 LEMONS, ZEST
2 CUPS FRESH TOMATOES, DICED	**2 CUPS** FRESH ITALIAN PARSLEY, CHOPPED
2 CUPS CHICKEN OR VEGETABLE STOCK OR WHITE WINE	SEA SALT & PEPPER TO TASTE

READY TO COOK

1. **IN** AN OVEN-PROOF PAN, BROWN THE VEAL SHANKS ON ALL SIDES.

2. **REMOVE** FROM THE PAN.

3. **ADD** THE ONIONS, CELERY, CARROTS AND 4 FINELY CHOPPED GARLIC CLOVES AND COOK UNTIL THE ONIONS ARE JUST BEGINNING TO SOFTEN.

4. **ADD** WINE OR STOCK AND BRING TO A BOIL.

5. **CONTINUE** TO BOIL VEGETABLES FOR ANOTHER 2 MINUTES.

6. **REDUCE** HEAT AND ADD TOMATOES, THYME, OREGANO, SEA SALT AND PEPPER.

7. **PLACE** THE VEAL SHANKS BACK INTO THE PAN, COVER, AND BAKE AT **350°F** FOR 2 HOURS OR UNTIL THE VEAL IS VERY TENDER.

8. **PUT** 2 FINELY CHOPPED GARLIC CLOVES IN A BOWL AND MASH SLIGHTLY WITH A FORK.

9. **ADD** THE LEMON ZEST AND PARSLEY AND MIX WELL.

Serve veal shanks with a sprinkle of garlic and parsley mixture over top and couscous on the side.

SHEPHERD'S PIE
with Macedoine

24 OUNCES LEAN GROUND BEEF	**2 CUPS** POTATOES, PEELED & CUBED
8 OUNCES LEAN GROUND PORK	**2 CUPS** CAULIFLOWER
2 CUPS ONIONS, FINELY CHOPPED	**1/2 CUP** GREEN ONIONS, CHOPPED
4 CLOVES GARLIC, FINELY CHOPPED	**2 TABLESPOONS** BUTTER
2 CUPS FROZEN MACEDOINE MIX, COOKED	**1/4 CUP** SKIM MILK
1 TABLESPOON FLOUR	SEA SALT & PEPPER TO TASTE
14 OUNCES PREPARED BEEF GRAVY	

READY TO COOK

1. **COOK** POTATOES WITH CAULIFLOWER IN BOILING WATER UNTIL SOFT.

2. **DRAIN**, SAVING SOME OF THE LIQUID FOR LATER USE.

3. **MASH** POTATOES AND CAULIFLOWER, USING HAND MIXER, ADDING SEA SALT, PEPPER, BUTTER, MILK AND RESERVED LIQUID IF NECESSARY.

4. **STIR** IN CHOPPED GREEN ONIONS AND SET ASIDE.

5. **IN** LARGE SKILLET, COOK ONIONS UNTIL JUST SOFT.

6. **ADD** GARLIC, GROUND BEEF AND PORK AND COOK UNTIL THE MEAT IS BROWNED, CHOPPING UP ANY LARGER PIECES.

7. **ADD** FLOUR, 1 TEASPOON OF SALT AND 1/2 TEASPOON OF PEPPER, STIRRING CONSTANTLY.

8. **ADD** MIXED FROZEN VEGETABLES AND GRAVY INTO THE MIXTURE AND HEAT FOR 7 MINUTES.

9. **PLACE** IN A CASSEROLE DISH AND SPREAD THE MIXTURE EVENLY IN THE BOTTOM.

10. **ADD** MASHED POTATOES AND CAULIFLOWER OVERTOP AND A SPRINKLE OF PAPRIKA.

11. **BAKE** AT **350°F** FOR 45 MINUTES UNTIL THE WHOLE MIXTURE IS BUBBLY.

12. **TURN** OVEN TO BROIL AND BROWN THE TOP, WATCHING CAREFULLY SO IT DOES NOT BURN.

Serve very hot to enjoy!

PER SERVING: 536 CALORIES // 36G CARBOHYDRATE // 58G PROTEIN // 14G FAT

CREOLE BEEF

24 OUNCES BEEF OR STEWING BEEF, CUBED	**1/4 CUP** BEEF BROTH
1/2 CUP LIME JUICE	**4 CUPS** SWEET CORN
1 CHILI PEPPER, SEEDS REMOVED & FINELY CHOPPED	**1 CUP** ONIONS, FINELY CHOPPED
4 CLOVES GARLIC, FINELY CHOPPED	**1 CUP** GREEN & RED PEPPERS, FINELY CHOPPED
2 TEASPOONS GROUND CINNAMON	**1/2 CUP** FRESH TOMATOES, DICED
1/4 CUP FRESH GINGER, FINELY CHOPPED	**1/2 CUP** CELERY, CHOPPED
1 TEASPOON GROUND CLOVES	**1 TEASPOON** CAYENNE PEPPER
1/2 TEASPOON GROUND NUTMEG	**1 TEASPOON** BUTTER
4 BAY LEAVES	**1/4 CUP** SKIM MILK
1 TEASPOON GRAPE SEED OIL	SEA SALT & PEPPER TO TASTE

READY TO COOK

1. **CUT** THE BEEF INTO 1" CUBES AND PUT IN A BOWL.
2. **ADD** LIME JUICE, CHILI PEPPER, CHOPPED GARLIC, SEA SALT, PEPPER, CINNAMON, GINGER, AND GROUND CLOVES.
3. **COVER** AND MARINATE OVERNIGHT, STIRRING OCCASIONALLY.
4. **WHEN** READY TO COOK, ADD 1 TEASPOON OF GRAPE SEED OIL TO AN OVEN PAN AND COOK BEEF, WITH THE MARINADE, FOR ABOUT 15 MINUTES.
5. **ADD** BAY LEAVES, NUTMEG, BEEF BROTH AND SOME PEPPER.
6. **COVER** THE PAN, PLACE IN OVEN AND BAKE AT **350°F** FOR 2 HOURS.
7. **STIR** OCCASIONALLY.
8. **IN** A LARGE SAUCEPAN, MELT BUTTER AND ADD ONIONS, PEPPERS, TOMATOES AND CELERY AND COOK UNTIL ONIONS ARE SOFT.
9. **ADD** SEA SALT, PEPPER, CAYENNE PEPPER, CORN AND MILK.
10. **COOK** 15 MINUTES, ADJUSTING SEASONING IF NECESSARY.

Serve beef with a spoonful of vegetable mixture on top.

VERATI **TIPS**
MARINATE 12 HOURS, COVERED, IN REFRIGERATOR FOR BEST RESULTS!

PER SERVING: 562 CALORIES // 45G CARBOHYDRATE // 69G PROTEIN // 13G FAT

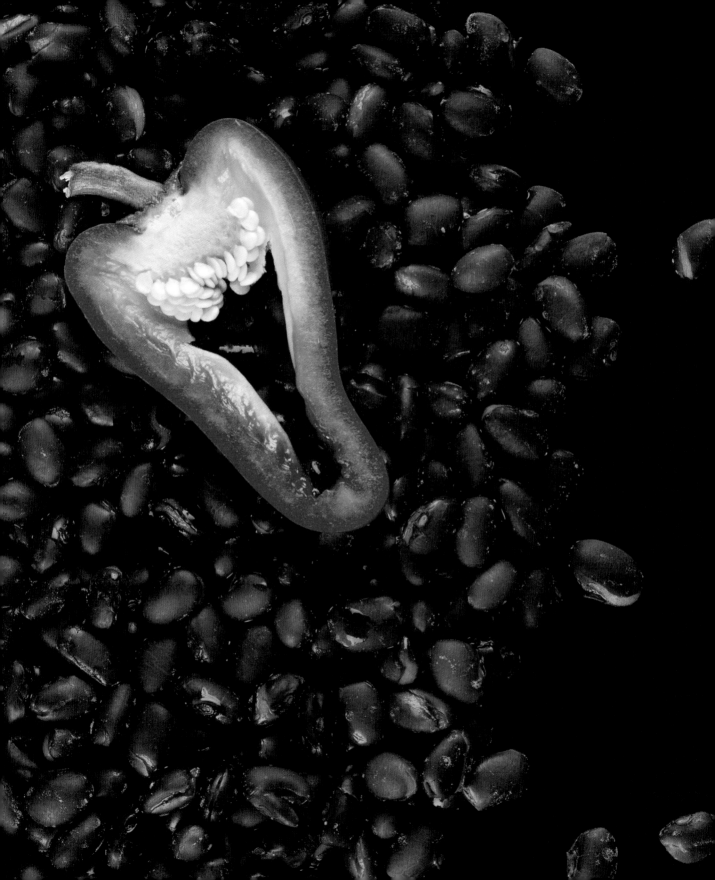

SPICY MEXICAN PORK

24 OUNCES LEAN PORK, CUBED

2 CUPS ONIONS, CHOPPED

4 CLOVES GARLIC, CHOPPED

2 CUPS FRESH TOMATOES, DICED

2 CUPS FRESH GREEN BEANS

1 CUP SWEET RED PEPPERS, CHOPPED

1 CUP GREEN PEPPERS, CHOPPED

1 CUP BLACK BEANS

2 TABLESPOONS CHILI POWDER (*SEE PAGE 173*)

1 TEASPOON DRIED OREGANO

1 TEASPOON GROUND CUMIN

1 TEASPOON GROUND CORIANDER

1/2 TEASPOON GROUND CINNAMON

1/8 TEASPOON GROUND CLOVES

1 TEASPOON GRAPE SEED OIL

SEA SALT & PEPPER TO TASTE

READY TO COOK

1. SOAK BLACK BEANS IN WATER OVERNIGHT.

2. RINSE AND COOK UNTIL TENDER.

3. COOK THE PORK CUBES IN OIL IN A LARGE PAN UNTIL THE MEAT IS LIGHTLY BROWNED ON ALL SIDES. REMOVE TO A SEPARATE BOWL.

4. ADD ONIONS AND GARLIC TO THE PAN AND COOK FOR 2 MINUTES.

5. ADD CHILI POWDER AND COOK FOR AN ADDITIONAL MINUTE.

6. PUT THE PORK AND ALL THE OTHER INGREDIENTS AND SEASONINGS, EXCEPT THE GREEN BEANS, INTO THE PAN AND SIMMER, COVERED, FOR 2 HOURS, STIRRING OCCASIONALLY.

7. ADD THE GREEN BEANS AND SIMMER ANOTHER 15 MINUTES OR UNTIL THE PORK IS VERY TENDER.

SERVE PORK WITH A SPOONFUL OF SPICY SAUCE OVER TOP.

PER SERVING: 635 CALORIES // 56G CARBOHYDRATE // 63G PROTEIN // 14G FAT

MOCK DUCK
with Broccoli

32 OUNCES FLANK STEAK	**1 TEASPOON** DRIED SAGE
2 CUPS FRESH BREAD, CUBED	**1 TEASPOON** DRIED SAVORY
1 CUP ONIONS, CHOPPED	**2 TABLESPOONS** BEEF STOCK
1 CUP CELERY, FINELY CHOPPED	**5 CUPS** BROCCOLI, BLANCHED (*SEE PAGE 129*)
1/2 CUP GREEN PEPPERS, FINELY CHOPPED	SEA SALT & PEPPER TO TASTE
1/2 CUP RED PEPPERS, FINELY CHOPPED	STRING

READY TO COOK

1. **PLACE** FRESH BREAD CUBES, ONIONS, CELERY, RED AND GREEN PEPPERS, SAGE, SAVORY, SEA SALT AND PEPPER IN BOWL AND MIX WELL.

2. **ADD** 2 TABLESPOONS OF BEEF STOCK TO MOISTEN AND MIX AGAIN.

3. **POUND** OUT THE FLANK STEAK INTO A RECTANGULAR SHAPE AND SEASON WITH SEA SALT AND PEPPER.

4. **PLACE** THE STUFFING IN THE MIDDLE OF THE STEAK AND ROLL UP.

5. **TIE** WITH STRONG STRING.

6. **BLANCH** THE BROCCOLI.

7. **BAKE** AT **350°F** FOR ABOUT 40 MINUTES.

Serve mock duck with broccoli on the side.

VERATITRICK

WHEN PREPARING THE STUFFING, MAKE SURE THE MIXTURE IS MOIST BUT NOT WET.

PER SERVING: 551 CALORIES // 24G CARBOHYDRATE // 66G PROTEIN // 12G FAT

SAUSAGE
and Bean Stew

4 HOT ITALIAN SAUSAGES	**3 CUPS** CHICKEN BROTH
2 CUPS WHITE KIDNEY BEANS	**2 CUPS** FRESH GREEN BEANS, WHOLE
2 CUPS ONIONS, CHOPPED	**1/2 TEASPOON** CAYENNE PEPPER OR CHILI POWDER *(SEE PAGE 173)*
2 CLOVES GARLIC, FINELY CHOPPED	**1 TABLESPOON** GRAINY MUSTARD
1 CUP CELERY, CHOPPED	**1 TEASPOON** GRAPE SEED OIL
1 CUP CARROTS, CHOPPED	SEA SALT & PEPPER TO TASTE

READY TO COOK

1. **SOAK** KIDNEY BEANS OVERNIGHT.
2. **RINSE** AND BOIL IN WATER TILL TENDER.
3. **HEAT** OIL IN PAN AND BROWN SAUSAGES, TURNING CONSTANTLY FOR ABOUT 5 MINUTES.
4. **ADD** ONIONS, GARLIC, CELERY, CARROTS, SEA SALT, PEPPER, CHILI POWDER OR CAYENNE PEPPER, AND MUSTARD TO THE PAN AND ON **MEDIUM** HEAT FOR ANOTHER 10 MINUTES, STIRRING CONSTANTLY.
5. **ADD** THE CHICKEN BROTH, KIDNEY BEANS AND SIMMER, COVERED FOR ABOUT 45 MINUTES.
6. **ADD** FRESH GREEN BEANS AND SIMMER UNTIL THE BEANS ARE JUST TENDER.

Serve in a bowl for you to enjoy!

VERATI**TIPS**
SOAK KIDNEY BEANS OVERNIGHT

PER SERVING: 695 CALORIES // 58G CARBOHYDRATE // 47G PROTEIN // 22G FAT

LAMB & LENTIL
Casserole

16 OUNCES LEAN LAMB, CUT INTO 1/2" CUBES	**1/2 TEASPOON** CAYENNE PEPPER
1 TABLESPOON FLOUR	**1/2 TEASPOON** GROUND CINNAMON
4 CLOVES GARLIC, FINELY CHOPPED	**1/8 TEASPOON** GROUND ALLSPICE
2 CUPS ONIONS, COARSELY CHOPPED	**1 TEASPOON** DRIED CUMIN
2 CUPS POTATOES, PEELED AND CUT IN 1" CUBES	**2 CUPS** VEGETABLE BROTH, VEGETABLE STOCK OR WATER
1 CUP GREEN PEPPERS, COARSELY CHOPPED	**1 CUP** LENTILS, DRY
1/2 CUP CHILI PEPPERS, FINELY CHOPPED	**1 TEASPOON** DRIED CORIANDER
1 CUP CAULIFLOWER, COARSELY CHOPPED	**1/2 CUP** PARSLEY, CHOPPED
2 CUPS FRESH TOMATOES, QUARTERED	SEA SALT & PEPPER TO TASTE
1 TEASPOON GRAPE SEED OIL	

READY TO COOK

1. **SOAK** LENTILS IN WATER OVERNIGHT.

2. **RINSE** AND BOIL IN FRESH WATER TILL TENDER.

3. **DUST** LAMB CUBES IN FLOUR AND BROWN LIGHTLY IN OIL IN AN OVEN-PROOF PAN.

4. **ADD** ONIONS AND CONTINUE TO COOK FOR 2-3 MINUTES.

5. **ADD** GARLIC, SEA SALT, PEPPER, CINNAMON, CAYENNE PEPPER, ALLSPICE, CUMIN AND CORIANDER AND COOK ANOTHER 1-2 MINUTES.

6. **ADD** POTATOES, GREEN PEPPERS, CAULIFLOWER AND TOMATOES AND MIX WELL.

7. **ADD** VEGETABLE BROTH OR WATER.

8. **COVER** AND BAKE AT **350⁰F** FOR 45 MINUTES UNTIL THE LAMB IS COOKED.

9. **REMOVE** FROM OVEN, STIR IN THE LENTILS AND PARSLEY AND BAKE, UNCOVERED, FOR ANOTHER 15 MINUTES.

Serve Casserole on table for everyone to enjoy!

VERATI **TIPS**
SOAK LENTILS OVERNIGHT

PER SERVING: 440 CALORIES // 37G CARBOHYDRATE // 46G PROTEIN // 11G FAT

LAMB MOUSSAKA
with Low Fat Cream Sauce

24 OUNCES GROUND LAMB	**1** EGGPLANT, SLICED
1 CUP ONIONS, FINELY CHOPPED	**2 TEASPOONS** OLIVE OIL
2 CLOVES GARLIC, FINELY CHOPPED	**1 CUP** SKIM MILK
2 CUPS DICED TOMATOES	**1 TABLESPOON** CORN STARCH
6 OUNCES TOMATO JUICE	**DASH** GROUND NUTMEG
1/2 CUP FINE BREAD CRUMBS	**1/8 CUP** LOW FAT PARMESAN CHEESE
1 EGG WHITE, BEATEN	**4 CUPS** MIXED GREEN SALAD
1 TEASPOON DRIED PARSLEY	**4 OUNCES** LOW FAT LOW CARB HOUSE DRESSING (*SEE PAGE 95*)
1 TEASPOON DRIED OREGANO	SEA SALT & PEPPER TO TASTE
1/4 TEASPOON GROUND CINNAMON	

READY TO COOK

1. **DIP** THE EGGPLANT SLICES INTO THE BEATEN EGG, THEN INTO THE BREAD CRUMBS AND PUT ON AN OILED COOKIE SHEET.
2. **BAKE** AT **325°F** UNTIL THE EGGPLANT IS SOFT.
3. **SAUTÉ** THE ONIONS AND GARLIC IN THE REMAINING OIL UNTIL SOFT.
4. **ADD** THE GROUND LAMB, SEA SALT AND PEPPER AND BROWN LIGHTLY.
5. **ADD** THE DICED TOMATOES AND TOMATO JUICE, PARSLEY, OREGANO AND CINNAMON.
6. **SIMMER**, UNCOVERED, UNTIL THE LIQUID IS REDUCED AND THE MIXTURE IS THICK.
7. **COMBINE** THE CORN STARCH AND MILK IN A BOWL AND ADD TO THE PAN. STIR CONSTANTLY TO PREVENT LUMPING.
8. **ADD** THE NUTMEG, SEA SALT AND PEPPER AND REMOVE FROM HEAT.
9. **PUT** A LAYER OF EGGPLANT ON THE BOTTOM OF A 9" X 13" CASSEROLE DISH.
10. **PUT** A LAYER OF THE LAMB MIXTURE ON TOP OF THE EGGPLANT.
11. **POUR** SOME OF THE CREAM SAUCE OVER THE EGGPLANT AND LAMB LAYERS.
12. **REPEAT** UNTIL YOU HAVE ANOTHER 2 LAYERS.
13. **POUR** THE REMAINING SAUCE OVER TOP AND SPRINKLE WITH THE LOW FAT PARMESAN CHEESE.
14. **BAKE** AT **350°F** FOR 50 MINUTES OR UNTIL THE CASSEROLE IS BUBBLY.

Serve moussaka with green salad drizzled with low fat low carb house dressing.

CHILI
Con Carne

1 CUP ONIONS, CHOPPED	**6 OUNCES** TOMATO PASTE
2 CUPS GREEN PEPPERS, CHOPPED	**2 CLOVES** GARLIC, WHOLE
2 CUPS SWEET RED PEPPERS, CHOPPED	**2** BAY LEAVES
1 CUP MUSHROOM CAPS, CHOPPED	**1 1/2 TABLESPOONS** CHILI POWDER (*SEE PAGE 173*)
4 CLOVES GARLIC, CHOPPED	**1/2 TEASPOON** TABASCO SAUCE
20 OUNCES GROUND ROUND STEAK	**1 TEASPOON** BROWN SUGAR OR SUGAR SUBSTITUTE
1 TABLESPOON DIJON MUSTARD	**1/2 TEASPOON** CAYENNE PEPPER
1/2 CUP DRY RED WINE	**BUNCH** CILANTRO, CHOPPED
1 CUP RED KIDNEY BEANS	SEA SALT & PEPPER TO TASTE
1 CUP KERNEL CORN	

READY TO COOK

1. **COOK** GROUND MEAT AND GARLIC, BEGINNING WITH **LOW HEAT** UNTIL MEAT RENDERS SOME OF ITS FAT.

2. **SEPARATE** MEAT WITH A FORK AND COOK UNTIL MEAT IS BROWNED.

3. **REMOVE** FROM PAN AND SET ASIDE.

4. **ADD** ONIONS AND MUSHROOMS TO A PAN AND COOK FOR 2 MINUTES.

5. **REMOVE** THEM FROM THE PAN.

6. **IN** A LARGE POT, PUT CHOPPED ONIONS, PEPPERS, MUSTARD, RED WINE, KIDNEY BEANS, CORN, TOMATO PASTE, GARLIC CLOVES, BAY LEAVES, CHILI POWDER, TABASCO, CAYENNE PEPPER, BROWN SUGAR, SEA SALT AND PEPPER. MIX WELL.

7. **SIMMER** FOR 1 HOUR OVER **LOW HEAT**, STIRRING OCCASIONALLY.

8. **AFTER** 1 HOUR, ADD THE MEAT AND BRING TO A BOIL FOR 2-3 MINUTES, STIRRING CONSTANTLY.

9. **SIMMER** FOR ANOTHER HOUR.

10. **REMOVE** BAY LEAVES AND GARLIC CLOVES BEFORE SERVING.

Serve with cilantro on top.

PER SERVING: 570 CALORIES // 41G CARBOHYDRATE // 59G PROTEIN // 9G FAT

SAUCES
Easy + Twist + Funky

#1 BBQ SAUCE EASY & BASIC ⬇⬇⬇

1/4 CUP ONIONS, PUREED

1 TABLESPOON BROWN SUGAR

1 CUP KETCHUP

1 TABLESPOON WHITE VINEGAR

1 TABLESPOON WORCESTERSHIRE SAUCE

• •

#2 BBQ SAUCE ADD A SPICY TWIST ⬇⬇⬇

1/4 CUP ONIONS, PUREED

1 CUP KETCHUP

1 CUP TOMATO SAUCE

3 TABLESPOONS BROWN SUGAR

1 1/2 TEASPOONS HOISIN SAUCE

1/2 TEASPOON GARLIC POWDER

1/2 TEASPOON WORCESTERSHIRE SAUCE

1/4 TEASPOON SMOKED PAPRIKA

1/4 TEASPOON CAYENNE PEPPER OR CHILI POWDER (SEE PAGE 173)

• •

#3 FUNKY BBQ SAUCE ⬇⬇⬇

7 TEASPOONS VERATI TAGINE BLEND (SEE PAGE 173)

5 CLOVES GARLIC, FINELY CHOPPED

1 CUP RED ONIONS, FINELY CHOPPED

3 CUPS KETCHUP

1/2 TEASPOON CAYENNE PEPPER

3 TABLESPOONS BROWN SUGAR

2 OUNCES LEMON JUICE

SEA SALT & PEPPER TO TASTE

• •

READY TO COOK

1. COOK ONIONS IN A PAN **2. ADD** ALL INGREDIENTS **3. COOK** OVER **LOW** HEAT FOR 10 MINUTES **4. LET** COOL TO ROOM TEMPERATURE, ABOUT 30 MIN **5. KEEP** REFRIGERATED.

IT IS BEST TO LET IT SIMMER FOR A COUPLE OF HOURS!
-CHEF VERATI

Ideal

FISH
SEAFOOD

OCEAN OF FREEDOM

...

TIPS
TRICKS

WRITE TO **CHEFVERATI@IDEALPROTEIN.COM**
FIND US ON **CHEF VERATI'S FACEBOOK PAGE**
VISIT **LOWFATLOWCARB.COM**

EAT

Best at lunch time

FACT # 7 ·· 317

SWORDFISH WITH A BITE OF FREEDOM WALNUT PESTO 319

MACKEREL WITH RATATOUILLE ····················· 321

BASA FILLETS WITH BELGIAN ENDIVES ············· 322

BACON BASA WITH LEEKS & CAPERS ··············· 322

FLOUNDER FILLETS WITH PORTUGUESE SAUCE ········ 323

GRILLED SCALLOP KEBOBS ························· 323

SOLE & OKRA IN CHILI SAUCE ···················· 325

HADDOCK FILLETS WITH SUN-DRIED TOMATOES

& GOAT CHEESE SALAD ··························· 326

GARLIC SOLE FILLETS WITH MUSHROOMS & ASPARAGUS 327

MAHI MAHI WITH CUCUMBER SALSA ················· 330

BAKED POLLOCK WITH SPICY TOMATO SAUCE ········ 331

PAN-COOKED SALMON WITH FRESH TOMATO SALSA ·· 333

HADDOCK IN ITALIAN-STYLE SAUCE ················ 334

SNAPPER MEXICAN-STYLE ························· 335

SEA SCALLOPS IN CREAMY BASIL SAUCE ············ 337

SAUTÉ ED SCALLOPS WITH PARMESAN RAPINIS ······· 338

SEAFOOD SKEWERS WITH SESAME BOK CHOY ········ 338

CUMIN PERCH WITH WATERCRESS SALAD ············· 339

BAKE SALMON STEAKS WITH PARSLEY BUTTER ······· 339

STEAMED MUSSELS WITH TOMATO & CUCUMBER SALAD 341

GARLIC SHRIMP WITH AVOCADO SALAD ·············· 342

SMOTHERED TILAPIA WITH MASHED CAULIFLOWERS ·· 342

BAKED SOLE FLORENTINE ON A BED ON SPINACH ····· 343

SWORDFISH STEAKS WITH GRILLED PEPPERS ·········· 343

LAYERED LOBSTER QUICHE WITH BROCCOLI & PARMESAN 344

HAKE FILLETS WITH GOAT CHEESE ·················· 345

SEAFOOD CASSEROLE ····························· 347

SOLE WITH AVOCADO & GRAPEFRUIT SALSA ·········· 348

TUNA STEAKS WITH HERBED RUTABAGA ·············· 349

SALMON WITH DILL SAUCE & ASPARAGUS ············· 351

ROLLED FLOUNDER WITH CREAMY HERB SAUCE ········ 352

PREPARE SEAFOOD // SHRIMPS + CLAMS + CRAB ···· 353

CARBS
Best at dinner time

FACT # 8 ·· 355

TUNA STEAKS A BITE OF MANGO SALSA FREEDOM ···· 357

BAKED COD WITH SPICY TOMATO SAUCE ············· 358

COD & BEAN CASSEROLE ······························ 359

BAKED FISH & CHIPS ································· 361

COD CAKES ON LEEKS & ONIONS ···················· 362

CRISPY MUSTARD COATING FLOUNDER ················ 362

CURRY PERCH LENTILS & ARTICHOKE ················ 363

MUSSELS LINGUINE WITH TOMATO SAUCE ············· 363

PENNE WITH CLAM SAUCE ···························· 365

CITRUS SWORDFISH WITH WALDORF-STYLE SALAD ·· 366

4 WHOLE FISH WITH ROASTED VEGETABLES ········· 367

SALMON CAKES WITH VEGETABLE PATTIES ·········· 369

WRAPPED TILAPIA INDIVIDUAL PARCHMENT ·········· 370

ALASKAN POLLOCK IN CHINESE-STYLE SAUCE ········ 371

MEDITERRANEAN TUNA WITH TWO-BEANS & POTATO SALAD 374

SOLE FILLETS & VEGGIE RICE WITH A CREAMY GINGER

SOY SAUCE ·· 375

CURRIED SHRIMP WITH SNOW PEAS ················· 377

POLLOCK FILLET CARROTS & SPINACH ··············· 378

TILAPIA BEANS CHIPOTLE SAUCE ····················· 378

TILAPIA FILLETS WITH CHIPOTLE PEPPER ············· 379

CHILI SCALLOPS STIR-FRY ························· 381

QUICK SALMON & PASTA CASSEROLE ················· 382

SOLE FILLETS LEMON & GARLIC ····················· 382

SHRIMP LINGUINE ROSÉ E SAUCE ····················· 383

COD FILLETS & RAPINI WITH KIDNEY BEANS ········· 383

ROASTED GARLIC SHRIMP WITH WILD RICE & GREEN SALAD 387

HADDOCK & BARLEY HOT POT ····················· 388

HADDOCK CHILI TOMATOES WITH SEASONED SWEET POTATOES 389

HOT POT SCALLOP ································· 391

PERCH FILLETS WITH SWEET POTATO CAKES ········ 392

HEARTY FISH STEW ································ 393

RAZOR CLAMS WITH CHILI & GARLIC ··············· 396

PIE SHELL // EASY ································ 397

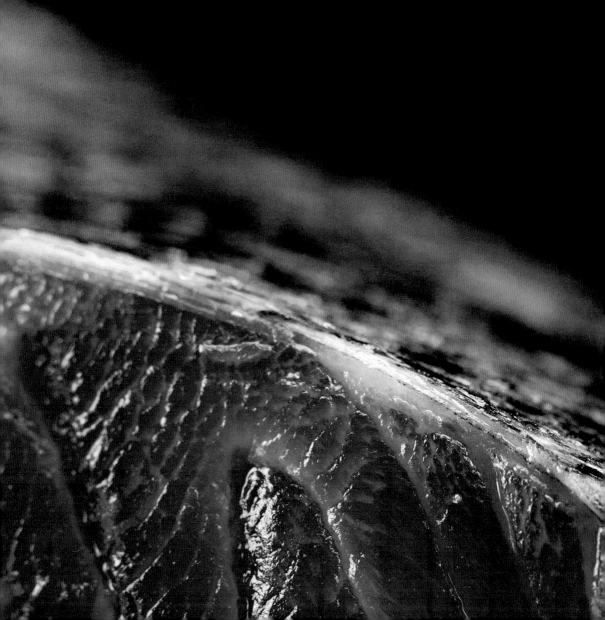

FAT

↓ ↓ ↓ ↓ ↓ ↓ ↓ ↓ ↓

CARBS

— best at lunch time —

FACT #7

ESSENTIAL

HEALTHY FATS ARE POWERFUL NATURAL ANTI-INFLAMMATORIES. OMEGA-3 FATS ARE THE BEST FATS FOR ALLEVIATING INFLAMMATION. TRY ADDING SOME ANTI-INFLAMMATORY FATS SUCH AS EXTRA-VIRGIN OLIVE OIL, AVOCADO OIL, FLAXSEED OIL, HEMPSEED OIL OR WALNUT OIL TO YOUR DAILY DIET.

INFLAMMATION

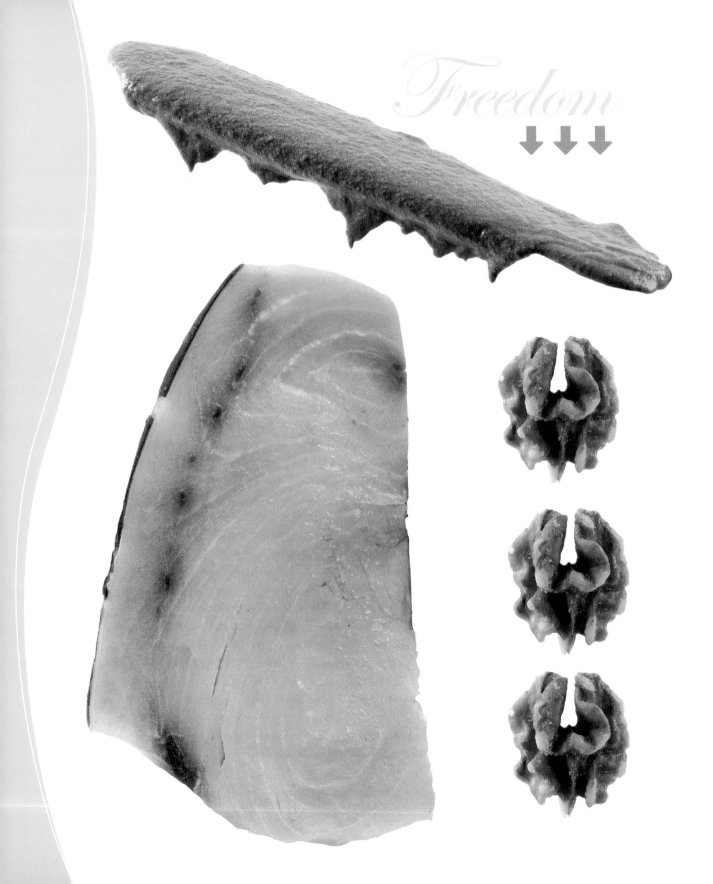

Freedom

SWORDFISH
with a Bite of Freedom Walnut Pesto

32 OUNCES SWORDFISH (4 FILLETS)

1 TABLESPOON LIME JUICE

1 CUP FRESH BASIL

1/8 CUP WALNUTS, PIECES

2 TABLESPOONS OLIVE OIL

8 CUPS MIXED GREEN SALAD

4 OUNCES LOW FAT LOW CARB HOUSE DRESSING (*SEE PAGE 95*)

SEA SALT & PEPPER TO TASTE

READY TO COOK

1. SEASON THE SWORDFISH WITH LIME JUICE AND MARINATE FOR 15-20 MINUTES. 2. PUT THE BASIL AND WALNUT PIECES, SEA SALT AND PEPPER IN A BLENDER OR FOOD PROCESSOR AND PROCESS UNTIL THE BASIL AND WALNUTS ARE GROUND. 3. SLOWLY ADD THE OLIVE OIL AND CONTINUE TO BLEND UNTIL SMOOTH. 4. PUT THE SWORDFISH ON A RACK UNDER AN OVEN GRILL PRE-HEATED TO 400°F. 5. COOK FOR 3-4 MINUTES ON EACH SIDE. 6. SERVE SWORDFISH WITH A LITTLE OF THE BASIL-WALNUT PESTO AND MIXED GREEN SALAD ON THE SIDE.

▶ GO NUTS!
ADD SOME CRUNCH TO YOUR SALAD; ENJOY EVERY BITE OF *Freedom*
A HANDFUL OF NUTS IS ALL YOU NEED; EATING TOO MANY CAN PROMOTE WEIGHT GAIN.

PER SERVING: 425 CALORIES // 25G FAT // 49G PROTEIN // 8G CARBOHYDRATE.

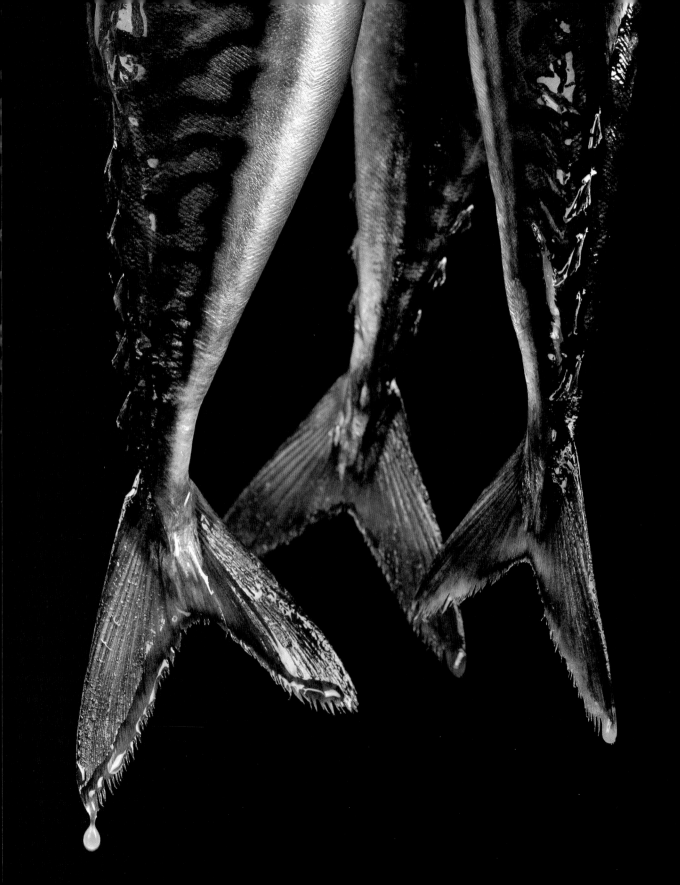

MACKEREL
with Ratatouille

24 OUNCES MACKEREL (4 FILLETS)

1 TEASPOON GRAPE SEED OIL

1 CUP GREEN ONIONS, CHOPPED

4 CLOVES GARLIC, CHOPPED

2 CUPS FRESH ZUCCHINIS, CUBED

2 CUPS FRESH EGGPLANTS, CUBED

1 CUP GREEN PEPPERS, CUBED

2 CUPS TOMATOES, DICED

1 CUP TOMATO SAUCE

1 TEASPOON OREGANO

1 TEASPOON BASIL

1 CUP PITTED BLACK OLIVES

1 TEASPOON GRAPE SEED OIL

SEA SALT & PEPPER TO TASTE

READY TO COOK

1. HEAT THE OIL IN A LARGE PAN.

2. SAUTÉ THE GARLIC UNTIL SOFT.

3. ADD THE EGGPLANTS, GREEN PEPPERS, ZUCCHINIS, TOMATOES AND TOMATO SAUCE.

4. BRING TO A BOIL AND THEN, REDUCE HEAT.

5. ADD THE OREGANO AND BASIL.

6. SIMMER, COVERED, FOR 45 MINUTES.

7 STIR IN THE BLACK OLIVES AND GREEN ONIONS.

8. SEASON THE MACKEREL WITH SEA SALT AND PEPPER TO TASTE.

9. BRUSH WITH OIL AND PLACE IN A PREHEATED 350°F OVEN.

10. COOK 4-5 MINUTES.

11. TURN, BRUSH WITH OIL AGAIN AND COOK ANOTHER 4-5 MINUTES OR UNTIL THE FISH FLAKES EASILY WITH A FORK.

SERVE MACKEREL WITH RATATOUILLE SAUCE ON THE SIDE.

PER SERVING: 598 CALORIES // 38G FAT // 43G PROTEIN // 9G CARBOHYDRATE

BASA FILLETS
with Belgian Endives

32 OUNCES BASA (4 FILLETS)

4 CUPS (8 LARGE PIECES) BELGIAN ENDIVES

2 CUPS TOMATOES, DICED

1 CUP SOUR CREAM

2 CUPS GREEN ONIONS, SLICED THINLY

2 TABLESPOONS DILL

1 TEASPOON GARLIC POWDER

2 TABLESPOONS CAPERS

1 TEASPOON GRAPE SEED OIL

1/4 CUP VEGETABLE BROTH

SEA SALT & PEPPER TO TASTE

READY TO COOK ↓↓↓

1. PLACE THE ENDIVES IN A ROASTING PAN. **2. ADD** THE VEGETABLE BROTH TO THE PAN AND PLACE IT IN A PREHEATED **350°F** OVEN. **3. ROAST** FOR ABOUT 15 MINUTES. **4. PLACE** THE TOMATOES, SOUR CREAM, SEA SALT, PEPPER AND CAPERS IN A SAUCEPAN. **5. BRING** TO A BOIL. **6. SEASON** THE BASA FILLETS WITH DILL AND GARLIC POWDER. **7. PLACE** THE FILLETS ON TOP OF THE ENDIVES AND POUR THE TOMATO AND SOUR CREAM MIXTURE OVER TOP. **8. ADD** GREEN ONIONS. **9. BAKE** ANOTHER 20 MINUTES OR UNTIL THE FISH IS DONE AND THE ENDIVES ARE SOFT.

Serve with endives under the fish.

PER SERVING: 447 CALORIES: // 25G FAT // 68G PROTEIN // 11G CARBOHYDRATE

BACON BASA
with Leeks and Capers

32 OUNCES BASA (4 FILLETS)

4 SLICES OF BACON, CHOPPED

4 CUPS LEEKS, SLICED

3 TABLESPOONS CAPERS

1/4 CUP LEMON JUICE

1 CUP GREEN ONIONS, CHOPPED

1 CUP FRESH PARSLEY, CHOPPED

1 TEASPOON FRESH SAGE, FINELY CHOPPED

2 TABLESPOONS GRAPE SEED OIL

4 CUPS MIXED SALAD GREENS

2 OUNCES LOW FAT LOW CARB HOUSE DRESSING (*SEE PAGE 95*)

SEA SALT & PEPPER TO TASTE

READY TO COOK ↓↓↓

1. HEAT THE OIL IN A LARGE FRYING PAN. **2. SAUTÉ** THE LEEKS UNTIL SOFT AND REMOVE THEM FROM THE PAN. **3. ADD** THE BACON AND COOK UNTIL CRISP. **4. ADD** THE BASA FILLETS AND COOK 3 MINUTES ON EACH SIDE. **5. RETURN** THE LEEKS TO THE PAN **6. ADD** THE LEMON JUICE, SEA SALT, PEPPER AND SAGE. **7. COVER** AND SIMMER ANOTHER 5-7 MINUTES.

Serve with capers, green onions and parsley on top and mixed green salad on the side.

PER SERVING: 437 CALORIES // 23G FAT // 49G PROTEIN // 12G CARBOHYDRATE

FLOUNDER FILLETS
with Portuguese Sauce

24 OUNCES FLOUNDER FILLETS

2 TABLESPOONS LEMON JUICE

1 CUP GREEN ONIONS, FINELY CHOPPED

4 CLOVES GARLIC, FINELY CHOPPED

2 CUPS FRESH TOMATOES, CHOPPED

2 CUPS TOMATO SAUCE

1 CUP FRESH PARSLEY, CHOPPED

2 TEASPOONS GRAPE SEED OIL

1 TABLESPOON BUTTER

3 CUPS FRESH CAULIFLOWER FLORETS

SEA SALT & PEPPER TO TASTE

READY TO COOK ↓↓↓

1. SEASON THE FLOUNDER FILLETS WITH LEMON JUICE, SEA SALT AND PEPPER AND ALLOW TO MARINATE WHILE PREPARING THE SAUCE. **2. HEAT** ONE TABLESPOON OF OIL AND THE BUTTER IN A LARGE PAN AND SAUTÉ THE ONIONS AND GARLIC UNTIL SOFT. **3. ADD** THE FRESH TOMATOES AND HEAT FOR ABOUT 5 MINUTES TO REDUCE SOME OF THE TOMATO LIQUID. ADD THE TOMATO. **4. ADD** THE TOMATO SAUCE AND SIMMER FOR ABOUT 15 MINUTES, UNTIL THE SAUCE IS FAIRLY THICK. **5. BOIL** THE CAULIFLOWER UNTIL JUST TENDER. **6. DRAIN**, COVER AND SET ASIDE. **7. BRUSH** BOTH SIDES OF THE FLOUNDER FILLETS WITH THE REMAINING TABLESPOON OF GRAPE SEED OIL AND PLACE ON A RACK. **8. PLACE** THE RACK IN THE OVEN AT 350F FOR 10-15 MINUTES, TURNING ONCE AND BRUSHING AGAIN WITH THE OIL IF THE TOPS BECOME TOO DRY. **9. REMOVE** FROM THE OVEN.

Serve flounder fillets and cauliflower with a spoonful of tomato sauce and a dash of parsley.

PER SERVING: 572 CALORIES // 21G FAT // 44G PROTEIN // 11G CARBOHYDRATE

GRILLED SCALLOP
Kebobs

20 OUNCES SCALLOPS

8 SLICES OF BACON

4 CUPS CHERRY TOMATOES, HALVES

1 TEASPOON OLIVE OIL

1 TEASPOON TARRAGON

1 TEASPOON CAYENNE PEPPER

1 TEASPOON BASIL

8 LARGE SKEWERS

4 CUPS BABY SPINACH

2 OUNCES LOW FAT LOW CARB HOUSE DRESSING (*SEE PAGE 95*)

SEA SALT & PEPPER TO TASTE

READY TO COOK ↓↓↓

1. THREAD THE SCALLOPS, TOMATOES AND BACON SLICES ONTO THE SKEWERS. **2. WHISK** THE OLIVE OIL, TARRAGON, CAYENNE PEPPER AND BASIL TOGETHER IN A SMALL BOWL, THEN BRUSH THE SCALLOPS, TOMATOES AND BACON WITH THE OIL MIXTURE. **3. PLACE** THE SKEWERS ON A RACK UNDER THE OVEN BROILER AND COOK FOR 5 MINUTES. **4. TURN** THE SKEWERS OVER AND BRUSH SECOND SIDE WITH THE OIL MIXTURE. **5. BROIL** ANOTHER 5 MINUTES.

Serve kebobs with wilted baby spinach.

PER SERVING: 380 CALORIES // 19G FAT // 42G PROTEIN // 8G CARBOHYDRATE

SOLE & OKRA
in Chili Sauce

32 OUNCES SOLE (4 FILLETS)

6 CUPS FRESH OKRA, WHOLE

1 TABLESPOON LEMON JUICE

1/4 CUP PLAIN YOGURT

1 TEASPOON DRIED CUMIN

1 TEASPOON DRIED CORIANDER

2 TEASPOONS CHINESE CHILI GARLIC SAUCE

2 TABLESPOONS TOMATO PASTE

2 CUPS TOMATOES, DICED

1 TEASPOON VINEGAR

2 TABLESPOONS GRAPE SEED OIL

2 TABLESPOONS BUTTER

SEA SALT & PEPPER TO TASTE

READY TO COOK

1. MARINATE THE SOLE FILLETS IN THE LEMON JUICE AND YOGURT FOR 30 MINUTES

2. FRY THE OKRA IN THE BUTTER AND OIL UNTIL LIGHTLY BROWNED.

3. IN A SAUCEPAN, COMBINE THE CHILI GARLIC SAUCE, TOMATO PASTE, DICED TOMATOES, VINEGAR, SEA SALT, PEPPER, CUMIN AND CORIANDER AND SIMMER FOR ABOUT 10 MINUTES.

4. PUT THE SOLE FILLETS, INCLUDING THE MARINADE, INTO AN OVEN-PROOF CASSEROLE DISH.

5. LAY THE OKRA ON TOP OF THE FISH AND POUR THE CHILI SAUCE OVER TOP.

6. COVER AND BAKE FOR 30 MINUTES.

SERVE WITH THE SAUCE AND OKRA ON TOP OF THE SOLE FILLETS.

MARINATE OVERNIGHT, COVERED, IN YOUR REFRIGERATOR FOR BEST RESULTS!

PER SERVING: 461 CALORIES // 19G FAT // 59G PROTEIN // 8G CARBOHYDRATE

HADDOCK FILLETS
with Sun-dried Tomatoes and Goat Cheese Salad

32 OUNCES HADDOCK (4 FILLETS)	**2 CUPS** CUCUMBERS, CUBED
1 TEASPOON GRAPE SEED OIL	**5 CUPS** FRESH SPINACH, CHOPPED
1 TEASPOON GARLIC POWDER	**1 CUP** GOAT CHEESE, CUBED
1 TEASPOON ONION POWDER	**2 TEASPOONS** OLIVE OIL
8 PIECES OF SUN-DRIED TOMATOES	**1 TEASPOON** LEMON JUICE
2 TEASPOONS LEMON ZEST, GRATED	**2 TEASPOONS** FRESH OREGANO
1 CUP RED ONIONS, SLICED IN ROUNDS	SEA SALT & PEPPER TO TASTE

READY TO COOK

1. **SEASON** THE HADDOCK WITH SEA SALT, PEPPER, GARLIC POWDER AND ONION POWDER AND SEAR IN OIL FOR 6-8 MINUTES.

2. **ADD** THE SUN-DRIED TOMATOES TO THE PAN WITH THE GRATED LEMON ZEST.

3. **COOK** ANOTHER 6-8 MINUTES OR UNTIL THE FILLETS FLAKE EASILY WITH A FORK.

4. **IN A LARGE BOWL**, COMBINE THE RED ONIONS, CUCUMBERS, SPINACH AND GOAT CHEESE.

5. **WHISK** THE OLIVE OIL, LEMON JUICE AND OREGANO TOGETHER THEN POUR OVER THE SPINACH MIXTURE.

Serve haddock fillets with spinach and goat cheese salad on the side.

PER SERVING: 581 CALORIES // 24G FAT // 64G PROTEIN // 12G CARBOHYDRATE.

GARLIC SOLE FILLETS
with Mushrooms and Asparagus

32 OUNCES SOLE (4 FILLETS)

1 TEASPOON DRIED PARSLEY

1 TEASPOON LEMON JUICE

4 CLOVES GARLIC, FINELY CHOPPED

1 TEASPOON GRAPE SEED OIL

1 TABLESPOON BUTTER

4 CUPS MUSHROOMS, SLICED

4 CUPS ASPARAGUS, SPEARS

SEA SALT & PEPPER TO TASTE

READY TO COOK

1. **SEASON** THE SOLE FILLETS WITH SEA SALT, PEPPER AND PARSLEY.

2. **COOK** THE MUSHROOMS IN BUTTER AND 1 TEASPOON OF OIL UNTIL THEY JUST BEGIN TO SOFTEN AND REMOVE FROM HEAT.

3. **STEAM** THE ASPARAGUS UNTIL DONE AND KEEP WARM.

4. **PREHEAT** A PAN WITH THE OIL AND ADD THE GARLIC.

5. **SAUTÉ** FOR 1 MINUTE AND ADD THE SOLE.

6. **COOK** FOR ABOUT 2 MINUTES AND TURN SOLE OVER; THE FIRST SIDE SHOULD HAVE ALREADY BROWNED.

7. **BROWN** THE SECOND SIDE AND CHECK FOR DONENESS BEFORE REMOVING FROM THE HEAT.

Serve sole fillets with a hint of lemon juice on top, mushrooms and asparagus on the side.

VERATI TIPS
SOLE FILLETS COOK QUITE QUICKLY. THEREFORE, REMEMBER TO REMOVE THE FISH IMMEDIATELY FROM THE HEATED PAN WHEN THEY ARE DONE!

PER SERVING: 484 CALORIES // 24G FAT // 60G PROTEIN // 5G CARBOHYDRATE.

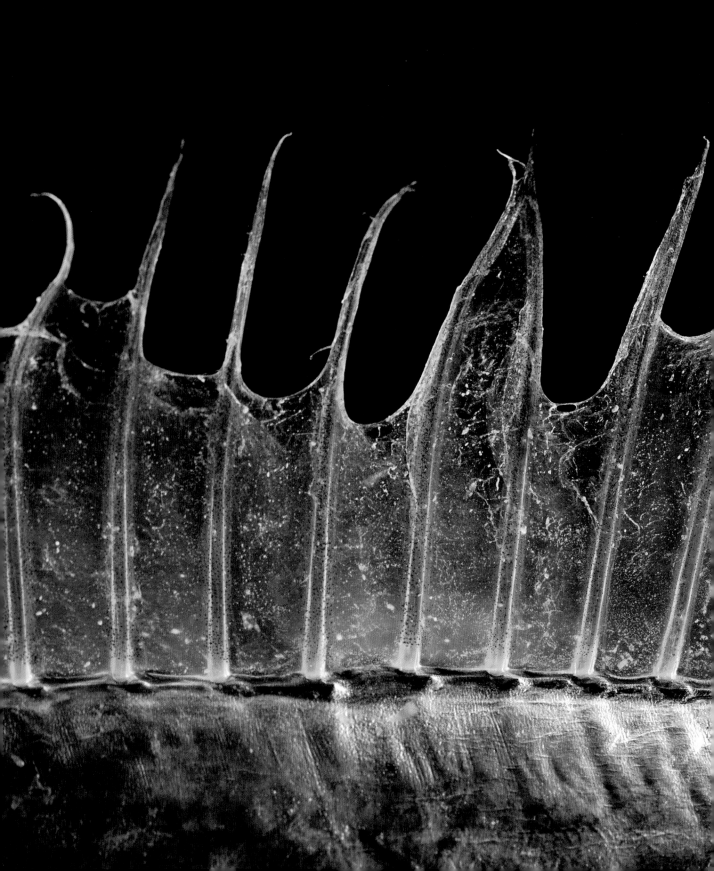

CHEF
VERATi.

WHENEVER I CAN, I CATCH MY OWN FISH.
IT IS A REAL GIFT TO EAT FOOD THAT IS FRESH.
WHAT A LIFESTYLE!
-CHEF VERATI

MAHI MAHI
with Cucumber Salsa

32 **OUNCES** MAHI MAHI (4 FILLETS)

2 **TABLESPOONS** GRAPE SEED OIL

1 **TABLESPOON** HONEY

2 **CUPS** STRAWBERRIES, CUBED

2 **CUPS** SEEDLESS CUCUMBERS, CUBED

1 **CUP** SWEET RED PEPPERS, CHOPPED

1 **CUP** GREEN BELL PEPPERS, CHOPPED

2 **CUPS** BOSTON LETTUCE LEAVES, WHOLE

1 **TABLESPOON** LIME JUICE

3 **TEASPOONS** FRESH MINT, CHOPPED

1/2 **TEASPOON** HOT PEPPER SAUCE

8 **TABLESPOONS** SOUR CREAM

SEA SALT & PEPPER TO TASTE

READY TO COOK

1. **IN A LARGE BOWL**, COMBINE THE STRAWBERRIES AND CUCUMBERS AS WELL AS THE RED AND GREEN PEPPERS WITH THE LIME JUICE, HONEY, HOT PEPPER SAUCE AND MINT.

2. **TOSS** UNTIL THE LIME JUICE AND PEPPER SAUCE ARE WELL AMALGAMATED.

3. **LEAVE** AT ROOM TEMPERATURE WHILE PREPARING THE FISH.

4. **SEASON** THE MAHI MAHI WITH SEA SALT AND PEPPER AND BRUSH BOTH SIDES WITH OIL. .

5. **PLACE** MAHI MAHI ON A RACK IN THE OVEN AND COOK 3-4 MINUTES PER SIDE.

6. **WHEN** THE FISH IS DONE, REMOVE FROM THE OVEN.

Serve mahi mahi on a bed of boston lettuce leaves with a spoonful of salsa and a hint of sour cream over top.

PER SERVING: 426 CALORIES // 18G FAT // 55G PROTEIN // 9G CARBOHYDRATE

BAKED POLLOCK
with Spicy Tomato Sauce

32 OUNCES POLLOCK (4 FILLETS)

6 BACON RASHERS, CHOPPED

2 CUPS TOMATOES, DICED

1 CUP TOMATO SAUCE

1 CUP GREEN ONIONS, FINELY CHOPPED

4 CLOVES GARLIC, FINELY CHOPPED

1 CUP SWEET YELLOW PEPPERS, CUBED

1 CUP SWEET RED PEPPERS, CUBED

1 CUP GREEN BELL PEPPERS, CUBED

2 CUPS SMALL WHITE MUSHROOMS, WHOLE

2 TABLESPOONS TOMATO PASTE

1 TEASPOON CHILI POWDER *(SEE PAGE 173)*

1 CHIPOTLE PEPPER, CHOPPED

1 TEASPOON OREGANO

1 TEASPOON BASIL

1 BUNCH FRESH CORIANDER, CHOPPED

SEA SALT & PEPPER TO TASTE

READY TO COOK

1. **HEAT** THE BACON IN A FRYING PAN UNTIL WELL RENDERED.

2. **ADD** THE GARLIC AND SAUTÉ FOR 1 MINUTE.

3. **ADD** THE TOMATO PASTE AND COOK FOR 1-2 MINUTES.

4. **ADD** THE MUSHROOMS AS WELL AS THE RED, YELLOW AND GREEN PEPPERS AND COOK FOR 1 MINUTE.

5. **ADD** THE TOMATOES, TOMATO PASTE, CHIPOTLE, CHILI POWDER, SEA SALT, PEPPER, OREGANO AND BASIL.

6. **SIMMER** FOR 10 MINUTES.

7. **PLACE** THE POLLOCK FILLETS ON THE BOTTOM OF AN OVEN CASSEROLE AND POUR THE SAUCE OVER TOP.

8. **BAKE** IN THE OVEN AT **350°F** FOR 30 MINUTES OR UNTIL THE FISH FLAKES EASILY WITH A FORK.

Serve with fresh coriander on the top.

PAN-COOKED SALMON
with Fresh Tomato Salsa

24 OUNCES SALMON (4 FILLETS)	**1 TEASPOON** LIME JUICE
4 CUPS FRESH TOMATOES, DICED	**2 TEASPOONS** LEMON JUICE
1 CUP GREEN ONIONS, FINELY CHOPPED	**1/2 TEASPOON** CAYENNE PEPPER OR CHILI POWDER (*OPTIONAL*) (*SEE PAGE 173*)
1 CUP SWEET RED PEPPERS, CHOPPED	**1 TEASPOON** GARLIC SALT
1 CUP GREEN PEPPERS, CHOPPED	**1 TEASPOON** ONION POWDER
1 CUP CUCUMBERS, DICED	**1 TEASPOON** OLIVE OIL
1 CUP FRESH CILANTRO, CHOPPED	**1 TEASPOON** GRAPE SEED OIL
1 TEASPOON GROUND CORIANDER	SEA SALT & PEPPER TO TASTE

READY TO COOK

1. **MIX** ALL THE INGREDIENTS TOGETHER IN A BOWL, COVER, AND ALLOW TO MARINATE AT ROOM TEMPERATURE FOR 30 MINUTES.
2. **PLACE** IN A HEATED PAN WITH THE OIL AND COOK ON MEDIUM HEAT FOR ABOUT 5-8 MINUTES.
3. **WHEN** IT IS ALMOST COOKED THROUGH, REMOVE FROM THE HEAT AND PUT A TIGHT-FITTING COVER ON THE PAN.
4. **LET** REST FOR 5 MINUTES.

Serve salmon fillets with fresh salsa on the side.

VERATI**TIPS**
YOU WILL BE ABLE TO TELL HOW MUCH OF THE SALMON
IS COOKED AS IT CHANGES COLOR.

PER SERVING: 445 CALORIES // 26G FAT // 40G PROTEIN // 9G CARBOHYDRATE.

HADDOCK
in Italian-Style Sauce

32 OUNCES HADDOCK (4 FILLETS)

8 SLICES OF PANCETTA HAM, SLICED

3 CUPS FRESH TOMATOES, CUBED

1 CUP ONIONS, CHOPPED

2 CLOVES GARLIC, FINELY CHOPPED

1 CUP SWEET RED PEPPERS, CHOPPED

1 CUP GREEN BELL PEPPERS, CHOPPED

2 CUPS MUSHROOMS, SLICED

1 TABLESPOON TOMATO PASTE

1 TEASPOON FRESH OREGANO, CHOPPED

1 TEASPOON FRESH BASIL, CHOPPED

1/2 TEASPOON CAYENNE PEPPER

1 BAY LEAF

2 TABLESPOONS GRAPE SEED OIL

SEA SALT & PEPPER TO TASTE

READY TO COOK

1. **IN** A LARGE PAN, SAUTÉ THE ONIONS AND PANCETTA HAM UNTIL SOFT.

2. **ADD** THE GARLIC AND COOK FOR 1-2 MINUTES.

3. **ADD** THE MUSHROOMS AND PEPPERS AND COOK FOR 2 MINUTES.

4. **ADD** THE TOMATOES, OREGANO, BASIL, SEA SALT, PEPPER, CAYENNE AND BAY LEAF AND SIMMER 15-20 MINUTES.

5. **PLACE** THE HADDOCK FILLETS IN AN OVEN-PROOF PAN AND POUR THE SAUCE OVER TOP. COVER AND BAKE 20-25 MINUTES OR UNTIL THE FISH FLAKES EASILY WITH A FORK.

Serve with slices of panchetta on top.

PER SERVING: 486 CALORIES // 19G FAT // 58G PROTEIN // 9G CARBOHYDRATE

SNAPPER
Mexican-Style

24 OUNCES SNAPPER (4 FILLETS)	**1 TEASPOON** CHIPOTLE PEPPER, FINELY CHOPPED
1 TABLESPOON LEMON JUICE	**1 TEASPOON** MARJORAM
1 CUP GREEN ONIONS, FINELY CHOPPED	**1 TEASPOON** THYME
4 CLOVES GARLIC, FINELY CHOPPED	**1 TEASPOON** CHILI POWDER *(OPTIONAL)* *(SEE PAGE 173)*
4 CUPS TOMATOES, DICED	**1 TEASPOON** GRAPE SEED OIL
1 TEASPOON OREGANO	**1 TEASPOON** BUTTER
1 CUP GREEN BELL PEPPERS, CHOPPED	**1/4 CUP** SOUR CREAM
1 CUP SWEET RED PEPPERS, CHOPPED	SEA SALT & PEPPER TO TASTE

READY TO COOK

1. **HEAT** THE OIL AND BUTTER IN A FRYING PAN AND SAUTÉ THE GARLIC UNTIL SOFTENED.

2. **ADD** THE TOMATOES, RED AND GREEN PEPPERS AND CHIPOTLE PEPPER AND SIMMER FOR 10 MINUTES.

3. **ADD** THE OREGANO, MARJORAM, THYME AND CHILI POWDER. STIR WELL.

4. **SEASON** THE SNAPPER WITH SEA SALT AND PEPPER TO TASTE AND DRIZZLE THE LEMON JUICE OVER TOP.

5. **PLACE** IN AN OVEN CASSEROLE.

6. **POUR** THE TOMATO SAUCE OVER TOP AND BAKE AT **350⁰F** FOR ABOUT 30 MINUTES OR UNTIL THE FISH IS COOKED.

Serve snapper fillets with a dash of sour cream and green onions over top.

PER SERVING: 369 CALORIES // 17G FAT // 51G PROTEIN // 10G CARBOHYDRATE.

/ 335 /

SEA SCALLOPS
in Creamy Basil Sauce

32 OUNCES SEA SCALLOPS

2 TABLESPOONS LIME JUICE

2 TABLESPOONS GRAPE SEED OIL

1/2 CUP 35% COOKING CREAM

1 TEASPOON GRAINY DIJON MUSTARD

4 TABLESPOONS LEMON JUICE

1/2 CUP FRESH BASIL, CHOPPED

8 CUPS FRESH ASPARAGUS, SPEARS & BLANCHED (*SEE PAGE 129*)

SEA SALT & PEPPER TO TASTE

READY TO COOK

1. **MARINATE** THE SCALLOPS IN THE LIME JUICE FOR SEVERAL HOURS.

2. **IN** A BOWL, WHISK TOGETHER OR BLEND BRIEFLY IN A BLENDER OR FOOD PROCESSOR THE CREAM, MUSTARD, LEMON JUICE, FRESH BASIL AND 1 TABLESPOON OF GRAPE SEED OIL.

3. **HEAT** THE REMAINING TABLESPOON OF GRAPE SEED OIL ON MEDIUM-HIGH HEAT.

4. **COOK** THE SCALLOPS QUICKLY, ABOUT 2 MINUTES PER SIDE, AND REMOVE FROM THE HEAT.

5. **STEAM** THE ASPARAGUS UNTIL TENDER.

Serve the scallops and asparagus covered with creamy basil sauce.

SAUTÉED SCALLOPS
with Parmesan Rapini

32 OUNCES SCALLOPS

4 STRIPS BACON, CHOPPED

2 TEASPOONS GRAPE SEED OIL

1 TEASPOON BUTTER

4 CLOVES GARLIC, FINELY CHOPPED

3 CUPS FRESH TOMATOES, CHOPPED

1 TABLESPOON TOMATO PASTE

1 CUP FRESH PARSLEY, CHOPPED

1 TEASPOON FRESH BASIL, CHOPPED

4 CUPS RAPINI

1 TABLESPOON PARMESAN CHEESE, GRATED

SEA SALT & PEPPER TO TASTE

READY TO COOK ⬇⬇⬇

1. HEAT 1 TEASPOON OF OIL IN A PAN AND SAUTÉ THE BACON AND GARLIC UNTIL SOFT BUT NOT BROWNED. **2. ADD** THE FRESH TOMATOES, TOMATO PASTE, BASIL, SEA SALT AND PEPPER. **3. COOK** ABOUT 12-15 MINUTES UNTIL THE TOMATOES ARE COOKED AND THE JUICE IS SOMEWHAT REDUCED. **4. STEAM** THE RAPINI UNTIL JUST TENDER. **5. DRAIN** AND STIR IN THE PARMESAN CHEESE. **6. KEEP** WARM. **7. HEAT** 1 TEASPOON OF OIL AND THE BUTTER IN A FRYING PAN AND SAUTÉ THE SCALLOPS QUICKLY, FOR ABOUT 2-3 MINUTES. **8. POUR** THE SAUCE INTO THE PAN WITH THE SCALLOPS AND COOK ANOTHER 2-3 MINUTES.

Serve scallops with rapini.

PER SERVING: 408 CALORIES // 21G FAT // 42G PROTEIN // 11G CARBOHYDRATE

SEAFOOD SKEWERS
with Sesame Bok Choy

16 OUNCES SCALLOPS

16 OUNCES SHRIMP, PEELED & DEVEINED *(SEE PAGE 353)*

2 TEASPOONS GRAPE SEED OIL

1 TABLESPOON CHINESE HOISIN SAUCE

1 TEASPOON CHINESE GARLIC CHILI SAUCE

4 SKEWERS

1 CUP GREEN BELL PEPPERS, CUBED

8 CUPS BABY BOK CHOY

2 TEASPOONS SESAME SEEDS

1 TEASPOON SESAME OIL

SEA SALT & PEPPER TO TASTE

READY TO COOK ⬇⬇⬇

1. STEAM THE BABY BOK CHOY WHOLE UNTIL JUST TENDER. **2. DRAIN** AND SEASON WITH SESAME SEEDS AND SESAME OIL. **3. KEEP** WARM. **4. IN** A BOWL, COMBINE THE HOISIN SAUCE AND GARLIC CHILI SAUCE. **5. THREAD** THE SCALLOPS, SHRIMP AND GREEN PEPPERS ALTERNATELY ON THE SKEWERS. **6. PREHEAT** THE OVEN GRILL TO 425° F. **7. BASTE** THE SCALLOPS AND SHRIMP WITH THE SAUCE UNTIL WELL COATED. **8. PLACE** SKEWERS ON A RACK OVER A COOKIE SHEET AND COOK FOR 3 MINUTES UNDER THE GRILL. **9. TURN** THE SKEWERS OVER AND BASTE AGAIN WITH THE SAUCE. **10. COOK** FOR ANOTHER 3 MINUTES OR UNTIL THE SHRIMP ARE PINK AND THE SCALLOPS ARE DONE.

Serve skewers with a spoonful of the remaining sauce on top and sesame bok choy on the side.

PER SERVING: 368 CALORIES // 15G FAT // 52G PROTEIN // 7 CARBOHYDRATE

CUMIN PERCH
with Watercress Salad

24 **OUNCES** PERCH (4 FILLETS)

2 **TABLESPOONS** GRAPE SEED OIL

2 **TABLESPOONS** CUMIN

1 **TEASPOON** DRIED CORIANDER

4 **CUPS** MUSHROOMS, SLICED

2 **CUPS** FRESH SPINACH, COARSELY CHOPPED

2 **CUPS** FRESH WATERCRESS, COARSELY CHOPPED

1/2 **CUP** SLIVERED ALMONDS

2 **TABLESPOONS** LIME JUICE

2 **OUNCES** LOW FAT LOW CARB HOUSE DRESSING (*SEE PAGE 95*)

SEA SALT & PEPPER TO TASTE

READY TO COOK ⬇⬇⬇

1. TOAST THE ALMONDS BY PLACING THEM ON A SHEET IN THE OVEN FOR A FEW MINUTES. **2. WATCH** THEM CAREFULLY SO THEY DO NOT BURN. **3. IN** A LARGE BOWL, COMBINE THE SPINACH, WATERCRESS, TOASTED ALMONDS AND LIME JUICE. **4. TOSS** WELL. **5. SAUTÉ** THE MUSHROOMS UNTIL JUST TENDER AND SET ASIDE. **6. SEASON** THE PERCH FILLETS WITH SEA SALT AND PEPPER TO TASTE. **7. HEAT** 1 TABLESPOON OF THE OIL IN A FRYING PAN AND QUICKLY BROWN THE FILLETS ON EACH SIDE. **8. COOK** UNTIL THE FILLETS FLAKE EASILY WITH A FORK. **9. PLACE** THEM ON A PLATTER AND KEEP WARM. **10. PUT** THE COOKED MUSHROOMS IN THE FRYING PAN, SEASON WITH CUMIN AND CORIANDER AND TOSS OVER LOW HEAT FOR 2-3 MINUTES.

Serve the perch fillets on the spinach and watercress salad and drizzle with house dressing.

PER SERVING: 383 CALORIES // 16G FAT // 47G PROTEIN // 7G CARBOHYDRATE

BAKE SALMON STEAKS
with Parsley Butter

24 **OUNCES** SALMON (4 STEAKS), ABOUT 3/4" THICK

2 **TEASPOONS** GRAPE SEED OIL

2 **TABLESPOONS** BUTTER

3 **TABLESPOONS** DRIED PARSLEY

1/4 **CUP** LEMON JUICE

8 **CUPS** GREEN BEANS

SEA SALT & PEPPER TO TASTE

READY TO COOK ⬇⬇⬇

1. STEAM THE GREEN BEANS UNTIL COOKED AND SET ASIDE. **2. IN** A BOWL, COMBINE THE BUTTER, PARSLEY, SEA SALT AND PEPPER BY MIXING WITH A SPOON. **3. FORM** INTO 4 SMALL BALLS AND PLACE IN REFRIGERATOR WHILE COOKING THE SALMON. **4. PREHEAT** THE OVEN TO 425°F THEN SET TO **BOIL. 5. BRUSH** THE SALMON STEAKS WITH A LITTLE OIL AND PLACE THEM ON A RACK UNDER THE BROILER. **6. GRILL** 5 MINUTES ON EACH SIDE.

Serve with a splash of lemon juice and a portion of green beans arranged in the hollow of the steaks and top with the butter and parsley balls.

PER SERVING: 535 CALORIES // 34G FAT // 42G PROTEIN // 10G CARBOHYDRATE

STEAMED MUSSELS
with Tomato and Cucumber Salad

4 POUNDS MUSSELS, CLEANED & DEBEARDED (*SEE PAGE 353*)

1 CUP GREEN ONIONS, CHOPPED

1 CUP CELERY, CHOPPED

1/3 CUP LEMON JUICE

1 CUP 35% COOKING CREAM

2 TEASPOONS DRIED PARSLEY

1/4 CUP FRESH PARSLEY, CHOPPED

1 TEASPOON BUTTER

2 CUPS FRESH TOMATOES, SLICED

2 CUPS CUCUMBERS, SLICED

1 TEASPOON FRESH CHIVES, CHOPPED

1 TEASPOON FRESH OREGANO, CHOPPED

4 CUPS ARUGULA

2 OUNCES LOW FAT LOW CARB HOUSE DRESSING (*SEE PAGE 95*)

SEA SALT & PEPPER TO TASTE

READY TO COOK

1. **PLACE** THE MUSSELS IN A LARGE STOCK POT.

2. **ADD** THE ONIONS, CELERY, SEA SALT, PEPPER, PARSLEY AND LEMON JUICE, SAVING 1 TABLESPOON OF LEMON JUICE FOR THE CREAM SAUCE.

3. **COVER** THE POT AND COOK ABOUT 5 MINUTES, UNTIL THE MUSSELS OPEN.

4. **DRAIN,** RESERVING THE LIQUID.

5. **DISCARD** ANY MUSSELS WHICH HAVE NOT OPENED.

6. **PUT** THE RESERVED COOKING LIQUID IN A PAN AND REDUCE BY HALF.

7. **ADD** CREAM AND BUTTER AND HEAT UNTIL THE BUTTER MELTS.

8. **ADD** THE SEA SALT AND FRESH PARSLEY AND THE RESERVED TABLESPOON OF LEMON JUICE.

9. **PLACE** THE MUSSELS IN SOUP BOWLS AND POUR THE SAUCE OVER THEM.

Serve with arugula and freshly sliced tomatoes and cucumbers seasoned with fresh chives and oregano.

PER SERVING: 483 CALORIES // 23G FAT // 56G PROTEIN // 12G CARBOHYDRATE.

GARLIC SHRIMP
with Avocado Salad

32 OUNCES	SHRIMP, PEELED & DEVEINED *(SEE PAGE 353)*
2 CUPS	AVOCADO, SLICED
1 CUP	GREEN ONIONS, FINELY CHOPPED
3 CLOVES	GARLIC, FINELY CHOPPED
5 CUPS	ARUGULA
1/2 CUP	FRESH CILANTRO, CHOPPED
1/2 CUP	FRESH MINT, CHOPPED
1/2 CUP	FRESH BASIL, CHOPPED
2 TEASPOONS	OLIVE OIL
1 TEASPOON	BUTTER
2 TEASPOONS	LEMON JUICE
1/2 TEASPOON	LEMON ZEST
	SEA SALT & PEPPER TO TASTE

READY TO COOK ⬇⬇⬇

1. COMBINE THE AVOCADO SLICES, GREEN ONIONS, CILANTRO, MINT AND BASIL IN A BOWL. **2. DRIZZLE** LEMON JUICE OVER TOP AND MARINATE FOR 10 MINUTES. **3. SAUTÉ** THE GARLIC IN OIL AND BUTTER FOR 2 MINUTES. **4. ADD** THE SHRIMP AND COOK UNTIL THE SHRIMP ARE PINK **5. PLACE** THE ARUGULA IN A LARGE BOWL. **6. ADD** THE AVOCADO MIXTURE, SHRIMP AND GARLIC AND TOSS UNTIL WELL COATED.

Serve shrimp with a tad of lemon zest and avocado salad on the side.

PER SERVING: 414 CALORIES // 17G FAT // 61G PROTEIN // 5G CARBOHYDRATE

SMOTHERED TILAPIA
with Mashed Cauliflowers

24 OUNCES	TILAPIA (4 FILLETS)
1/2 TEASPOON	PAPRIKA
1 CUP	TOMATOES, DICED
1 CUP	RED PEPPERS, SLICED
1 CUP	YELLOW PEPPERS, SLICED
4 CUPS	CAULIFLOWER FLORETS
1 CUP	GREEN ONIONS, FINELY CHOPPED
4 CLOVES	GARLIC, FINELY CHOPPED
2 TABLESPOONS	BUTTER
3 TEASPOONS	OIL
1/2 CUP	35% COOKING CREAM
3 TEASPOONS	DRIED PARSLEY
	SEA SALT & PEPPER TO TASTE

READY TO COOK ⬇⬇⬇

1. SEASON THE TILAPIA FILLETS WITH SEA SALT, PEPPER AND PAPRIKA. **2. PREHEAT** A PAN WITH 2 TEASPOONS OF OIL AT **MEDIUM-HIGH** AND COOK THE RED AND YE LOW PEPPERS FOR 2 MINUTES. **3. ADD** THE DICED TOMATOES AND THEIR JUICE AND BRING TO A BOIL. **4. TURN DOWN** THE HEAT IMMEDIATELY TO SIMMER AND PLACE THE SEASONED TILAPIA FILLETS ON TOP OF THE TOMATO MIXTURE. **5. COOK** COVERED, FOR 3-4 MINUTES. **6. SAUTÉ** THE GARLIC IN 1 TEASPOON OF OIL FOR 1-2 MINUTES UNTIL SOFT BUT NOT BROWN. **7. BOIL** THE CAULIFLOWER FLORETS UNTIL SOFT AND DRAIN, RESERVING 1/2 CUP OF THE LIQUID. **8. USING** A BLENDER OR FOOD PROCESSOR, MASH THE CAULIFLOWER FLORETS WITH THE BUTTER, GREEN ONIONS, SEA SALT AND PEPPER UNTIL THEY REACH THE CONSISTANCY OF MASHED POTATOES, ADDING THE CREAM AND A LITTLE OF THE RESERVED COOKING LIQUID IF NECESSARY.

Serve tilapia fillets with a dash of parsley on top and mashed cauliflower on the side.

PER SERVING: 412G CALORIES // 17G FAT // 42G PROTEIN // 9G CARBOHYDRATE

BAKE SOLE FLORENTINE
on a Bed on Spinach

32 **OUNCES** SOLE (4 FILLETS)

5 **CUPS** FRESH SPINACH

2 **CUPS** MUSHROOMS, SLICED

1 **CUP** GREEN ONIONS, FINELY CHOPPED

2 **CLOVES** GARLIC, FINELY CHOPPED

2 **TABLESPOONS** GRAPE SEED OIL

1 1/2 **CUPS** 35% COOKING CREAM

2 **TABLESPOONS** FRESH PARSLEY, CHOPPED

SEA SALT & PEPPER TO TASTE

READY TO COOK ⬇⬇⬇

1. **IN** A SAUCEPAN, HEAT THE OIL. 2. **SAUTÉ** THE GARLIC AND MUSHROOMS FOR 2-3 MINUTES. 3. **ADD** THE CREAM AND STIR UNTIL THE SAUCE BEGINS TO THICKEN SLIGHTLY. 4. **PLACE** THE FRESH SPINACH ON THE BOTTOM OF A CASSEROLE DISH. 5. **LAY** THE SOLE FILLETS ON TOP OF THE SPINACH. 6. **POUR** THE SAUCE OVER THE FISH AND SPINACH AND BAKE AT 350⁰F FOR 25 MINUTES.

Serve the sole fillets and spinach with a dash of chopped parsley over top.

PER SERVING: 418 CALORIES // 22G FAT // 60G PROTEIN // 7G CARBOHYDRATE

SWORDFISH STEAKS
with Grilled Peppers

24 **OUNCES** SWORDFISH (4 STEAKS)

4 **TABLESPOONS** LEMON JUICE

4 **TABLESPOONS** OLIVE OIL

4 **CLOVES** GARLIC, FINELY CHOPPED

2 **TEASPOONS** DRIED OREGANO

2 **TEASPOONS** DRIED MARJORAM

1 **TEASPOON** GRAPE SEED OIL

8 **CUPS** RED, GREEN, YELLOW PEPPERS, SLICED

SEA SALT & PEPPER TO TASTE

READY TO COOK ⬇⬇⬇

1. **COMBINE** THE LEMON JUICE, OLIVE OIL, GARLIC, OREGANO, MARJORAM, SEA SALT AND PEPPER. 2. **RESERVE** 3 TABLESPOONS OF THE MIX FOR THE PEPPERS IN A SEPARATE BOWL. 3. **MARINATE** THE SWORDFISH FOR ABOUT 30 MINUTES. 4. **REMOVE** FROM THE MARINADE AND PLACE IN A PREHEATED FRYING PAN WITH 1 TEASPOON OF GRAPE SEED OIL AND COOK FOR 5-7 MINUTES EACH SIDE OR UNTIL DONE. 5. **SERVE** WITH GRILLED PEPPERS. 6. **CUT** THE PEPPERS IN HALF AND REMOVE SEEDS AND MEMBRANE. 7. **PLACE** SKIN-SIDE UP UNDER THE OVEN GRILL AND GRILL UNTIL THE SKIN IS CHARRED. 8. **REMOVE** AND ALLOW TO COOL ENOUGH TO HANDLE. 9. **REMOVE** THE SKINS AND SLICE THE PEPPERS INTO STRIPS.

Serve swordfish steaks with grilled peppers on the side topped with reserved marinade.

PER SERVING: 514 CALORIES // 28G FAT // 45G PROTEIN // 12G CARBOHYDRATE

LAYERED LOBSTER
Quiche with Broccoli and Parmesan

1 PREPARED OR STORE-BOUGHT PIE SHELL (*SEE PAGE 397*)

24 OUNCES LOBSTER MEAT, CANNED

1 CUP 35% COOKING CREAM

4 EGGS

1/8 TEASPOON NUTMEG

1/8 TEASPOON CAYENNE PEPPER

1 CUP PARMESAN CHEESE, GRATED

2 CUPS BROCCOLI, CUBED

6 CUPS BABY SPINACH

4 OUNCES LOW FAT LOW CARB HOUSE DRESSING (*SEE PAGE 95*)

SEA SALT & PEPPER TO TASTE

READY TO COOK

1. **COOK** THE PIE SHELL IN A **350°F** OVEN FOR 15 MINUTES. REMOVE AND SET ASIDE.

2. **DRAIN** AND CHOP THE LOBSTER.

3. **BEAT** THE EGGS AND PUT IN A BOWL WITH THE CREAM, NUTMEG, CAYENNE PEPPER, SEA SALT AND PEPPER. STIR WELL.

4. **SPREAD** THE GRATED CHEESE OVER THE BOTTOM OF THE PIE SHELL.

5. **SPREAD** A LAYER OF BROCCOLI OVER THE CHEESE.

6. **DISTRIBUTE** THE LOBSTER EVENLY OVER THE BROCCOLI.

7. **POUR** THE EGG AND MILK MIXTURE OVER THE LOBSTER.

8. **BAKE** IN A **350°F** OVEN FOR 50 MINUTES OR UNTIL THE CENTRE IS "ALMOST" FIRM.

9. **REMOVE** AND ALLOW TO REST FOR 10 MINUTES.

Serve with a spinach salad.

PER SERVING: 521 CALORIES // 26G FAT // 48G PROTEIN // 13G CARBOHYDRATE.

/ 344 /

HAKE FILLETS
with Goat Cheese

32 OUNCES HAKE FILLETS (4 FILLETS)

2 CUPS DICED TOMATOES

1 TABLESPOON FRESH OREGANO, CHOPPED

1 TABLESPOON FRESH CHIVES, CHOPPED

1 TABLESPOON FRESH SAGE, FINELY CHOPPED

1/2 CUP GOAT CHEESE, CRUMBLED

4 CUPS FENNEL, THINLY SLICED

1 TABLESPOON GRAPE SEED OIL

2 TABLESPOONS LEMON JUICE

1 TEASPOON CARAWAY SEEDS

2 CUPS GREEN ONIONS, THINLY SLICED

2 CUPS SWEET RED PEPPERS, THINLY SLICED

SEA SALT & PEPPER TO TASTE

READY TO COOK

1. **COMBINE** THE FENNEL, GREEN ONIONS AND RED PEPPERS IN A BOWL.
2. **DRIZZLE** THE LEMON JUICE AND GRAPE SEED OIL OVER TOP.
3. **STIR** IN THE CARAWAY SEEDS AND ALLOW TO SIT AT ROOM TEMPERATURE FOR 30 MINUTES.
4. **IN** A PAN, COMBINE THE TOMATOES, OREGANO, CHIVES AND SAGE AND SIMMER FOR ABOUT 5 MINUTES.
5. **HEAT** 1 TABLESPOON OF THE OIL IN A LARGE FRYING PAN AND PLACE THE HAKE FILLETS IN THE BOTTOM OF THE PAN, DON'T OVERLAP THE FILLETS.
6. **POUR** THE TOMATOES OVER TOP AND COOK ON **LOW HEAT** FOR ABOUT 15 MINUTES UNTIL THE FISH FLAKES EASILY WITH A FORK.
7. **JUST** BEFORE REMOVING THE FISH FROM THE PAN, SPRINKLE THE GOAT CHEESE OVER TOP AND COOK, COVERED, FOR 1 MINUTE.

Serve with the fennel.

SEAFOOD CASSEROLE

10 OUNCES WHITE FISH, CUBED

10 OUNCES CRAB, CHOPPED (*SEE PAGE 353*)

10 OUNCES SHRIMP, PEELED & DEVEINED (*SEE PAGE 353*)

1 TEASPOON GRAPE SEED OIL

2 TABLESPOONS BUTTER

1 CUP 35% COOKING CREAM

1/8 TEASPOON NUTMEG

8 CUPS CHEDDAR CHEESE, GRATED

8 CUPS MIXED GREEN SALAD

4 OUNCES LOW FAT LOW CARB HOUSE DRESSING (*SEE PAGE 95*)

SEA SALT & PEPPER TO TASTE

READY TO COOK

1. SAUTÉ THE WHITE FISH AND CRAB MEAT IN THE OIL FOR ABOUT 10 MINUTES OR UNTIL DONE.

2. ADD THE SHRIMP AND COOK UNTIL PINK.

3. COMBINE THE CREAM AND NUTMEG IN A PAN AND HEAT, STIRRING CONSTANTLY UNTIL THE SAUCE IS SMOOTH.

4. ADD THE FISH TO THE SAUCE AND POUR INTO A CASSEROLE DISH.

5. SPREAD THE CHEESE EVENLY OVER TOP AND BAKE AT 350°F FOR 30 MINUTES.

SERVE CASSEROLE WITH MIXED GREEN SALAD ON THE SIDE.

A CASSEROLE RICH IN OMEGA 3'S!

PER SERVING: 470 CALORIES // 19G FAT // 44G PROTEIN // 5G CARBOHYDRATE

SOLE
with Avocado and Grapefruit Salsa

24 OUNCES SOLE (4 FILLETS)	**4 TABLESPOONS** GRAPEFRUIT JUICE
1 CUP AVOCADO, SLICED	**2 TEASPOONS** GRAPE SEED OIL
1 CUP GRAPEFRUIT, CHOPPED	**1/2 TEASPOON** HOT PEPPER SAUCE
1 CUP RED ONIONS, FINELY SLICED	**1 TEASPOON** PAPRIKA
1 CUP SWEET RED PEPPERS, FINELY SLICED	**4 CUPS** MIXED GREEN SALAD
2 TABLESPOONS FRESH MINT, CHOPPED	**2 OUNCES** LOW FAT LOW CARB HOUSE DRESSING (*SEE PAGE 95*)
2 TABLESPOONS FRESH CORIANDER, CHOPPED	SEA SALT & PEPPER TO TASTE
2 TABLESPOONS FRESH PARSLEY, CHOPPED	

READY TO COOK

1. **COMBINE** THE AVOCADO, GRAPEFRUIT, RED ONIONS AND RED PEPPERS WITH THE MINT, CORIANDER, GRAPEFRUIT JUICE, HOT PEPPER SAUCE AND 1 TEASPOON OF GRAPE SEED OIL.

2. **TOSS** WELL AND SET ASIDE.

3. **HEAT** THE REMAINING TEASPOON OF OIL IN A PAN AND COOK THE SOLE FILLETS UNTIL THE FISH FLAKES EASILY WITH A FORK.

4. **SPRINKLE** WITH PARSLEY BEFORE SERVING.

Serve sole with avocado and grapefruit salsa, mixed green salad on the side.

TUNA STEAKS
with Herbed Rutabaga

32 OUNCES TUNA (4 STEAKS)

2 TEASPOONS GRAPE SEED OIL

4 CUPS ROASTED RUTABAGA, CUBED

1 FRESH SAGE LEAF, FINELY CHOPPED

1 TABLESPOON FRESH OREGANO, CHOPPED

1 TABLESPOON FRESH CHIVES, CHOPPED

4 CUPS MIXED GREEN SALAD

2 OUNCES LOW FAT LOW CARB HOUSE DRESSING (*SEE PAGE 95*)

SEA SALT & PEPPER TO TASTE

READY TO COOK

1. **BOIL** THE RUTABAGA IN LIGHTLY SALTED WATER UNTIL JUST TENDER.

2. **DRAIN** AND PLACE IN A BOWL.

3. **TOSS** WITH THE SAGE, OREGANO, CHIVES AND 1 TEASPOON OF OIL.

4. **PLACE** ON A COOKIE SHEET AND BAKE AT **375⁰F** FOR 5 MINUTES.

5. **SWITCH** THE OVEN TO **BROIL** AND CONTINUE COOKING FOR ANOTHER 4-6 MINUTES.

6. **BRUSH** THE TUNA STEAKS WITH THE REMAINING TEASPOON OF OIL, SEA SALT AND PEPPER.

7. **PLACE** ON A RACK UNDER THE BROILER AND BROIL 2-3 MINUTES EACH SIDE.

Serve your tuna medium rare or rare and a mixed green salad on the side.

SALMON
with Dill Sauce and Asparagus

24 OUNCES SALMON (4 FILLETS)

2 TEASPOONS GRAPE SEED OIL

1 TEASPOON BUTTER

DASH OF LEMON JUICE

8 CUPS ASPARAGUS, SPEARS

2 TABLESPOONS DRIED OR FRESH DILL

1/4 CUP SOUR CREAM

SEA SALT & PEPPER TO TASTE

READY TO COOK

1. **STEAM** THE ASPARAGUS UNTIL COOKED.

2. **WARM** THE OIL AND BUTTER IN A NON-STICK PAN.

3. **SPRINKLE** SALMON FILLETS WITH SEA SALT AND PEPPER AND PLACE SKIN-SIDE DOWN IN THE PAN.

4. **COOK** AT LOW TEMPERATURE FOR ABOUT 5 MINUTES, UNTIL THE FILLETS ARE COOKED THROUGH.

5. **ADD** A DASH OF LEMON JUICE TO THE PAN.

6. **TURN** OFF THE HEAT, COVER AND LEAVE FOR ANOTHER 5 MINUTES.

7. **MIX** DILL WITH THE SOUR CREAM. STIR WELL.

Serve salmon fillets with fresh salsa on the side.

VERATI**TIPS**
YOU WILL BE ABLE TO SEE HOW MUCH OF THE SALMON
IS COOKED AS IT CHANGES COLOR.

PER SERVING: 469 CALORIES // 26G FAT // 39G PROTEIN // 7G CARBOHYDRATE

ROLLED FLOUNDER
with Creamy Herb Sauce

32 OUNCES FLOUNDER (4 FILLETS)

1 TEASPOON OREGANO

1 TEASPOON LEMON ZEST, GRATED

1 LEMON, JUICE

1/2 CUP 35% COOKING CREAM

2 TABLESPOONS BUTTER

PINCH OF NUTMEG

1 TEASPOON FRESH OREGANO, CHOPPED

1 TEASPOON FRESH MARJORAM, CHOPPED

1 TEASPOON FRESH PARSLEY, CHOPPED

SEA SALT & PEPPER TO TASTE

READY TO COOK

1. **SEASON** THE FLOUNDER FILLETS WITH SEA SALT, PEPPER, OREGANO AND GRATED LEMON ZEST.

2. **ROLL** UP EACH FILLET AND PLACE THEM SEAM-SIDE DOWN IN A BAKING DISH.

3. **DRIZZLE** THE LEMON JUICE OVER THE FISH AND BAKE AT **350°F** FOR 15 MINUTES OR UNTIL THE FISH IS COOKED.

4. **PUT** THE BUTTER IN A SAUCEPAN.

5. **COMBINE** THE CREAM AND CORNSTARCH AND ADD TO THE PAN.

6. **STIR** CONSTANTLY TO PREVENT LUMPING.

7. **ADD** THE SEA SALT, NUTMEG, OREGANO, MARJORAM AND PARSLEY AND CONTINUE TO STIR OVER HEAT UNTIL THE SAUCE IS SMOOTH.

Serve flounder fillets with a spoonful of creamy herb sauce over top and mixed green salad on the side.

VERATI TIPS

IF THE HERB SAUCE SEEMS TOO THICK AFTER ADDING THE CORNSTARCH, JUST POUR A LITTLE MORE MILK INTO THE MIX.

PER SERVING: 345 CALORIES // 16G FAT // 56G PROTEIN // 5G CARBOHYDRATE.

PREPARE SEA FOOD
Shrimps + Clams + Crab

#1 SHRIMP, DEVEINED ⬇⬇⬇

1. LOOK AT THE END OF THE SHRIMP WHERE THE HEAD USED TO BE, THERE SHOULD BE A SMALL FLAP. **2. PULL** THIS FLAP TOWARDS THE TAIL UNTIL IT COMES OFF REVEILING THE "VEIN"; A SMALL BLACK TUBULE. **3. PLACE** THE SHRIMP IN COLD WATER AND WIPE THE VEIN AWAY. IF YOU CAN'T FIND ONE, DON'T WORRY, IT JUST MEANS THAT SHRIMP DIDN'T GET HIS LAST SUPPER!

#2 MUSSELS, DEBEARD ⬇⬇⬇

1. CHECK TO MAKE SURE THEIR SHELLS ARE TIGHTLY CLOSED. **2. DISCARD** MUSSELS WITH CRACKED SHELLS. **3. IF** SOME ARE OPEN, TAP THEM GENTLY AGAINST THE COUNTER. **4. AFTER** A FEW MINUTES DISCARD THE MUSSELS THAT ARE STILL OPEN. **5. LOOK** AT THE CRACK WHERE THE TWO SHELLS MEET, YOU WILL SEE A LITTLE BROWN THREAD. THIS IS "THE BEARD". **6. GRASP** THE BEARD AND PULL IT OUT AND TOWARDS THE HINGE END OF THE MUSSEL. **7. REMOVE** IT COMPLETELY AND DISCARD.

#3 CRAB, PREPARING THE MEAT ⬇⬇⬇

1. PLACE CRAB ON A TABLE, BELLY-SIDE UP. **2. REMOVE** THE ABDOMEN WITH YOUR FINGERS. **3. TURN** OVER AND REMOVE OUTER SHELL BY INSERTING YOUR THUMB BETWEEN THE BODY AND THE SHELL AT REAR OF CRAB AND PULLING THE SHELL UP FIRMLY. **4. TWIST** OFF CLAWS AND LEGS. **5. CRACK** OPEN THE LEG SHELLS USING A NUTCRACKER OR SMALL HAMMER. **6. PICK** OUT MEAT. **7. PULL** OFF THE SPONGY GILLS AND SMALL PADDLES AT THE FRONT OF THE CRAB AND DISCARD. **8. SNAP** THE BODY IN HALF. **9. PICK** OUT MEAT.

NEVER FEAR! IN THE SPIRIT OF LEARNING NEW THINGS... HERE ARE SOME LITTLE TRICKS TO PREPARE YOUR SEAFOOD!
-CHEF VERATI

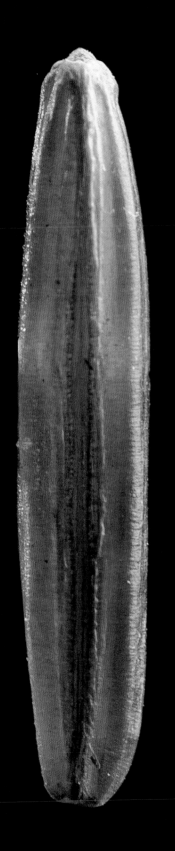

CARBS

↓ ↓ ↓ ↓ ↓ ↓ ↓ ↓ ↓

 FAT

best at dinner time

FACT # 8

ADEQUATE

THE INTAKE OF CARBOHYDRATES BLOCK THE BREAKDOWN OF PROTEIN AND PREVENTS MUSCLE WASTING. TRY ADDING HEALTHY CARBS TO YOUR DAILY DIET. IT IS BEST TO INCORPORATE THEM IN YOUR BREAKFAST AND IN YOUR DINER.

MUSCLES

+

Freedom

TUNA STEAKS
a Bite of Mango Salsa Freedom

24 OUNCES TUNA (4 STEAKS)

2 CUPS FRESH MANGO, CUBED

2 CUPS CUCUMBERS, CUBED

1 CUP RED ONIONS, VERY FINELY SLICED

1/2 CUP FRESH MINT, CHOPPED

1/2 CUP FRESH CORIANDER, CHOPPED

1 CUP SWEET RED PEPPERS, CHOPPED

1 TEASPOON GRAPE SEED OIL

2 TABLESPOONS LIME JUICE

4 CUPS MIXED GREEN SALAD

2 OUNCES LOW FAT LOW CARB HOUSE DRESSING (*SEE PAGE 95*)

SEA SALT & PEPPER TO TASTE

READY TO COOK

1. IN A LARGE BOWL, COMBINE THE MANGO, CUCUMBERS, ONIONS, MINT, CORIANDER AND RED PEPPERS WITH THE LIME JUICE. 2. MIX WELL AND MARINATE FOR 30 MINUTES AT ROOM TEMPERATURE. 3. PREHEAT THE OVEN TO 425° F. 4. SEASON THE TUNA STEAKS WITH SEA SALT, PEPPER AND OIL. 5. PLACE THE TUNA STEAKS ON A RACK IN THE CENTRE OF THE OVEN AND GRILL 2-3 MINUTES EACH SIDE. 6. TURNING ONCE AND BRUSHING WITH MORE OIL IF NECESSARY. 7. SERVE GRILLED TUNA STEAKS ALONGSIDE REFRESHING MANGO SALSA.

▶ MANGO, TANGO, SALSA
ADD SWEETNESS TO EVERYDAY MEALS;
ENJOY EVERY BITE OF *Freedom*
SOME FRUITS CONTAIN MORE SUGAR THAN OTHERS;
GET FAMILIAR WITH THEIR GLYCEMIC INDEX.

PER SERVING: 441 CALORIES // 32G CARBOHYDRATE // 52G PROTEIN // 12G FAT

BAKED COD
with Spicy Tomato Sauce

32 OUNCES COD (4 FILLETS)	**1 TEASPOON** CHILI POWDER (*SEE PAGE 173*)
4 TABLESPOONS FLOUR	**2** BAY LEAVES
1 CUP ONIONS, CHOPPED	**1 TEASPOON** BASIL
1 CUP SWEET RED PEPPERS, SLICED	**1 TEASPOON** OREGANO
2 CUPS TOMATO SAUCE	**1 TEASPOON** LEMON ZEST, GRATED
2 CUPS MUSHROOMS, SLICED	**1 TEASPOON** GRAPE SEED OIL
2 CUPS GREEN PEAS	**2 CUPS** WILD RICE, COOKED
2 CLOVES GARLIC, FINELY CHOPPED	SEA SALT & PEPPER TO TASTE

READY TO COOK

1. **COOK** THE RICE IN WATER ON STOVE TOP, IN A STEAMER OR IN THE MICROWAVE UNTIL THE RICE IS SOFT, ADDING A LITTLE MORE WATER IF NECESSARY.
2. **ADD** SEA SALT AND PEPPER TO FLOUR AND DREDGE PIECES OF COD IN THE MIXTURE.
3. **PLACE** IN AN OVEN PAN AND SET ASIDE.
4. **SAUTÉ** THE ONIONS UNTIL THEY BEGIN TO SOFTEN.
5. **ADD** GARLIC, MUSHROOMS, RED PEPPERS AND SAUTÉ ANOTHER 1-2 MINUTES.
6. **ADD** TOMATO SAUCE, GREEN PEAS, CHILI POWDER, BAY LEAVES, BASIL AND OREGANO.
7. **BRING** TO A BOIL, REDUCE HEAT AND COOK ANOTHER 3 MINUTES.
8. **ADD** LEMON ZEST.
9. **POUR** TOMATO SAUCE OVER THE COD FILLETS.
10. **BAKE** IN THE OVEN AT **350⁰F** FOR 45 MINUTES OR UNTIL FISH FLAKES WHEN TESTED WITH A FORK.

Serve fillets over steamed rice and top with a spoonful of tomato sauce.

PER SERVING: 668 CALORIES // 63G CARBOHYDRATE // 67G PROTEIN // 13G FAT

COD & BEAN
Casserole

1 POUND COD (4 FILLETS)	**1 CUP** TOMATO JUICE
1 CUP WHITE KIDNEY BEANS, COOKED	**1 CUP** VEGETABLE STOCK
2 CUPS ONIONS, CHOPPED	**1 TABLESPOON** FRESH THYME
3 CLOVES GARLIC, FINELY CHOPPED	**1 TABLESPOON** FRESH BASIL
1 CUP CELERY, CHOPPED	**1 TEASPOON** GRAPE SEED OIL
1 CUP CARROTS, SLICED	**2 TABLESPOONS** PARSLEY
2 CUPS POTATOES, PEELED & CUBED	**2 TABLESPOONS** LOW FAT PARMESAN CHEESE
2 CUPS TOMATOES, DICED	SEA SALT & PEPPER TO TASTE

READY TO COOK

1. **HEAT** OIL AND SAUTÉ THE ONIONS AND GARLIC UNTIL JUST SOFTENED.
2. **ADD** CELERY, CARROTS, POTATOES AND TOMATOES, ALONG WITH THEIR JUICE, AND SIMMER FOR 10 MINUTES.
3. **ADD** THYME AND BASIL, AS WELL AS SEA SALT AND PEPPER TO TASTE, AND SIMMER ANOTHER 2-3 MINUTES.
4. **POUR** HALF THE ONIONS AND TOMATO MIXTURE INTO AN OVEN-PROOF DISH.
5. **ADD** HALF THE BEANS.
6. **LAY** THE FISH FILLETS OVER TOP, AND THEN, ADD THE REMAINING BEANS AS WELL AS THE REST OF THE ONIONS AND TOMATO MIXTURE.
7. **POUR** THE VEGETABLE STOCK OVER TOP AND BAKE IN THE OVEN AT **350°F** FOR ABOUT 30 MINUTES.

Serve with a dash of parsley and parmesan cheese over top.

VERATI *Twist*
FOR A VARIATION, TRY RAPINI AND MUSHROOMS INSTEAD OF THE VEGETABLES.

PER SERVING: 679 CALORIES // 59G CARBOHYDRATE // 70G PROTEIN // 7G FAT

BAKED
Fish and Chips

32 OUNCES COD (4 FILLETS)	**2 CUPS** SWEET POTATOES, PEELED & CUT IN WEDGES
4 TABLESPOONS FLOUR	**1 TABLESPOON** OIL
2 TEASPOONS PAPRIKA	**4 CUPS** CABBAGE, GRATED
1 CUP PANKO OR COARSE BREAD CRUMBS	**1** CARROT, GRATED
1 EGG	**2 OUNCES** LOW FAT LOW CARB HOUSE DRESSING (*SEE PAGE 95*)
1 TABLESPOON SKIM MILK	SEA SALT & PEPPER TO TASTE

READY TO COOK

1. **COMBINE** FLOUR, SEA SALT, PEPPER AND PAPRIKA IN A BOWL.
2. **IN** A SEPARATE BOWL, BEAT EGG AND MILK TOGETHER.
3. **PLACE** BREAD CRUMBS ON A FLAT PLATE.
4. **DIP** COD FILLETS INTO FLOUR MIXTURE FIRST, THEN INTO EGG MIXTURE AND FINALLY COAT WITH BREAD CRUMBS.
5. **PLACE** FILLETS ON AN OILED PAN AND BAKE IN THE OVEN AT **400°F** FOR 12 MINUTES.
6. **TURN** FILLETS OVER AND BAKE ANOTHER 10 MINUTES OR UNTIL THE FISH IS COOKED.
7. **TOSS** SWEET POTATOES WITH OIL, REMAINING SEA SALT AND PAPRIKA AND SPREAD EVENLY ON AN OILED BAKING PAN.
8. **BAKE** IN THE OVEN ALONGSIDE THE FISH FOR ABOUT 15 MINUTES OR UNTIL SOFT ON THE INSIDE, CRISP ON THE OUTSIDE.
9. **SLICE** CABBAGE THINLY AND TOSS WITH GRATED CARROTS AND SALAD DRESSING.

Serve hot fillets and crispy baked sweet potatoes along with cabbage and carrot salad.

PER SERVING: 474 CALORIES // 46G CARBOHYDRATE // 48G PROTEIN // 14G FAT

COD CAKES
on Leeks and Onions

24 **OUNCES** COD, COOKED & SHREDDED

1 **TEASPOON** GROUND GINGER

1 EGG

1/2 **CUP** BREAD CRUMBS, FINELY GROUND

1 **CUP** POTATOES, PEELED, COOKED & MASHED

2 **TEASPOONS** GRAPE SEED OIL

4 **CUPS** LEEKS, CHOPPED

4 **CUPS** RED ONIONS, FINELY SLICED

1 **CUP** TOMATO SAUCE

1 **TABLESPOON** FRESH PARSLEY, CHOPPED

SEA SALT & PEPPER TO TASTE

READY TO COOK ⬇⬇⬇

1. IN 1 TABLESPOON OF OIL, SAUTÉ THE ONIONS AND LEEKS, ADDING A TABLESPOON OF WATER TO THE PAN IF THERE IS NOT ENOUGH OIL. **2. COVER** AND SIMMER ABOUT 10 MINUTES UNTIL BOTH LEEKS AND ONIONS ARE SOFT. **3. IN** A LARGE BOWL, COMBINE THE COD, SHREDDED AS FINELY AS POSSIBLE, WITH THE GINGER, EGG, SEA SALT AND PEPPER. **4. ADD** THE MASHED POTATOES AND BLEND AGAIN. **5. FORM** 4 ROUND CAKES WITH THE COD MIXTURE. **6. DREDGE** THE CAKES IN THE BREAD CRUMBS, COATING ALL SIDES. **7. HEAT** 1 TABLESPOON OF OIL IN A FRYING PAN AND COOK THE COD CAKES ON **LOW** HEAT, TURNING TO MAKE SURE THEY BROWN EVENLY ON BOTH SIDES.

Serve cod on top of onion and leek mixture, adding a spoonful of tomato sauce over each cake, and garnish with some chopped parsley.

PER SERVING: 470 CALORIES // 41G CARBOHYDRATE // 45G PROTEIN // 11G FAT

CRISPY MUSTARD
Coating Flounder

32 **OUNCES** FLOUNDER (4 FILLETS)

1 **CUP** PANKO BREAD CRUMBS

4 **TABLESPOONS** GRAINY MUSTARD

1/4 **CUP** SKIM MILK

1 EGG, BEATEN

1 **TEASPOON** ONION POWDER

1 **TABLESPOON** LEMON JUICE

1 **TEASPOON** GRAPE SEED OIL

2 **CUPS** BROWN RICE, COOKED

8 **CUPS** MIXED GREEN SALAD

SEA SALT & PEPPER TO TASTE

READY TO COOK ⬇⬇⬇

1. COOK THE RICE IN WATER ON THE STOVE TOP OR IN THE MICROWAVE UNTIL THE RICE IS SOFT. **2. COMBINE** THE PANKO, SEA SALT AND PEPPER TO TASTE AND ONION POWDER IN A SHALLOW BOWL. **3. IN** ANOTHER BOWL, COMBINE THE EGG AND MILK. **4. COAT** THE FLOUNDER FILLETS ON BOTH SIDES WITH THE MUSTARD. **5. DIP** EACH FILLET INTO THE EGG AND MILK MIXTURE FIRST, THEN INTO THE PANKO MIXTURE. **6. HEAT** THE OIL IN A FRYING PAN AND COOK THE FLOUNDER FILLETS 3 MINUTES PER SIDE, UNTIL THE FILLETS ARE GOLDEN AND THE FISH FLAKES EASILY WITH A FORK.

Serve fish with a drizzle of lemon juice, brown rice and green salad as side dishes.

PER SERVING: 749 CALORIES // 76G CARBOHYDRATE // 62G PROTEIN // 11G FAT

CURRY PERCH
Lentils and Artichoke

20 OUNCES	PERCH (4 FILLETS)
1 CUP	ARTICHOKE HEARTS, MARINATED
1 CUP	GREEN ONIONS, FINELY CHOPPED
1 CUP	LENTILS, COOKED
2 CUPS	SWEET POTATOES, CUBED
1/2 TEASPOON	CAYENNE PEPPER
1 TEASPOON	CUMIN, GROUND
1 TEASPOON	CORIANDER, GROUND
1 TEASPOON	CURRY, POWDER
1 TABLESPOON	OIL
4 CUPS	CAULIFLOWER
SEA SALT & PEPPER TO TASTE	

READY TO COOK ⬇⬇⬇

1. SEASON THE FISH FILLETS WITH SEA SALT, CAYENNE PEPPER, CUMIN, CORIANDER AND CURRY POWDER. **2. PLACE** IN A PRE-HEATED PAN WITH OIL AND COOK FOR 1-2 MINUTES ON EACH SIDE. **3. ADD** THE SWEET POTATOES, LENTILS AND CAULIFLOWER AND SIMMER 8 MINUTES OR UNTIL THE FISH FLAKES WITH A FORK AND THE POTATOES ARE COOKED. **4. ADD** THE ARTICHOKE HEARTS AND HEAT FOR ANOTHER 3-4 MINUTES.

Serve with a handful of green onions on top.

PER SERVING: 492 CALORIES // 58G CARBOHYDRATE // 42G PROTEIN // 10G FAT

MUSSELS LINGUINE
with Tomato Sauce

4 POUNDS	MUSSELS, CLEANSED & DEBEARDED (*SEE PAGE 353*)
1 CUP	ONIONS, FINELY CHOPPED
4 CLOVES	GARLIC, FINELY CHOPPED
1/2 CUP	FRESH BASIL, CHOPPED
1/2 CUP	FRESH PARSLEY, CHOPPED
2 CUPS	TOMATOES, DICED
12 OZ	LINGUINE
1 TEASPOON	GRAPE SEED OIL
6 CUPS	MIXED GREEN SALAD
4 OUNCES	LOW FAT LOW CARB HOUSE DRESSING (*SEE PAGE 95*)
SEA SALT & PEPPER TO TASTE	

READY TO COOK ⬇⬇⬇

1. COOK THE PASTA IN BOILING WATER UNTIL JUST TENDER. DRAIN AND SET ASIDE. **2. IN** A LARGE FRYING PAN, SAUTÉ THE ONIONS AND GARLIC IN 1 TEASPOON OF THE OIL UNTIL BOTH THE ONIONS AND GARLIC ARE SOFT BUT NOT BROWNED. **3. ADD** THE DICED TOMATOES, SEA SALT AND PEPPER, PARSLEY AND BASIL AND COOK FOR ABOUT 5-7 MINUTES. **4. ADD** THE MUSSELS TO THE PAN AND COOK, COVERED, FOR 5 MINUTES. **5. CHECK** TO MAKE SURE ALL THE MUSSELS HAVE OPENED AND DISCARD ANY THAT HAVE NOT. **6. POUR** THE MUSSELS AND SAUCE OVER THE COOKED LINGUINE.

Serve pasta with green salad.

PER SERVING: 633 CALORIES // 57G CARBOHYDRATE // 58G PROTEIN // 12G FAT

PENNE
with Clam Sauce

1 1/2 CUPS PENNE PASTA *(SEE PAGE 215)*	**1 TEASPOON** FRESH THYME
4 POUNDS BABY CLAMS	**1/2 CUP** WHITE WINE
1 CUP TOMATOES, DICED	**1/2 CUP** VEGETABLE BROTH
1 CUP ONIONS, FINELY CHOPPED	**1/2 CUP** LOW FAT PARMESAN CHEESE, GRATED
4 CLOVES GARLIC, FINELY CHOPPED	**1/2 CUP** FRESH PARSLEY, CHOPPED
1 CUP GREEN PEPPERS, CHOPPED	**4 CUPS** ASPARAGUS, SPEARS
1 CUP SWEET RED PEPPERS, CHOPPED	SEA SALT & PEPPER TO TASTE
1/2 TEASPOON DRIED CHILI FLAKES	

READY TO COOK

1. **PUT** THE PENNE IN A LARGE POT WITH BOILING WATER AND COOK UNTIL AL DENTE.

2. **IN** ANOTHER LARGE POT, BRING THE WINE TO A BOIL.

3. **ADD** THE BABY CLAMS AND COOK THEM COVERED FOR ABOUT 5-7 MINUTES, UNTIL OPENED.

4. **RESERVE** THE LIQUID.

5. **IN** LARGE FRYING PAN, COOK THE ONIONS, GARLIC AS WELL AS THE GREEN AND RED PEPPERS UNTIL ONIONS BEGIN TO SOFTEN.

6. **ADD** THE CHILI FLAKES, THYME, DICED TOMATOES AND RESERVED CLAM LIQUID.

7. **CONTINUE** TO COOK FOR 10 MINUTES.

8. **ADD** THE VEGETABLE BROTH AND BRING TO A BOIL.

9. **ADD** THE CLAMS AND COOKED PENNE AND MIX WELL.

10. **STEAM** ASPARAGUS.

Serve penne sprinkled with parmesan cheese and fresh parsley alongside steamed asparagus.

VERATI**TIPS**
AL DENTE MEANS "TO THE TOOTH". WHEN PASTA IS COOKED AL DENTE,
THERE SHOULD BE A SLIGHT RESISTANCE IN THE CENTER OF THE PASTA WHEN CHEWED.

PER SERVING: 490 CALORIES // 71G CARBOHYDRATE // 30G PROTEIN // 7G FAT

CITRUS SWORDFISH
with Waldorf-Style Salad

24 OUNCES SWORDFISH (4 STEAKS)	**2 CUPS** SEEDLESS GRAPES
1 TABLESPOON LIME JUICE	**1/2 CUP** WALNUTS, HALVES
2 TABLESPOONS LEMON JUICE	**1/2 CUP** RAISINS
1/2 CUP PLAIN LOW FAT YOGURT	**2 CUPS** FRESH SPINACH LEAVES
1 TABLESPOON FRESH CORIANDER, CHOPPED	**2 CUPS** FRESH ARUGULA
1 TEASPOON GRAPE SEED OIL	**1/2 CUP** FRESH PARSLEY, CHOPPED
2 CUPS CELERY, CHOPPED	SEA SALT & PEPPER TO TASTE
2 CUPS APPLES, CHOPPED	

READY TO COOK

1. **COMBINE** CELERY, APPLES, WALNUTS, RAISINS, GRAPES AND PARSLEY IN A BOWL.
2. **POUR** YOGURT AND LIME JUICE OVER TOP AND MIX WELL.
3. **ALLOW** TO MARINATE AT ROOM TEMPERATURE WHILE THE FISH IS COOKING.
4. **SEASON** THE SWORDFISH STEAKS WITH SEA SALT AND PEPPER TO TASTE.
5. **HEAT** THE OIL IN A PAN AND COOK THE SWORDFISH FOR ABOUT 5-8 MINUTES PER SIDE.
6. **WHEN** THE FISH IS ALMOST DONE, POUR 2 TABLESPOONS OF LEMON JUICE INTO THE PAN AND CONTINUE TO COOK FOR 1 MINUTE.

Serve hot swordfish on a bed of spinach and arugula leaves, topping fillets with remaining lemon liquid.

4 WHOLE FISH
with Roasted Vegetables

48 OUNCES WHITEFISH (4 FISH)	**2 CUPS** OKRA, WHOLE
1/2 CUP RED ONIONS, THINLY SLICED	**2 CUPS** CAULIFLOWER, CHOPPED
1/2 CUP CELERY LEAVES, CHOPPED	**1 CUP** WHITE ONIONS, QUARTERED
1/2 CUP FRESH PARSLEY, CHOPPED	**1 CUP** SWEET POTATOES, PEELED & CUBED
1 LEMON, THINLY SLICED	**2 CUPS** ASPARAGUS, SPEARS
1/2 TEASPOON FRESH BASIL	**2 TEASPOONS** GRAPE SEED OIL
1 TEASPOON FRESH OREGANO	SEA SALT & PEPPER TO TASTE

READY TO COOK

1. **CLEAN,** SCALE, REMOVE THE HEAD AND WIPE THE INSIDE OF THE FISH WITH A PAPER TOWEL.
2. **PLACE** RED ONIONS, CELERY LEAVES, CHOPPED PARSLEY AND LEMON SLICES EVENLY ALONG THE CAVITY.
3. **LIGHTLY** OIL A PIECE OF HEAVY FOIL AND WRAP THE FISH TIGHTLY.
4. **PLACE** ON A BAKING SHEET AND HEAT IN THE OVEN AT **350⁰F** FOR 45 MINUTES.
5. **PLACE** THE OKRA, CAULIFLOWER, WHITE ONIONS, SWEET POTATOES AND ASPARAGUS IN AN OVEN PAN.
6. **POUR** THE OIL OVER THE VEGETABLES AND ADD BASIL, OREGANO, AS WELL AS SEA SALT AND PEPPER, AND TOSS WELL.
7. **COVER** THE PAN WITH FOIL AND BAKE IN THE OVEN ALONGSIDE THE FISH, REMOVING THE FOIL FOR THE LAST 15 MINUTES.
8. **WHEN** THE FISH IS COOKED, REMOVE FROM THE OVEN AND CAREFULLY OPEN THE FOIL, AVOIDING THE HOT STEAM COMING OUT
OF THE PACKET. CAUTIOUSLY REMOVE THE FISH FROM THE BONES BEFORE SERVING.

Serve the vegetables hot or cold as a salad with the whole fish on the top.

VERATI**TIPS**

WHILE HOLDING THE FISH BY THE TAIL, SCRAPE THE BLADE OF A SHARP KNIFE IN SHORT, SHARP
BURSTS AGAINST THE GRAIN OF THE SCALES AND BACK AGAIN, WORKING THE KNIFE FROM THE TAIL
TO THE HEAD. RINSE THE FISH, THEN SLICE THE LENGTH OF THE BELLY OF THE FISH AND PULL OUT
THE GUTS. CUTTING THEM OUT AT THE TOP. SLICING DOWNWARDS JUST BEHIND THE GILL PLATES,
SEVER THE HEAD. YOU CAN ALSO ASK YOUR LOCAL FISH STORE TO DO IT FOR YOU.

PER SERVING: 680 CALORIES // 51G CARBOHYDRATE // 50G PROTEIN // 21G FAT

SALMON CAKES
with Vegetable Patties

2 CANS PINK PACIFIC SALMON IN WATER	**1/2 CUP** CORNMEAL
1/2 CUP GREEN ONIONS, VERY FINELY CHOPPED	**1** EGG
3 CUPS CAULIFLOWER, CHOPPED	**1 TEASPOON** DRIED DILL
3 CUPS POTATOES, PEELED, CUBED	**1 TABLESPOON** DRIED PARSLEY
8 CUPS MIXED GREEN SALAD	**1 TABLESPOON** LEMON JUICE
4 OUNCES LOW FAT LOW CARB HOUSE DRESSING (*SEE PAGE 95*)	**1 TEASPOON** GRAPE SEED OIL
1/2 CUP FINE BREAD CRUMBS	SEA SALT & PEPPER TO TASTE

READY TO COOK

1. **BOIL** THE CAULIFLOWER AND POTATOES UNTIL COOKED, DRAIN AND RESERVE 1/2 CUP OF THE LIQUID.

2. **ADD** THE PARSLEY, SEA SALT AND PEPPER.

3. **MASH OR BLEND** UNTIL SMOOTH, ADDING SOME OF THE RESERVED LIQUID IF NECESSARY.

4. **WHEN** COOL ENOUGH TO HANDLE, MAKE 4 PATTIES FROM THE MIXTURE AND SET ASIDE.

5. **MIX** THE SALMON, GREEN ONIONS, DILL, EGG, LEMON JUICE, PEPPER TO TASTE AND BREAD CRUMBS.

6. **MASH** UNTIL EVERYTHING IS WELL COMBINED AND FORM INTO 4 PATTIES.

7. **COAT** ALL PATTIES WITH THE CORNMEAL AND FRY IN OIL UNTIL BROWN ON EACH SIDE.

Serve salmon cakes and vegetable patties along with mixed green salad.

WRAPPED TILAPIA
Individual Parchment

24 OUNCES TILAPIA (4 FILLETS)

4 PIECES PARCHMENT PAPER

1 CUP GREEN ONIONS, CHOPPED

1 TABLESPOON LEMON ZEST, GRATED

8 SLICES LEMON, THINLY SLICED

2 TEASPOONS GRAPE SEED OIL

2 CUPS RED ONIONS, THINLY SLICED

1 CUP CELERY, CHOPPED

4 CUPS TOMATOES, DICED

1 CUP TOMATO JUICE

1 TEASPOON FRESH OREGANO

2 CLOVES GARLIC, FINELY CHOPPED

2 CUPS RICE, COOKED

SEA SALT & PEPPER TO TASTE

READY TO COOK

1. **LIGHTLY** OIL THE 4 PIECES OF PARCHMENT PAPER WITH 1 TABLESPOON OF THE GRAPE SEED OIL.

2. **PLACE** A PORTION OF TILAPIA ON EACH PIECE OF PAPER AND EVENLY DISTRIBUTE THE GREEN ONIONS, LEMON ZEST, LEMON SLICES AND PEPPER AMONG THE 4 FILLETS.

3. **FOLD** THE PARCHMENT PAPER AROUND THE TILAPIA TO SEAL THE PACKETS.

4. **PLACE** ON A PAN AND BAKE IN THE OVEN AT **350⁰F** FOR 12-15 MINUTES.

5. **HEAT** 1 TEASPOON OF THE REMAINING GRAPE SEED OIL IN A FRYING PAN.

6. **ADD** THE CELERY AND ONIONS AND SAUTÉ FOR 2-3 MINUTES.

7. **ADD** THE GARLIC AND COOK AN ADDITIONAL MINUTE.

8. **ADD** THE TOMATOES WITH THEIR JUICE AND THE FRESH OREGANO.

9. **BRING** TO A BOIL AND REDUCE HEAT.

10. **COOK** AT LOW HEAT FOR 10 MINUTES OR UNTIL SOME OF THE JUICE HAS REDUCED.

Serve with a spoonful of onion and tomato sauce over each fillet.

ALASKAN POLLOCK
in Chinese-Style Sauce

32 OUNCES ALASKAN POLLOCK (4 FILLETS)

4 PIECES ALUMINUM FOIL

1 CUP RED ONIONS, FINELY SLICED

1" PIECE FRESH GINGER, PEELED & CHOPPED

2 TABLESPOONS LOW-SODIUM SOY SAUCE

2 TABLESPOONS GRAPE SEED OIL

2 TEASPOONS SESAME OIL

1 TABLESPOON SESAME SEEDS

1 CUP BROWN RICE, COOKED

2 1/2 CUPS WATER

1/2 CUP GREEN ONIONS, CHOPPED

4 CUPS MUSHROOMS, SLICED

1 CUP CELERY, CHOPPED

1 CUP SWEET RED PEPPERS, CHOPPED

1 CUP GREEN BELL PEPPERS, CHOPPED

SEA SALT & PEPPER TO TASTE

READY TO COOK

1. **COOK** THE RICE IN WATER ON STOVE TOP OR IN THE MICROWAVE UNTIL THE RICE IS SOFT, ADDING A LITTLE MORE WATER IF NECESSARY. ALLOW IT TO COOL FOR 10 MINUTES.

2. **HEAT** 1 TABLESPOON OF THE GRAPE SEED OIL IN A FRYING PAN AND SAUTÉ THE ONIONS, MUSHROOMS, CELERY AND RED AND GREEN PEPPERS UNTIL THE ONIONS AND CELERY ARE TENDER.

3. **ADD** THE RICE AND 1 TABLESPOON OF SOY SAUCE AND MIX WELL. COOK FOR 2-3 MINUTES, COVER AND TURN OFF THE HEAT.

4. **ALLOW** TO REST, COVERED, UNTIL THE FISH IS READY TO BE SERVED.

5. **SEASON** THE FISH WITH SEA SALT AND PEPPER AND DIVIDE INTO 4 PORTIONS.

6. **PREPARE** 4 PIECES OF ALUMINUM FOIL LARGE ENOUGH TO WRAP EACH OF THE FISH PORTIONS.

7. **BRUSH** A LITTLE OF THE REMAINING GRAPE SEED OIL ON EACH OF THE PIECES OF FOIL.

8. **LAY** THE FISH ON THE FOIL AND COVER WITH THE RED ONIONS, CHOPPED GINGER AND SESAME SEEDS.

9. **SPRINKLE** THE REMAINING SOY SAUCE OVER THE FISH AND SEAL INSIDE THE ALUMINUM FOIL.

10. **BAKE** IN THE OVEN AT **350º F** FOR 10-15 MINUTES.

Serve the fillets with a dash of sesame oil and mushroom fried rice on the side.

PER SERVING: 726 CALORIES // 63G CARBOHYDRATE // 39G PROTEIN // 19G FAT

CHEF
VERATi.

YOU DON'T WANT TO WASTE
A DROP OF THAT YOGURT SAUCE! LOL
-CHEF VERATI

MEDITERRANEAN TUNA
with Two-Beans and Potato Salad

20 OUNCES TUNA (4 STEAKS)	**1 TABLESPOON** CAPERS
4 1/2 POTATOES, PEELED & QUARTERED	**1 TABLESPOON** GRAINY DIJON MUSTARD
2 CUPS GREEN BEANS	**2 TEASPOONS** OREGANO
1 CUP GREEN ONIONS, CHOPPED	**2 TEASPOONS** THYME
1/2 CUP BLACK OLIVES	**1/8 TEASPOON** ALLSPICE
1 CUP LOW FAT FETA CHEESE	**1 TEASPOON** OLIVE OIL
1 CUP WHITE KIDNEY BEANS, COOKED	**1 TEASPOON** LEMON JUICE
1/2 CUP LOW FAT GREEK YOGURT	SEA SALT & PEPPER TO TASTE

READY TO COOK

1. **COMBINE** THE OREGANO, THYME, ALLSPICE, OLIVE OIL, LEMON JUICE, SEA SALT AND PEPPER IN A BOWL.
2. **COAT** THE TUNA STEAKS WITH THE MIXTURE.
3. **GRILL OR BROIL** THE TUNA STEAKS FOR 3 MINUTES PER SIDE OR BAKE FOR 7-10 MINUTES IN THE OVEN AT **375⁰ F**.
4. **COOK** THE POTATOES AND GREEN BEANS UNTIL JUST TENDER.
5. **DRAIN** AND PUT IN A LARGE BOWL.
6. **ADD** THE CHOPPED GREEN ONIONS, OLIVES, FETA CHEESE AND WHITE KIDNEY BEANS.
7. **ADD** THE YOGURT, CAPERS, MUSTARD, SEA SALT AND PEPPER AND TOSS TO COAT WELL.

Serve tuna steaks with warm two-beans and potato salad as a side dish.

PER SERVING: 716 CALORIES // 56G CARBOHYDRATE // 63G PROTEIN // 14G FAT

SOLE FILLETS & VEGGIE RICE
with a Creamy Ginger Soy Sauce

32 OUNCES SOLE (4 FILLETS)

2 TABLESPOONS LOW SODIUM SOY SAUCE

2" PIECE FRESH GINGER, PEELED & CHOPPED

2 TABLESPOONS VINEGAR

1 TEASPOON BROWN SUGAR

2 TABLESPOONS GRAPE SEED OIL

1 CUP BROWN RICE, COOKED

2 CUPS MUSHROOMS, SLICED

1 CUP SWEET RED PEPPERS, SLICED

1 CUP GREEN BELL PEPPERS, SLICED

2 CUPS FRESH SNOW PEAS, WHOLE

1 CUP GREEN ONIONS, CHOPPED

1/4 CUP SESAME SEEDS

1 TEASPOON SESAME OIL

SEA SALT& PEPPER TO TASTE

READY TO COOK

1. **HEAT** THE GINGER, SOY SAUCE, VINEGAR AND BROWN SUGAR IN A SMALL PAN FOR ABOUT 5 MINUTES. REMOVE FROM THE HEAT AND SET ASIDE.

2. **COOK** THE RICE IN WATER ON THE STOVE TOP OR IN THE MICROWAVE UNTIL THE RICE IS SOFT, ADDING A LITTLE MORE WATER IF NECESSARY.

3. **BLANCH** THE SNOW PEAS UNTIL TENDER AND DRAIN.

4. **IN** A FRYING PAN, SAUTÉ THE MUSHROOMS FOR 2-3 MINUTES IN 1 TABLESPOON GRAPE SEED OIL.

5. **ADD** THE SNOW PEAS WITH THE RED AND GREEN PEPPERS AND SAUTÉ ANOTHER FEW MINUTES, STIRRING OCCASIONALLY.

6. **REMOVE** FROM HEAT, COVER AND KEEP WARM.

7. **HEAT** THE GRAPE SEED OIL IN A PAN.

8. **SEASON** THE SOLE FILLETS WITH SEA SALT AND PEPPER AND BROWN QUICKLY ON BOTH SIDES.

9. **POUR** THE GINGER SAUCE OVER THE FISH AND SIMMER FOR 5-7 MINUTES OR UNTIL THE FISH IS COOKED.

Serve fillets with a hint of ginger sauce and a spoonful of vegetable mixture over cooked rice.
Top with a sprinkling of sesame seeds and a dash of sesame oil.

PER SERVING: 487 CALORIES // 23G CARBOHYDRATE // 63G PROTEIN // 11G FAT

CURRIED SHRIMP
with Snow Peas

32 **OUNCES** SHRIMP, PEELED & DEVEINED (*SEE PAGE 353*)

1 **CUP** ONIONS, CHOPPED

4 **CLOVES** GARLIC, FINELY CHOPPED

2 **CUPS** SWEET RED PEPPERS, CUBED

4 **CUPS** SNOW PEAS

1 **CUP** FRESH TOMATOES, DICED

1 **TABLESPOON** TOMATO PASTE

1 **TEASPOON** CHILI POWDER (*SEE PAGE 173*)

1 **TEASPOON** CORIANDER, GROUND

3 **TABLESPOONS** FRESH CORIANDER, CHOPPED

1/2 **CUP** COCONUT MILK

1 **TABLESPOON** GRAPE SEED OIL

2 **CUPS** RICE, COOKED

SEA SALT & PEPPER TO TASTE

READY TO COOK

1. **COOK** THE RICE IN WATER ON THE STOVE TOP OR IN THE MICROWAVE UNTIL THE RICE IS SOFT, ADDING A LITTLE MORE WATER IF NECESSARY.

2. **HEAT** THE OIL AND SAUTÉ THE ONIONS AND GARLIC UNTIL SOFT.

3. **ADD** THE TOMATOES AND COOK ON MEDIUM HEAT FOR 3-4 MINUTES.

4. **STIR** IN THE CHILI POWDER AND GROUND CORIANDER.

5. **ADD** THE RED AND GREEN PEPPERS AND COOK ANOTHER 3-4 MINUTES, STIRRING OCCASIONALLY.

6. **ADD** THE SHRIMP AND THE COCONUT MILK AND COOK FOR 2-3 MINUTES UNTIL THE SHRIMP ARE DONE.

Serve shrimp with a sprinkle of chopped fresh coriander on top alongside steamed rice.

PER SERVING: 771 CALORIES // 63G CARBOHYDRATE // 56G PROTEIN // 14G FAT

POLLOCK FILLET
Carrots and Spinach

32 OUNCES POLLOCK (4 FILLETS)

1 CUP RED ONIONS, SLICED IN ROUNDS

2 CLOVES GARLIC, FINELY CHOPPED

3 CUPS CARROTS, THINLY SLICED

4 CUPS FRESH SPINACH

1 CUP WILD RICE, COOKED

1 CUP LONG GRAIN RICE, COOKED

2 TEASPOONS BUTTER

1 TABLESPOON CORNMEAL

1 TABLESPOON LEMON JUICE

2 TEASPOONS LEMON, ZEST

1 TEASPOON TARRAGON

SEA SALT & PEPPER TO TASTE

READY TO COOK ↓↓↓

1. MARINATE THE POLLOCK FILLETS IN LEMON JUICE FOR 30 MINUTES. **2. COOK** THE RICE IN WATER ON THE STOVE TOP OR IN THE MICROWAVE UNTIL THE RICE IS SOFT. **3. IN** BOILING WATER, ADD THE CARROTS FOR 3-4 MINUTES. **4. DRAIN** AND SET SIDE. **5. HEAT** THE BUTTER IN A FRYING PAN AND COOK THE ONIONS FOR 2-3 MINUTES UNTIL THEY BEGIN TO SOFTEN. **6. ADD** THE GARLIC AND COOK FOR 1 MINUTE. **7. SEASON** THE POLLOCK WITH TARRAGON, SEA SALT, PEPPER AND CORNMEAL. **8. PLACE** IN THE PAN WITH THE ONIONS AND GARLIC. **9. PLACE** THE CARROTS OVER TOP. **10. ADD** THE VEGETABLE BROTH. **11. SIMMER** FOR 6-7 MINUTES OR UNTIL THE POLLOCK FLAKES EASILY WITH A FORK. **12. PLACE** THE FRESH SPINACH ON TOP OF THE POLLOCK AND COOK, COVERED, FOR 2 MINUTES UNTIL THE SPINACH IS WILTED.

Serve the fillets with a dash of lemon zest over top, alongside steamed long grain and wild rice.

PER SERVING: 425 CALORIES // 38G CARBOHYDRATE // 48 PROTEIN // 6G FAT

TILAPIA BEANS
Chipotle Sauce

20 OUNCES TILAPIA (4 FILLETS)

1 CUP BLACK BEANS, COOKED

4 CUPS SNOW PEAS

2 CUPS RED PEPPERS

1 CUP GREEN ONIONS

1 CHIPOTLE PEPPER, CHOPPED

1 CUP TOMATO SAUCE

1 TEASPOON GROUND GINGER

1 TEASPOON LEMON JUICE

1 TEASPOON GRAPE SEED OIL

SEA SALT & PEPPER TO TASTE

READY TO COOK ↓↓↓

1. IN A SAUCEPAN, COMBINE THE BLACK BEANS AND THEIR LIQUID WITH THE CHIPOTLE PEPPER, GINGER AND LEMON JUICE. **2. SIMMER** FOR 5 MINUTES. **3. ADD** THE SNOW PEAS AND COOK ON MEDIUM HEAT UNTIL THE SNOW PEAS ARE COOKED. **4. SEASON** THE TILAPIA FILLETS WITH SEA SALT AND PEPPER TO TASTE. **5. HEAT** THE OIL IN A FRYING PAN AND COOK THE FILLETS FOR 4-5 MINUTES, TURNING OVER ONCE. THE FISH SHOULD FLAKE EASILY WITH A FORK WHEN IT IS COOKED.

Serve fillets with a spoonful of black bean and chipotle sauce on top.

PER SERVING: 477 CALORIES // 49G CARBOHYDRATE // 42G PROTEIN // 5G FAT

TILAPIA FILLETS
with Chipotle Pepper

24 OUNCES TILAPIA (4 FILLETS)

1 CUP ONIONS, CHOPPED

2 CUPS SWEET POTATOES, PEELED, COOKED & MASHED

4 CUPS GREEN BEANS

1 CUP FRESH TOMATOES, DICED

2 CLOVES GARLIC, FINELY CHOPPED

2 TEASPOONS SMOKED PAPRIKA

1/4 TEASPOON CHIPOTLE PEPPERS

2 TABLESPOONS LEMON JUICE

1 TEASPOON GRAPE SEED OIL

SEA SALT & PEPPER TO TASTE

READY TO COOK ↓↓↓

1. HEAT THE OIL IN A FRYING PAN AND SAUTÉ THE ONION AND GARLIC UNTIL SOFT. **2. SEASON** THE TILAPIA WITH THE SMOKED PAPRIKA AND SAUTÉ IN THE SAME PAN FOR 2-3 MINUTES ON EACH SIDE. **3. ADD** THE DICED TOMATOES, LEMON JUICE AND CHIPOTLE PEPPERS. **4. SIMMER**, COVERED, FOR 5 MINUTES.

Serve with mashed sweet potatoes and steamed fresh green beans.

PER SERVING: 487 CALORIES // 38G CARBOHYDRATE // 38G PROTEIN // 4G FAT

CHILL SCALLOPS
Stir-Fry

24 OUNCES SCALLOPS	2 CUPS CARROTS, CUT IN STRIPS
2 TABLESPOONS FLOUR	2 CUPS FRESH FENNEL, SLICED THINLY
2 TEASPOONS OIL	1 CUP SWEET KERNEL CORN
4 CLOVES GARLIC, FINELY CHOPPED	1 CUP VEGETABLE BROTH OR CHICKEN STOCK
1 CUP SWEET RED PEPPERS, SLICED	1 TEASPOON CHILI POWDER *(SEE PAGE 173)*
1 CUP GREEN BELL PEPPERS, SLICED	2 TABLESPOONS LEMON JUICE
1 CUP GREEN ONIONS, CHOPPED	SEA SALT & PEPPER TO TASTE

READY TO COOK

1. BRING A SMALL POT OF WATER TO A BOIL.
2. ADD CARROTS AND FENNEL AND COOK FOR 2 MINUTES.
3. REMOVE FROM HEAT AND DRAIN.
4. COMBINE SEA SALT, CHILI POWDER AND FLOUR IN A BOWL AND DUST THE SCALLOPS WITH THE MIXTURE.
5. HEAT THE OIL IN A FRYING PAN AND SAUTÉ THE GARLIC FOR 2 MINUTES.
6. ADD THE SCALLOPS AND COOK FOR ANOTHER 2-3 MINUTES.
7. REMOVE THE SCALLOPS FROM THE PAN.
8. ADD THE RED AND GREEN PEPPERS, BOILED CARROTS, FENNEL AND CORN TO THE PAN ALONG WITH THE VEGETABLE BROTH.
9. BRING TO A BOIL AND REDUCE HEAT.
10. RETURN THE SCALLOPS TO THE PAN AND SIMMER FOR 1-2 MINUTES.

SERVE SCALLOPS AND VEGETABLES WITH A DRIZZLE OF LEMON JUICE ON TOP.

PER SERVING: 394 CALORIES // 39G CARBOHYDRATE // 44G PROTEIN // 7G FAT

QUICK SALMON
and Pasta Casserole

2 CUPS SALMON, CANNED

12 OUNCES WHOLE WHEAT PASTA (SEE PAGE 215)

1 CUP GREEN ONIONS, CHOPPED

4 CUPS FROZEN MIXED VEGETABLES

3 CUPS CHERRY TOMATOES, CUT IN HALF

2 CUPS SKIM MILK

2 TABLESPOONS CORN STARCH

1 TEASPOON GRAPE SEED OIL

1 TABLESPOON BUTTER

2 TABLESPOONS LOW FAT PARMESAN CHEESE

4 CLOVES GARLIC, FINELY CHOPPED

1/8 TEASPOON NUTMEG

SEA SALT & PEPPER TO TASTE

READY TO COOK ⬇ ⬇ ⬇

1. COOK THE PASTA UNTIL JUST TENDER, DRAIN, AND SET ASIDE. **2. PLACE** THE FROZEN VEGETABLES IN THE POT WITH THE WATER AND BRING THE WATER TO A BOIL. **3. COVER** THE POT AND SIMMER FOR ABOUT 4 TO 7 MINUTES. **4. DRAIN**, RESERVING SOME OF THE LIQUID. **5. COMBINE** THE PASTA AND VEGETABLES. **6. HEAT** THE OIL IN A PAN AND SAUTÉ THE GARLIC FOR 1 MINUTE. **7. ADD** THE GREEN ONIONS AND COOK ANOTHER MINUTE. **8. ADD** THE GARLIC AND ONIONS TO THE PASTA AND VEGETABLES. **9. MELT** THE BUTTER IN A SAUCE PAN. **10. BLEND** THE CORN STARCH INTO THE MILK AND ADD TO THE PAN WITH THE BUTTER. **11. STIR** CONSTANTLY UNTIL THE SAUCE BEGINS TO THICKEN. **12. ADD** THE SALMON, SEA SALT, PEPPER AND NUTMEG AND CONTINUE TO STIR UNTIL THE SALMON IS HEATED. **13. POUR** THE SAUCE OVER THE PASTA AND VEGETABLE MIXTURE AND MIX WELL. **14. STIR** IN THE CHERRY TOMATOES.

Serve with a sprinkle of parmesan cheese if desired.

PER SERVING: 791 CALORIES // 72G CARBOHYDRATE // 51G PROTEIN // 21G FAT

SOLE FILLETS
Lemon and Garlic

32 OUNCES SOLE (4 FILLETS)

1 CUP WHOLE WHEAT COUSCOUS

8 CUPS ASPARAGUS, SPEARS & BLANCHED (SEE PAGE 129)

1 TEASPOON GRAPE SEED OIL

4 CLOVES GARLIC, FINELY CHOPPED

3 TABLESPOONS LEMON JUICE

4 TABLESPOONS FRESH DILL

SEA SALT & PEPPER TO TASTE

READY TO COOK ⬇ ⬇ ⬇

1. PUT THE COUSCOUS IN A BOWL AND POUR IN BOILING WATER TO COVER. **2. ALLOW** TO SIT FOR 10 MINUTES UNTIL THE COUSCOUS HAS ABSORBED ALL THE WATER. **3. SEASON** WITH SEA SALT AND PEPPER AND FOLD IN THE FRESH DILL. **4. IN** ANOTHER BOWL, COMBINE LEMON JUICE, OIL AND GARLIC. **5. PLACE** THE FISH FILLETS ON A BAKING SHEET, MAKING SURE THAT THEY DO NOT OVERLAP. **6. POUR** THE LEMON, OIL AND GARLIC MIXTURE OVER TOP. **7. BROIL** FOR ABOUT 10-12 MINUTES OR UNTIL THE FISH IS COOKED.

Serve with couscous and asparagus, adding more flavor by pouring any remaining sauce.

PER SERVING: 537 CALORIES // 42G CARBOHYDRATE // 68G PROTEIN // 8G FAT

SHRIMP LINGUINE
Rosée Sauce

24 **OUNCES** SHRIMP, PEELED & DEVEINED (*SEE PAGE 353*)

12 **OZ** PACKAGE OF LINGUINE

1/2 **CUP** LOW FAT GOAT CHEESE

3 **CUPS** CHERRY TOMATOES, HALVES

1 **CUP** GREEN ONIONS, CHOPPED

3 **TABLESPOONS** CAPERS

4 **CUPS** MIXED GREEN SALAD

2 **OUNCES** LOW FAT LOW CARB HOUSE DRESSING (*SEE PAGE 95*)

3 **CLOVES** GARLIC, FINELY CHOPPED

1 **TEASPOON** OLIVE OIL

1 **TEASPOON** OREGANO

1 **TEASPOON** MARJORAM

1 **TEASPOON** BASIL

READY TO COOK ⬇ ⬇ ⬇

1. **COMBINE** THE GOAT CHEESE WITH TOMATOES, CAPERS, OREGANO, MARJORAM, BASIL, SEA SALT, PEPPER AND HALF THE AMOUNT OF GARLIC IN A BOWL AND ALLOW TO MARINATE FOR 30 MINUTES OR LONGER, STIRRING OCCASIONALLY. 2. **COOK** THE LINGUINE UNTIL JUST TENDER. 3. **DRAIN** AND KEEP WARM. 4. **HEAT** OIL IN A PAN AND SAUTÉ THE REMAINING GARLIC FOR 1 MINUTE. 5. **ADD** THE SHRIMP AND COOK UNTIL THEY TURN PINK. 6. **ADD** THE MARINADE AND GREEN ONIONS TO THE PAN AND STIR WELL.

Serve shrimp on a bed of linguine along with the green salad and house dressing as a side dish.

PER SERVING: 594 CALORIES // 49G CARBOHYDRATE // 51G PROTEIN // 12G FAT

COD FILLETS & RAPINI
with Kidney Beans

24 **OUNCES** COD FILLETS

4 **CUPS** RAPINI, CHOPPED

1 **CUP** ONIONS, CHOPPED

4 **CLOVES** GARLIC, FINELY CHOPPED

1 **CUP** MUSHROOMS, SLICED

1 **CUP** VEGETABLE STOCK

1 **CUP** COOKED WHITE KIDNEY BEANS

1 **CUP** FRESH TOMATOES, CHOPPED.

1 **TEASPOON** GRAPE SEED OIL

1 LEMON, WEDGES

SEA SALT & PEPPER TO TASTE

READY TO COOK ⬇ ⬇ ⬇

1. **HEAT** THE OIL IN A PAN AND SAUTÉ THE ONIONS AND GARLIC UNTIL THE ONIONS BEGINS TO SOFTEN. 2. **ADD** THE MUSHROOMS AND SAUTÉ ANOTHER 2-3 MINUTES. 3. **ADD** THE TOMATOES, THE KIDNEY BEANS AND VEGETABLE STOCK. 4. **SIMMER** FOR 10 MINUTES. 5. **ADD** THE COD FILLETS, RAPINI AND COOK, COVERED FOR ANOTHER 15 MINUTES OR UNTIL THE FISH FLAKES EASILY WITH A FORK.

Serve with lemon wedges.

PER SERVING: 424 CALORIES // 37G CARBOHYDRATE // 46G PROTEIN // 9G FAT

CHEF
VERATi.
My creative team... what a team...
That is all I have to say...
-Chef Verati

ROASTED GARLIC SHRIMP
with Wild Rice and Green Salad

32 OUNCES SHRIMP, PEELED & DEVEINED (*SEE PAGE 353*)

2 HEADS OF GARLIC

2 CUPS WILD RICE, COOKED

2 CUPS VEGETABLE BROTH OR WATER

1 CUP ONIONS, CHOPPED

1/2 TEASPOON LEMON ZEST, GRATED

2 TABLESPOONS LEMON JUICE

1 TEASPOON OIL

1 TABLESPOON BUTTER

8 CUPS MIXED GREEN SALAD

4 OUNCES LOW FAT LOW CARB HOUSE DRESSING (*SEE PAGE 95*)

SEA SALT & PEPPER TO TASTE

READY TO COOK

1. **WRAP** THE HEADS OF GARLIC IN FOIL AND ROAST IN THE OVEN AT **400°F** FOR 35 MINUTES.
2. **REMOVE** FROM THE OVEN AND, WHEN COOL ENOUGH TO HANDLE, SQUEEZE THE SOFT GARLIC INTO A BOWL.
3. **ADD** THE LEMON JUICE AND MIX WELL.
4. **HEAT** THE OIL IN A FRYING PAN AND SAUTÉ THE ONIONS UNTIL SOFT.
5. **ADD** THE WILD RICE AND STIR WELL.
6. **ADD** THE VEGETABLE BROTH OR WATER, SEA SALT AND PEPPER.
7. **BRING** TO A BOIL, THEN REDUCE THE HEAT, COVER AND SIMMER FOR 45-50 MINUTES OR UNTIL THE RICE IS TENDER. SET ASIDE.
8. **MELT** THE BUTTER IN A MEDIUM HOT PAN AND SAUTÉ THE SHRIMP UNTIL THEIR COLOR CHANGES FROM GRAY TO PINK.
9. **ADD** THE LEMON JUICE AND GARLIC MIXTURE TO THE PAN AND COOK FOR ANOTHER 1-2 MINUTES.

Serve shrimp with a sprinkle of lemon zest and wild rice and green salad as side dishes.

VERATITRICK

RICE CAN EASILY BE COOKED IN A MICROWAVE. ADD THE VEGETABLE BROTH OR WATER, SEA SALT AND PEPPER AND MICROWAVE ON HIGH IN FOUR MINUTE INCREMENTS UNTIL THE RICE IS COOKED, ADDING MORE WATER OR BROTH IF NECESSARY.

PER SERVING: 539 CALORIES // 56G CARBOHYDRATE // 57G PROTEIN // 6G FAT

HADDOCK & BARLEY
Hot Pot

2 **POUNDS** HADDOCK, CUBED	1 1/2 **CUPS** PEARL BARLEY
1 **CUP** ONIONS, CHOPPED	4 **CUPS** VEGETABLE STOCK
4 **CLOVES** GARLIC, FINELY CHOPPED	1 **TEASPOON** THYME
1 **CUP** CARROTS, SLICED	1 **TEASPOON** CHILI POWDER (*SEE PAGE 173*)
2 **CUPS** LEEKS, CHOPPED	1 **TEASPOON** PAPRIKA
1 **CUP** KERNEL CORN	1 **TEASPOON** PARSLEY
1 **CUP** PEAS	1 **TEASPOON** GRAPE SEED OIL
2 **CUPS** FRESH SPINACH, CHOPPED THINLY	SEA SALT & PEPPER TO TASTE

READY TO COOK

1. **HEAT** THE OIL IN A PAN AND SAUTÉ THE ONIONS AND LEEKS UNTIL SOFT.
2. **ADD** THE GARLIC AND COOK ANOTHER 2 MINUTES.
3. **PUT** THE ONIONS, LEEKS AND GARLIC INTO AN OVEN-PROOF PAN.
4. **LAY** THE HADDOCK PIECES ON TOP.
5. **ADD** THE CARROTS, CORN, PEAS, THYME, CHILI POWDER, PAPRIKA, SEA SALT AND PEPPER.
6. **ADD** THE BARLEY AND POUR THE VEGETABLE STOCK OVER TOP.
7. **COVER** AND BAKE IN THE OVEN AT **350⁰ F** FOR 50 MINUTES.
8. **REMOVE** THE COVER AFTER 50 MINUTES AND CHECK THE BARLEY FOR SOFTNESS.
9. **ADD** THE CHOPPED SPINACH AND PARSLEY AND STIR.
10. **COVER** AND COOK ANOTHER 10 MINUTES.

Serve in a cooking pan, it will become comfort food!

HADDOCK CHILI TOMATOES
with Seasoned Sweet Potatoes

32 OUNCES HADDOCK (4 FILLETS)

4 SHEETS HEAVY ALUMINUM FOIL

4 CLOVES GARLIC, FINELY CHOPPED

2 CUPS TOMATOES, DICED

2 TABLESPOONS CAPERS

1/4 TEASPOON CHILI POWDER (*SEE PAGE 173*)

1 TEASPOON LEMON JUICE

1 TEASPOON LEMON ZEST, GRATED

2 TEASPOONS GRAPE SEED OIL

6 CUPS SWEET POTATOES, PEEL & CUT IN WEDGES

1 TEASPOON OREGANO

1 TEASPOON BASIL

4 CUPS MIXED GREEN SALAD

2 OUNCES LOW FAT LOW CARB HOUSE DRESSING (*SEE PAGE 95*)

SEA SALT & PEPPER TO TASTE

READY TO COOK

1. **IN** A BOWL, COMBINE THE CHOPPED GARLIC, TOMATOES, CAPERS, CHILI POWDER, LEMON JUICE, LEMON ZEST, SEA SALT AND PEPPER.

2. **BRUSH** THE HADDOCK FILLETS WITH OIL AND PLACE ONE ON EACH OF THE SHEETS OF ALUMINUM FOIL.

3. **DIVIDE** THE TOMATO MIXTURE EVENLY AMONG THE 4 FILLETS AND SEAL THE FOIL FIRMLY AROUND EACH ONE.

4. **PLACE** THE 4 PACKETS ON AN OVEN SHEET AND BAKE IN THE OVEN AT **350⁰ F** FOR 20-25 MINUTES.

5. **SEASON** SWEET POTATOES WITH THE OREGANO, BASIL AND REMAINING OIL.

6. **PLACE** ON A COOKIE SHEET SO THAT THE POTATOES DO NOT OVERLAP.

7. **BAKE** 20-25 MINUTES IN THE OVEN ALONGSIDE THE FISH, TURNING ONCE.

Serve haddock fillets along with sweet potato wedges and green salad.

HOT POT
Scallop

20 OUNCES SCALLOPS	1 CUP POTATOES, DICED
6 STRIPS TURKEY BACON	2 TABLESPOONS GRAPE SEED OIL
2 CUPS ONIONS, CHOPPED	1 TEASPOON LEMON JUICE
1 CUP CELERY, CHOPPED	2 TABLESPOONS DRIED PARSLEY
1 CUP CARROTS, CUBED	1/2 CUP COCONUT MILK
1 CUP KERNEL CORN	1 CUP WATER OR CHICKEN BROTH
1 CAN PALM HEARTS, CUT IN 1" PIECES	SEA SALT & PEPPER TO TASTE
1 CUP FRESH TOMATOES, CHOPPED	

READY TO COOK

1. HEAT THE OIL IN A FRYING PAN AND SAUTE THE SCALLOPS OVER HIGH HEAT FOR 1 MINUTE.

2. REMOVE FROM THE PAN IMMEDIATELY AND KEEP WARM.

3. CUT THE BACON STRIPS IN HALF AND COOK IN THE SAME FRYING PAN UNTIL JUST CRISP.

4. REMOVE FROM THE PAN.

5. ADD THE ONIONS AND COOK FOR 2-3 MINUTES.

6. PLACE THE CELERY, CARROTS, CORN, FRESH TOMATOES AND DICED POTATOES IN THE PAN.

7. ADD THE CHICKEN BROTH AND SIMMER FOR 15 MINUTES UNTIL THE CARROTS, CELERY AND POTATOES ARE COOKED.

8. ADD THE SCALLOPS, BACON, PALM HEARTS AND COCONUT MILK AND REHEAT FOR 2-3 MINUTES.

SERVE THE HOT POT WITH A DASH OF LEMON JUICE AND GARNISH WITH PARSLEY.

PER SERVING: 490 CALORIES // 30G CARBOHYDRATE // 37G PROTEIN // 15G FAT

PERCH FILLETS
with Sweet Potato Cakes

24 OUNCES PERCH (4 FILLETS)

1 CUP ONIONS, SLICED

4 CLOVES GARLIC, FINELY CHOPPED

1 CUP SWEET RED PEPPERS, SLICED

1 CUP YELLOW PEPPERS, SLICED

1 CUP GREEN PEPPERS, SLICED

4 CUPS SWEET POTATOES, PEELED & CUBED

4 CUPS MIXED GREEN SALAD

2 OUNCES LOW FAT LOW CARB HOUSE DRESSING (*SEE PAGE 95*)

2 TEASPOONS GRAPE SEED OIL

1/4 CUP CORN MEAL

1 TEASPOON FRESH THYME, LEAVES

1 TEASPOON FRESH OREGANO, FINELY CHOPPED

1 TEASPOON FRESH SAGE, FINELY CHOPPED

1 TEASPOON GARLIC POWDER

1 TEASPOON ONION SALT

1 TEASPOON GROUND GINGER

1/8 TEASPOON ALLSPICE

SEA SALT & PEPPER TO TASTE

READY TO COOK

1. **HEAT** OIL IN A PAN AND SAUTÉ ONIONS AND GARLIC FOR 1-2 MINUTES.

2. **ADD** THE RED, YELLOW AND GREEN PEPPERS AND SAUTÉ AN ADDITIONAL 2 MINUTES.

3. **IN** A BOWL, COMBINE THE THYME, OREGANO, SAGE, GARLIC POWDER AND ONION SALT.

4. **COAT** THE PERCH FILLETS WITH THE MIXTURE ON BOTH SIDES.

5. **ADD** TO THE PAN WITH THE ONIONS, GARLIC AND PEPPERS.

6. **SIMMER** COVERED, FOR 7-8 MINUTES.

7. **COOK** THE SWEET POTATOES IN BOILING WATER, FOR 10 MINUTES.

8. **DRAIN** AND MASH, ADDING SEA SALT, PEPPER, GINGER AND ALLSPICE.

9. **FORM** INTO 4 PATTIES AND DREDGE IN CORN MEAL.

10. **HEAT** OIL IN PAN AND BROWN FOR 2-3 MINUTES EACH SIDE.

Serve the perch fillet on top of the potato cakes.

HEARTY FISH
Stew

32 OUNCES FISH, CUBED	**1 TEASPOON** THYME
2 CUPS ONIONS, COARSELY CHOPPED	**1/8 TEASPOON** NUTMEG
4 CLOVES GARLIC, FINELY CHOPPED	**2 TEASPOONS** PARSLEY
1 CUP CELERY INCLUDING LEAVES, COARSELY CHOPPED	**1 CUP** SKIM MILK
1 CUP CARROTS, COARSELY CHOPPED	**1 CUP** VEGETABLE STOCK
1 CUP KERNEL CORN	**1 TABLESPOON** CORN STARCH
2 CUPS RED POTATOES, QUARTERED	**1 TEASPOON** GRAPE SEED OIL
1 CUP ZUCCHINI, COARSELY CHOPPED	SEA SALT & PEPPER TO TASTE

READY TO COOK

1. **IN** A LARGE PAN, SAUTÉ THE ONIONS AND GARLIC IN GRAPE SEED OIL UNTIL JUST SOFT.
2. **ADD** THE CELERY, CARROTS, CORN AND POTATOES AND THE VEGETABLE STOCK AND COOK ANOTHER 5 MINUTES.
3. **IN** A SEPARATE BOWL, BLEND THE CORN STARCH INTO THE MILK AND ADD TO THE PAN.
4. **STIR** FOR 5 MINUTES ON LOW HEAT UNTIL THE MIXTURE BEGINS TO THICKEN.
5. **ADD** THE FISH, SEA SALT, PEPPER, THYME AND NUTMEG AND STIR WELL.
6. **SIMMER**, COVERED, FOR 25 MINUTES.

Serve with parsley on top.

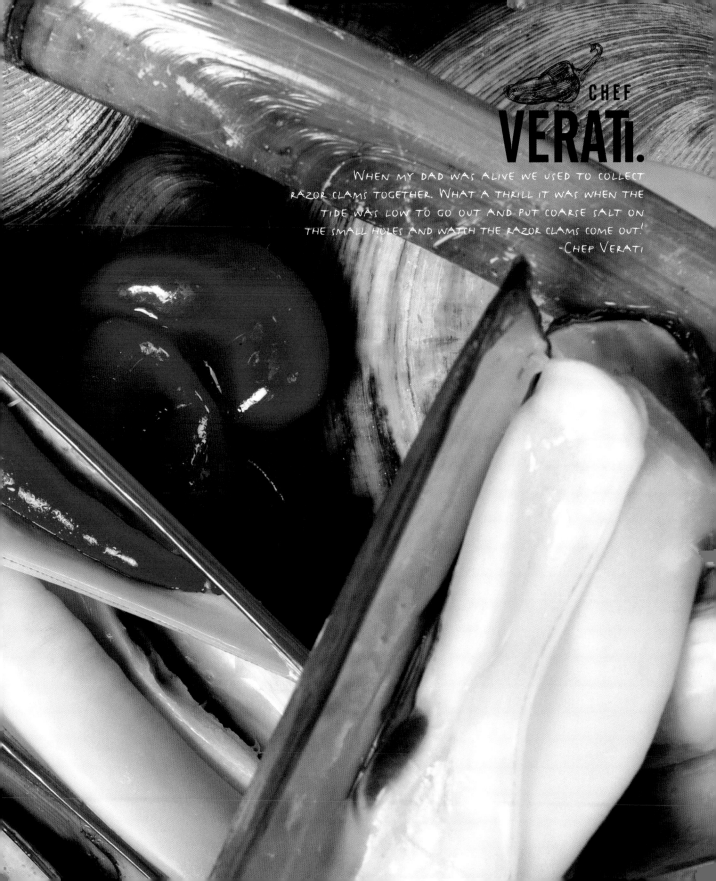

CHEF

VERATi.

When my dad was alive we used to collect razor clams together. What a thrill it was when the tide was low to go out and put coarse salt on the small holes and watch the razor clams come out!
-Chef Verati

RAZOR CLAMS
with Chili and Garlic

48 OUNCES RAZOR CLAMS, RINCED	**2 CUPS** CELERY, FINELY CHOPPED
16 OUNCES WHITE WINE	**2 CUPS** ONIONS, FINELY CHOPPED
1 CLOVE GARLIC, FINELY CHOPPED	**2 CUPS** LEEKS, FINELY CHOPPED
1 CHILI PEPPER, FINELY CHOPPED	**4 CUPS** RICE, COOKED
2 CUPS CARROTS, FINELY CHOPPED	SEA SALT & PEPPER TO TASTE

READY TO COOK

1. **COOK** THE RICE IN WATER ON THE STOVE TOP OR IN THE MICROWAVE UNTIL THE RICE IS SOFT.

2. **PUT** ALL THE INGREDIENTS IN A POT WITH A LID.

3. **COOK** AT MEDIUM HEAT UNTIL THE RAZOR CLAMS ARE OPEN.

4. **REMOVE** EVERYTHING EXEPT THE LIQUID AND SET ASIDE.

5. **REDUCE** THE COOKING LIQUID BY HALF.

6. **GENTLY** PULL CLAMS FROM SHELLS, SLICING THE MUSCLE THAT IS ATTACHED TO THE SHELL TO FREE THE MEAT.

7. **PUT** THE RAZOR CLAMS BACK IN THE POT.

Serve the razor clams on a bed of rice.

PER SERVING: 350 CALORIES // 85G CARBOHYDRATE // 52G PROTEIN // 12G FAT

PIE SHELL
Easy

#1 EASY PIE SHELL ↓↓↓

2 CUPS FLOUR
1 CUP BUTTER
3 OUNCES SUGAR

PINCH OF SALT
3 EGGS

· ·

READY TO COOK

1. MIX EVERYTHING LIGHTLY. **2. LET** THE DOUGH REST 30 MINUTES. **3. ROOL** IT OUT ABOUT 1/8 OF AN INCH THICK OR FREEZE IT.

NEVER MADE A PIE CRUST? I'LL WALK YOU
THROUGH IT! ONCE YOU TRY IT... YOU WILL NEVER
GO BACK TO THE SUPERMARKET FOR ONE!
-CHEF VERATI

Ideal

FREEDOM
A LIFESTYLE!
· · ·

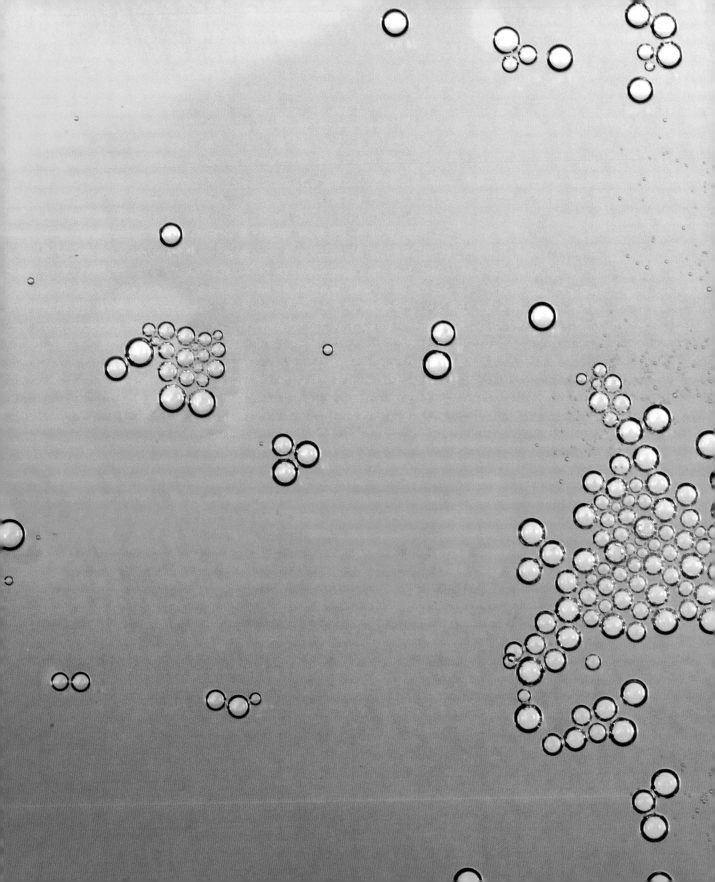

TIPS & TRICKS

WRITE TO **CHEFVERATI@IDEALPROTEIN.COM**
FIND US ON **CHEF VERATI'S FACEBOOK PAGE**
VISIT **LOWFATLOWCARB.COM**

FUN DAY
Best once a week

TROPICAL COCONUT CHICKEN STIR-FRY ·············· 405

ZESTY SALSA VERDE MANGO & GREEN PAPAYA ON SALMON 408

GUILT FREE COCONUT RICE &THAI GREEN CURRY CHICKEN 409

SHRIMP TACOS WITH WASABI MAYO ················ 410

CELERY & APPLE STUFFED FLOUNDER FILLETS ········ 410

APRICOT GLAZED PORK LOIN ···················· 411

ANGEL HAIR PASTA WITH CLAMS & PANCETTA ······· 411

FUNKY ROTINI WITH FRESH TUNA ················· 414

SPICE UP YOUR RICE TEXAS STYLE ················ 414

PEACH & PECAN STUFFED QUAIL ·················· 415

TUNA STEAK & WASABY MASHED POTATOES ········ 415

LAMB & POTATO CASSEROLE ···················· 417

DUCK IN ORANGE SAUCE ······················· 419

DOUBLE CHEESEBURGER WITH A FREEDOM SPECIAL SAUCE 420

SLOW COOKED BEEF WITH VEGETABLES ·············· 421

CREAMY FETTUCINE WITH SALMON ·················· 423

PORK SPARE RIBS WITH STUFFED POTATOES ········· 424

GREEK SHRIMP WITH TOMATO & FETA ··············· 425

THAT'S NO PLAIN POTATO BACON & CHEESE POTATO SKINS 427

SHRIMP & MANGO AVOCADO SALSA ················· 431

HALIBUT AVOCADO PEACH STRAWBERRY BLUEBERRY SALSA · 435

SPICE-CRUSTED PORK WITH PEACH SALSA ··········· 438

VEGETABLE & DILL RICE WITH SHRIMPS ·············· 439

ORANGE GLAZED BEEF WITH SNOW PEAS ············ 441

A WELL STACKED LASAGNA WITH VEAL
& TOMATO SAUCE & BÉCHAMEL ···················· 442

Each recipe serves four.

TROPICAL COCONUT
Chicken Stir-Fry

4 CHICKEN BREASTS, BONELESS, SKINLESS & SLICED

1 TABLESPOON GRAPE SEED OIL

1 ONION, DICED

2 CLOVES GARLIC, FINELY CHOPPED

1" PIECE FRESH GINGER, PEELED & CHOPPED

1 1/2 CUPS WATER

2 CUPS SWEET POTATOES, PEELED & CUBED

1/2 CUP COCONUT MILK

2 TABLESPOONS LOW FAT PEANUT BUTTER

1/2 TABLESPOON HOT CHILI PASTE

1 MANGO, PEELED & CUBED

3 TABLESPOONS GREEN ONIONS, MINCED

3 TABLESPOONS FRESH CILANTRO, CHOPPED

2 CUPS RICE, COOKED

SEA SALT & PEPPER TO TASTE

READY TO COOK

1. **COOK** THE RICE IN WATER ON STOVE TOP, IN A STEAMER OR IN THE MICROWAVE UNTIL THE RICE IS SOFT, ADDING A LITTLE MORE WATER IF NECESSARY.

2. **HEAT** OIL IN A WOK OR LARGE DEEP SKILLET.

3. **SEASON** CHICKEN WITH SEA SALT AND PEPPER AND COOK 5 TO 6 MINUTES, UNTIL BROWNED.

4. **REMOVE** CHICKEN FROM SKILLET AND RESERVE.

5. **ADD** ONIONS, GARLIC AND GINGER TO PAN AND COOK FOR ABOUT 3 MINUTES.

6. **ADD** WATER AND BRING TO A BOIL.

7. **ADD** SWEET POTATOES AND SIMMER UNCOVERED UNTIL TENDER AND ALMOST ALL THE LIQUID HAS EVAPORATED.

8. **COMBINE** THE COCONUT MILK WITH THE PEANUT BUTTER AND HOT CHILI PASTE.

9. **ADD** TO THE PAN AND BRING TO A BOIL.

10. **ADD** CHICKEN AND COOK 3 TO 5 MINUTES OR UNTIL CHICKEN IS COOKED THROUGH.

11. **ADD** MANGO AND COOK 1 TO 2 MINUTES LONGER OR JUST UNTIL HOT.

Serve with rice and sprinkle with green onions and cilantro.

ZESTY SALSA VERDE
Mango and Green Papaya on Salmon

2 TABLESPOONS ORANGE ZEST

2 ORANGES, PEELED & COARSELY CHOPPED

1 TEASPOON LEMON ZEST

3 TABLESPOONS FRESH LEMON JUICE

1/4 CUP OLIVE OIL

1/2 CUP FRESH FLAT-LEAF PARSLEY, CHOPPED

2 SCALLIONS, FINELY SLICED

3 TABLESPOONS FRESH MINT, CHOPPED

2 TABLESPOONS CAPERS, RINSED, DRAINED & COARSELY CHOPPED

4 CUPS CUCUMBERS, CHOPPED

1 CUP RED ONIONS, FINELY CHOPPED

2 MANGOS, DICED

2 GREEN PAPAYAS, DICED

1/4 CUP FRESH CORIANDER, CHOPPED

32 OUNCES SALMON (4 FILLETS) 3 INCH THICK, SKINLESS

SEA SALT & PEPPER TO TASTE

READY TO COOK

1. **COMBINE** ORANGE ZEST, ORANGES, LEMON ZEST, LEMON JUICE, OLIVE OIL, PARSLEY, SCALLIONS, MINT, CAPERS, CUCUMBERS, RED ONIONS, MANGO AND GREEN PAPAYAS.
2. **TOSS** LIGHTLY AND SEASON WITH SEA SALT AND PEPPER. SET ASIDE.
3. **PLACE** A GRILL PAN OVER **MEDIUM-HIGH** HEAT.
4. **BRUSH** THE SALMON ON BOTH SIDES WITH THE GRAPE SEED OIL AND SEASON WITH SEA SALT AND PEPPER.
5. **GRILL** FOR 3 TO 4 MINUTES ON EACH SIDE, UNTIL THE FISH FLAKES EASILY.
6. **TRANSFER** THE SALMON TO A PLATTER AND ALLOW TO REST FOR 5 MINUTES.
7. **SPOON** SOME SALSA VERDE ON TOP OF THE SALMON.

Serve with a sprinkle of fresh coriander on top.

VERATI *Twist*

HAVE A GRILLED SALMON AND TRY THIS RECIPE ON A GAS
OR CHARCOAL GRILL FOR MORE FLAVOR!

GUILT FREE COCONUT RICE
and Thai Green Curry Chicken

1 CUP LONG GRAIN BROWN RICE

1 CUP COCONUT MILK

2 CUPS VEGETABLE OR CHICKEN BROTH

16 OUNCES BONELESS SKINLESS CHICKEN, SLICED

2 TEASPOONS CORN STARCH

1 TABLESPOON SOY SAUCE

2 TABLESPOONS GRAPE SEED OIL

1 CUP SNAP PEAS, TRIMMED & BLANCHED (*SEE PAGE 129*)

1 CUP RED PEPPERS, SLICED

1 CUP RED ONIONS, SLICED

1 CUP BUTTON MUSHROOMS, HALVED

2 TABLESPOONS THAI GREEN CURRY PASTE

1 BUNCH FRESH BASIL, WHOLE

2 TABLESPOONS FRESH LIME JUICE

SEA SALT & PEPPER TO TASTE

READY TO COOK

1. **IN** A SAUCEPAN, COMBINE THE RICE WITH 1/2 CUP COCONUT MILK AND 1 1/2 CUPS BROTH AND STIR.

2. **BRING** TO A BOIL OVER **MEDIUM-HIGH** AND REDUCE HEAT TO **LOW**.

3. **COVER** AND SIMMER ABOUT 45 MINUTES OR UNTIL LIQUID HAS BEEN ABSORBED. SET ASIDE.

4. **IN** A BOWL COMBINE CHICKEN WITH CORN STARCH AND SOY SAUCE, MIXING WELL TO COAT CHICKEN AND LET SIT FOR 5 MINUTES.

5. **IN** A LARGE SKILLET, HEAT OIL OVER **MEDIUM** HEAT.

6. **COOK** CHICKEN UNTIL LIGHT BROWN.

7. **TRANSFER** TO CLEAN SKILLET AND ADD SNAP PEAS, RED PEPPERS AND ONIONS, SPRINKLE WITH SEA SALT AND PEPPER, STIRRING FREQUENTLY ABOUT 5 MINUTES OR UNTIL ONIONS BEGIN TO SOFTEN.

8. **STIR** IN CURRY PASTE.

9. **ADD** REMAINING COCONUT MILK, SCRAPING ANY BROWN RESIDUE FROM THE BOTTOM OF THE PAN.

10. **ADD** REMAINING CHICKEN BROTH AND RESERVED CHICKEN AND BRING TO A SIMMER.

11. **COOK** UNTIL VEGETABLES ARE TENDER CRISP AND SAUCE IS SLIGHTLY THICKENED, STIRRING OCCASIONALLY, ABOUT 5 MINUTES.

12. **REMOVE** FROM HEAT AND STIR IN BASIL AND LIME JUICE.

Serve over coconut rice.

SHRIMP TACOS
with *Wasabi Mayo*

32 OUNCES LARGE SHRIMPS, PEELED & DEVEINED (*SEE PAGE 353*)

3 TABLESPOONS TERIYAKI SAUCE

1/2 CUP LIGHT MAYONNAISE

2 TABLESPOONS WASABI

6 CUPS ENGLISH CUCUMBERS, SLICED

1 TABLESPOON RED ONIONS, FINELY CHOPPED

1 BUNCH FRESH CILANTRO, CHOPPED

1 AVOCADO, DICED

1 TABLESPOON HOT SWEET CHILI SAUCE

8 TORTILLAS, 6 INCH DIAMETER

2 CUPS ROMAINE LETTUCE, SHREDDED

SEA SALT & PEPPER TO TASTE

READY TO COOK ↓↓↓

1. TOSS SHRIMP WITH TERIYAKI SAUCE. **2. COOK** ON A HOT BARBECUE OR GRILL PAN AND RESERVE. **3. COMBINE** MAYONNAISE WITH WASABI, CUCUMBERS, ONIONS, AVOCADO AND CILANTRO. **4. ADD** SEA SALT, PEPPER AND CHILI SAUCE. **5. WRAP** TORTILLAS IN FOIL AND PUT IN A **300°F** OVEN FOR 15 MINUTES OR UNTIL WARM. **6. TO** ASSEMBLE, SPOON THE CENTRE OF EACH TORTILLA WITH THE MAYO AND VEGETABLE GARNISH. **7. ARRANGE** 2 OR 3 SHRIMPS ACROSS THE CENTER OF EACH TORTILLA. **8. TOP** WITH LETTUCE. **9. ROLL** EACH TORTILLA UP TIGHTLY.

Serve with leftover garnish on the side.

CELERY & APPLE
Stuffed Flounder Fillets

2 CUPS CELERY, COARSELY CHOPPED

1 CUP APPLES, DICED

1/4 TEASPOON GARLIC, MINCED

1/4 TEASPOON ONION POWDER

1/4 TEASPOON OREGANO

1 TABLESPOON OF GRAPE SEED OIL

32 OUNCES FLOUNDER (4 FILLETS)

1 CUP ORANGE JUICE

1 TABLESPOON CORN STARCH

1/4 CUP COLD WATER

1 ORANGE, SLICED

2 CUPS RICE, COOKED

8 CUPS MIXED VEGETABLES, BLANCHED (*SEE PAGE 129*)

READY TO COOK ↓↓↓

1. BLANCH VEGETABLES AND COOK RICE. **2. COMBINE** CELERY, APPLES, GARLIC, ONION POWDER AND OREGANO. **3. PLACE** ABOUT 1 TABLESPOON OF THE MIXTURE IN THE CENTRE OF EACH FILLET. **4. SAUTÉ** REMAINING CELERY AND APPLES WITH THE OIL AND LET COOL. **5. ROLL** UP FROM NARROW END AND FASTEN WITH TOOT PICKS. **6. PLACE** FISH ROLLS IN A SKILLET AND SEASON WITH SEA SALT AND PEPPER. **7. ADD** ORANGE JUICE AND BRING TO A BOIL. REDUCE HEAT AND SIMMER, COVERED, FOR 10 MINUTES. **8. ADD** RESERVED CELERY MIXTURE. **9. SIMMER**, UNCOVERED, 5 MINUTES LONGER. **10. MOVE** FISH TO SERVING PLATTER. **11. COMBINE** CORN STARCH AND WATER AND STIR INTO SKILLET. **12. COOK** AND STIR ABOUT 2 MINUTES OR UNTIL THICKENED. **13. SPOON** SAUCE OVER FISH.

Serve with rice, mixed green salad and garnish the fillets with halved orange slices.

APRICOT GLAZED
Pork Loin

32 OUNCES PORK LOIN ROAST, BONELESS, TRIMMED & TIED

2 CLOVES GARLIC, MINCED

1 TEASPOON FRESH ROSEMARY, CHOPPED

1 TEASPOON FRESH THYME, CHOPPED

1/2 TEASPOON PAPRIKA

4 OUNCES APRICOT JAM

2 TABLESPOONS VINEGAR CIDER

1/2 TEASPOON DRY MUSTARD

2 OUNCES WATER

8 CUPS MIXED VEGETABLES, BLANCHED (*SEE PAGE 129*)

SEA SALT & PEPPER TO TASTE

READY TO COOK ↓↓↓

1. IN A SMALL BOWL, COMBINE THE GARLIC, SEA SALT, PEPPER, THYME, ROSEMARY AND PAPRIKA. **2. RUB** SPICE MIXTURE ONTO THE ROAST, COATING IT COMPLETELY. **3. COVER** TIGHTLY WITH PLASTIC WRAP AND REFRIGERATE FOR 30 MINUTES. **4. PREHEAT** OVEN TO **375°F**. **5. UNWRAP** THE ROAST, SET ON A BAKING PAN AND COOK IN OVEN FOR 45 MINUTES OR UNTIL ALMOST COOKED. **6. IN** A SMALL SAUCEPAN, COMBINE THE APRICOT JAM, VINEGAR, DRY MUSTARD AND WATER. **7. STIR** OVER **LOW-MEDIUM** HEAT UNTIL THE MIXTURE BEGINS TO BUBBLE AND SIMMER FOR 1 MINUTE. **8. REMOVE** THE ROAST FROM THE OVEN AND POUR THE GLAZE OVER THE ROAST. **9. COOK** UNCOVERED FOR 10 MINUTES OR UNTIL AN INSTANT-READ THERMOMETER INSERTED IN THE CENTER REGISTERS **160°F**. **10. TRANSFER** THE ROAST TO A LARGE WARM PLATTER AND REMOVE THE TIES.

Serve with the pan juices if you wish and the vegetables of your choice!

ANGEL HAIR PASTA
with Clams and Pancetta

16 OUNCES ANGEL HAIR PASTA (*SEE PAGE 215*)

10 OUNCES PANCETTA OR BACON, DICED

1 CAN BABY CLAMS, WITH THEIR LIQUID

1 LEMON, ZEST & JUICED

3 TABLESPOONS CHIVES, FINELY CHOPPED

4 TABLESPOONS OLIVE OIL

4 CUPS ASPARAGUS, SPEARS, CHOPPED & BLANCHED (*SEE PAGE 129*)

4 CUPS ONIONS, SLICED

8 CUPS MIXED GREEN SALAD

4 OUNCES LOW FAT LOW CARB HOUSE DRESSING (*SEE PAGE 95*)

SEA SALT & PEPPER TO TASTE

READY TO COOK ↓↓↓

1. BLANCH THE ASPARAGUS. **2. COOK** THE PASTA AL DENTE, FOLLOWING PACKAGE INSTRUCTIONS. **3. DRAIN** AND SET ASIDE. **4. IN** A LARGE BOWL, PLACE THE PANCETTA IN A DRY SKILLET AND SAUTÉ UNTIL BROWNED. **5. DRAIN** ON PAPER TOWELS. **6. IN** THE SAME SKILLET SAUTÉ THE ONIONS UNTIL LIGHTLY BROWNED, ADD ALL THE REMAINING INGREDIENTS AND POUR OVER THE HOT PASTA.

Serve with a mixed green salad.

FUNKY ROTINI
with Fresh Tuna

4 CUPS BABY ARUGULA, COARSELY CHOPPED

4 CUPS CHERRY TOMATOES, HALVES

16 OUNCES ROTINI, COOKED

1 CUP BLACK OLIVES, PITTED

24 OUNCES FRESH TUNA, DICED

4 TABLESPOONS EXTRA VIRGIN OLIVE OIL

2 TABLESPOONS RICE VINEGAR

2 TABLESPOONS SOYA SAUCE

1/2 TEASPOON WASABI

3 TABLESPOONS MAYO

4 TABLESPOONS SUSHI GINGER

SEA SALT & PEPPER TO TASTE

READY TO COOK ⬇ ⬇ ⬇

1. COOK THE PASTA AL DENTE, FOLLOWING PACKAGE INSTRUCTIONS.
2. PUT THE ARUGULA, CHERRY TOMATOES AND PASTA IN A BOWL.
3. ADD THE OLIVES, TUNA, OLIVE OIL, VINEGAR, SOYA, WASABI, MAYO, GINGER AND TOSS.

Serve hot or cold.

SPICE UP YOUR RICE
Texas style

16 OUNCES GROUND BEEF

1 CUP ONIONS, CHOPPED

2 TABLESPOONS GRAPE SEED OIL

1 CUP GREEN PEPPERS, CHOPPED

2 STALKS CELERY, CHOPPED

1 CLOVE GARLIC, CHOPPED

2 CUPS TOMATOES, DICED

1 CUP LONG GRAIN RICE

1 CUP TOMATO JUICE

1/4 CUP WATER

1 TABLESPOON CHILI SAUCE

1 BUNCH FRESH CILANTRO, CHOPPED

SEA SALT & PEPPER TO TASTE

READY TO COOK ⬇ ⬇ ⬇

1. BROWN ONIONS AND GARLIC IN GRAPE SEED OIL. **2. ADD** THE MEAT AND CHILI SAUCE. **3. BROWN** THE BEEF FOR A FEW MINUTES. **4. ADD** GREEN PEPPERS AND CELERY AND COOK FOR 2 MORE MINUTES. **5. ADD** THE TOMATOES, THE TOMATO JUICE AND WATER AND BRING TO A BOIL. **6. ADD** RICE. **7. COVER** AND COOK ON **LOW** HEAT FOR 15 MINUTES.

Serve with fresh cilantro on the top.

PEACH &PECAN
Stuffed Quail

8 QUAILS

1 CUP DRIED PEACHES, CHOPPED

1/3 CUP PECANS, CHOPPED

1 EGG

16 OUNCES LEAN GROUND PORC

1/4 TABLESPOON NUTMEG, GRATED

3 TABLESPOONS GRAPE SEED OIL

8 SLICES MILD PANCETTA OR PROSCIUTTO, FINELY SLICED

1 CUP ONIONS, CHOPPED

1 1/2 CUPS WHITE WINE

4 CUPS LEEKS, CHOPPED

4 CUPS SHIITAKE MUSHROOMS, SLICED

SEA SALT & PEPPER TO TASTE

READY TO COOK ↓↓↓

1. PREHEAT OVEN TO 375°F. **2. IN** A BOWL, COMBINE THE PEACHES, PECANS, NUTMEG, EGG, LEAN GROUND PORK AND PANCETTA. SET ASIDE. **3. SEASON** THE INSIDE OF THE QUAIL WITH SEA SALT AND PEPPER AND STUFF WITH THE PEACH MIXTURE. **4. USE** TOOTHPICKS TO HOLD THE LEGS IN PLACE. **5. ON** THE STOVE, IN A LARGE SKILLET, BROWN THE QUAIL IN THE OIL AND ROAST IN THE OVEN FOR 20 MINUTES OR UNTIL COOKED. **6. REMOVE** FROM THE SKILLET AND KEEP WARM. **7. PLACE** 2 TABLESPOONS OF THE FAT FROM THE ROASTING IN THE SKILLET AND BROWN THE ONIONS IN IT. **8. DEGLAZE** WITH THE WINE AND REDUCE BY HALF. **9. ADD** LEEKS AND MUSHROOMS AND LET THEM COOK UNTIL THE LEEKS ARE TENDER.

Serve using the leeks and mushrooms as a nest.

TUNA STEAK &WASABY
Mashed Potatoes

3 CUPS POTATOES, CUBED

1/2 CUP MILK

2 TEASPOONS WASABI

1/2 CUP MIRIN WINE

2 TEASPOONS TOASTED SESAME OIL

4 TABLESPOONS LOW SODIUM TAMARI SOY SAUCE

2 TABLESPOONS HONEY

6 CLOVES GARLIC, MINCED

3" PIECE FRESH GINGER, PEELED & CHOPPED

4 TABLESPOONS GRAPE SEED OIL

24 OUNCES YELLOW FIN SUSHI-GRADE TUNA (4 X 1 INCH STEAKS)

8 CUPS BOK CHOY, BLANCHED (*SEE PAGE 129*)

SEA SALT & PEPPER TO TASTE

READY TO COOK ↓↓↓

1. BLANCH THE BOK CHOY. **2. BOIL** POTATOES IN SALT WATER, ABOUT 10-15 MINUTES. **3. STRAIN** AND PLACE IN A BIG BOWL. **4. ADD** MILK, WASABI, SEA SALT, PEPPER AND MASH TOGETHER. **5. HEAT** A SAUCEPAN ON **MEDIUM**, ADD MIRIN WINE, SESAME OIL, TAMARI, HONEY, GARLIC AND GINGER AND BRING TO A BOIL. **6. REDUCE** HEAT TO **LOW**, LET SIMMER FOR 5 MINUTES. **7. STRAIN** SAUCE TO REMOVE GARLIC AND GINGER. **8. IN** A FRYING PAN, HEAT GRAPE SEED OIL ON **HIGH** HEAT. **9. PLACE** TUNA STEAKS AND BASTE WITH TERIYAKI SAUCE. DO NOT OVERCOOK!

VERATI TIPS

YOU SHOULD SERVE YOUR TUNA MEDIUM RARE TO RARE. AIM FOR A NICE GOLDEN COLOUR ON THE OUTSIDE AND A PINK COLOR ON THE INSIDE.

LAMB & POTATO
Casserole

8 TO 12 LAMB CHOPS	**4 CUPS** CHICKEN STOCK
2 TABLESPOONS GRAPE SEED OIL	**4 CUPS** ZUCCHINIS, CUBED
2 CUPS ONIONS, SLICED THINLY	**4 CUPS** CARROTS, SLICED
4 CLOVES GARLIC, MINCED	**8 CUPS** MIXED GREEN SALAD
2 TABLESPOONS DRY PROVENCAL HERBS MIX	**4 OUNCES** LOW FAT LOW CARB HOUSE DRESSING (*SEE PAGE 95*)
3 CUPS POTATOES, PEELED & THINLY SLICED	SEA SALT & PEPPER TO TASTE

READY TO COOK

1. **PREHEAT** OVEN TO 375°F.

2. **IN** A LARGE SKILLET, SAUTÉ THE LAMB CHOPS IN THE OIL.

3. **ARRANGE** THE LAMB CHOPS IN A SINGLE LAYER IN AN OVEN-TO-TABLE CASSEROLE. SPRINKLE WITH SEA SALT AND PEPPER.

4. **PUT** A LAYER OF POTATOES, A LAYER OF ONIONS, A LAYER OF ZUCCHINIS AND A LAYER OF CARROTS ON THE LAMB CHOPS.

5. **SPRINKLE** WITH DRY PROVENCAL HERBS MIX AND GARLIC AND ADD STOCK.

6. **COVER** AND BAKE FOR 1 1/2 HOUR.

Serve with a green salad on the side.

DUCK
in Orange Sauce

32 OUNCES DUCK (4 BREASTS)

2 TEASPOONS ORANGE ZEST

1/4 CUP ORANGE MARMALADE

1/4 CUP WHITE WINE VINEGAR

3 CUPS VEAL STOCK

3 TABLESPOONS CORN STARCH

2 TABLESPOONS WATER

1 SMALL ORANGE, PEELED & SECTIONED

4 CUPS BABY CARROTS, BLANCHED (*SEE PAGE 129*)

4 CUPS PARSNIPS, BLANCHED (*SEE PAGE 129*)

SEA SALT & PEPPER TO TASTE

READY TO COOK

1. **BLANCH** VEGETABLES.

2. **PREHEAT** OVEN TO **475⁰F**.

3. **SEAR** THE DUCK BREASTS ON **HIGH** HEAT AND REMOVE HALF OF THE FAT FROM THE PAN.

4. **ADD** ORANGE MARMALADE AND ORANGE ZESTS.

5. **ADD** VINEGAR, VEAL STOCK AND LEMON JUICE, BRING TO A BOIL.

6. **ADD** BLANCHED VEGETABLES, THEN PUT THE PAN IN THE OVEN UNTIL DUCK BREASTS ARE COOKED.

Serve duck breasts medium rare with vegetables and oranges on top.

THE CHEAT DAY IS MANDATORY, INDULGE YOURSELF WITH FREEDOM!

DOUBLE CHEESEBURGER
with a Freedom Special Sauce

4 HAMBURGER BUNS	2 TABLESPOONS FRENCH SALAD DRESSING
48 OUNCES GROUND BISON OR LEAN GROUND BEEF	2 TABLESPOONS RELISH
8 SLICES PROCESSED CHEESE	1 TEASPOON BROWN SUGAR
8 LEAVES LETTUCE	2 TEASPOONS KETCHUP
1 TOMATO, SLICED	2 TEASPOONS WHITE VINEGAR
1/2 CUP ONIONS, FINELY CHOPPED	SEA SALT & PEPPER TO TASTE
3/4 CUP MAYONNAISE	

READY TO COOK

1. **IN** A BOWL, COMBINE MAYONNAISE, FRENCH SALAD DRESSING, RELISH, BROWN SUGAR, KETCHUP, WHITE VINEGAR, SEA SALT AND PEPPER AND SET ASIDE.
2. **PREHEAT** THE GRILL, SETTING THE BURNERS TO **HIGH**.
3. **COOK** OR FRY YOUR FRENCH FRIES.
4. **SHAPE** THE MEAT INTO 8 LARGE BUT VERY THIN PATTIES.
5. **GRILL** THE PATTIES UNTIL WELL-DONE.
6. **PLACE** THE CHEESE SLICES ON 4 OF THE PATTIES FOR THE LAST MINUTE OF COOKING.
7. **TOAST** THE BUNS.
8. **SPREAD** THE SAUCE ON THE BUN BOTTOMS.
9. **PUT** A PATTY ON EACH BUN BOTTOM.
10. **SPREAD** WITH SAUCE AND GARNISH WITH ONIONS AND LETTUCE.
11. **TOP** WITH THE REMAINING PATTIES.
12. **SPREAD** SAUCE ON THE BUN TOPS AND PLACE ON THE PATTIES.

Serve with French fries. Yummy!

SLOW COOKED BEEF
with Vegetables

2 CUPS SMALL NEW POTATOES, PEELED & HALVED

2 CUPS CARROTS, PEELED & HALVED LENGTHWISE

32 OUNCES BONELESS BEEF BLADE ROAST, CUBED (1.5 INCH)

2 TABLESPOONS GRAPE SEED OIL

2 CUPS ONIONS, SLICES

4 CLOVES GARLIC, MINCED

1 TABLESPOON FLOUR

1 CUP RED WINE

1 1/2 CUPS CHICKEN BROTH OR VEGETABLE BROTH

1 1/2 CUPS TOMATOES, DICED

3 BRANCHES FRESH THYME

8 CUPS MIXED GREEN SALAD

4 OUNCES LOW FAT LOW CARB HOUSE DRESSING (*SEE PAGE 95*)

SEA SALT & PEPPER TO TASTE

READY TO COOK

1. **PLACE** THE POTATOES AND CARROTS IN A SLOW COOKER AND SET ASIDE.

2. **IN** A LARGE SKILLET OVER **MEDIUM-HIGH** HEAT, BROWN THE MEAT IN THE OIL.

3. **SEASON** WITH SEA SALT AND PEPPER AND PLACE IN THE SLOW COOKER.

4. **IN** THE SAME SKILLET OVER **MEDIUM** HEAT, BROWN THE ONIONS AND GARLIC.

5. **DUST** WITH FLOUR AND COOK FOR 1 MORE MINUTE.

6. **ADD** THE WINE AND BRING TO A BOIL WHILE STIRRING.

7. **TRANSFER** THE MIXTURE TO THE SLOW COOKER AND ADD THE BROTH, TOMATOES AND THYME.

8. **COVER** AND COOK UNTIL THE MEAT IS EASILY CUT WITH A FORK, ABOUT 6 HOURS WITH THE COOKER SET TO **HIGH** OR 8 HOURS WITH THE COOKER SET TO **LOW**.

9. **REMOVE** THE THYME.

Serve with a mixed green salad on the side.

VERATI *Twist*

IF YOU DON'T HAVE A SLOW COOKER USE A ROASTING PAN.

CREAMY FETTUCINE
with *Salmon*

32 OUNCES SALMON (4 STEAKS)	2 CUPS 35 % CREAM OR HALF AND HALF
2 SCALLIONS, INCLUDING TOPS, THINLY SLICED	16 OUNCES FETTUCINE, COOKED
4 CUPS ASPARAGUS, SPEARS, CHOPPED & BLANCHED *(SEE PAGE 129)*	8 CUPS MIXED GREEN SALAD
4 CUPS LEEKS, FINELY SLICED	4 OUNCES LOW FAT LOW CARB HOUSE DRESSING *(SEE PAGE 95)*
2 TABLESPOONS GRAPE SEED OIL	SEA SALT & PEPPER TO TASTE
4 TABLESPOONS CAPERS, DRAINED & FINELY CHOPPED	

READY TO COOK

1. COOK THE PASTA AL DENTE, FOLLOWING PACKAGE INSTRUCTIONS.
2. COOK LEEKS AND SALMON IN A SKILLET WITH THE OIL.
3. ADD CREAM, SCALLIONS AND CAPERS.
4. COOK OVER MEDIUM HEAT FOR 5 MINUTES STIRRING OCCASIONALLY.
5. PUT THE FETTUCCINE IN THE CREAM.

SERVE WITH MIXED GREEN SALAD ON THE SIDE.

EAT FOR PLEASURE, NOT BY
COMPULSION OR EMOTION

PORK SPARE RIBS
with Stuffed Potatoes

64 OUNCES PORK SPARE RIBS, SPLIT IN RACKS

4 TEASPOONS SMOKED PAPRIKA

2 TEASPOONS HOT HUNGARIAN PAPRIKA

1 TEASPOON DRY MUSTARD

2 CLOVES FRESH GARLIC, CHOPPED

1/8 CUP BROWN SUGAR

1/4 CUP KETCHUP

1/4 CUP PREPARED MUSTARD

1/4 CUP WATER

2 TABLESPOONS PREPARED MUSTARD

1 TEASPOON GROUND GINGER

1/4 CUP SOY SAUCE

8 CUPS MIXED GREEN SALAD

4 OUNCES LOW CARBOHYDRATE HOUSE DRESSING (*SEE PAGE 95*)

SEA SALT & PEPPER TO TASTE

READY TO COOK

1. **COMBINE** ALL THE INGREDIENTS FOR THE MARINADE, MIX WELL AND SET ASIDE.

2. **RUB** THE SPARE RIBS WELL WITH THE PAPRIKA, SEA SALT, SUGAR AND DRY MUSTARD.

3. **PLACE** IN A COVERED OVEN PAN AND BAKE FOR 1 HOUR AT **350⁰F**.

4. **REMOVE** THE RIBS FROM THE PAN.

5. **DRAIN** ANY EXCESS FAT.

6. **BASTE** THE RIBS GENEROUSLY WITH THE MARINADE ON ONE SIDE AND PLACE IN THE OVEN TO **BROIL** FOR 10 MINUTES.

7. **TURN** THE RIBS AND BASTE THE OTHER SIDE AND RETURN TO THE OVEN FOR ANOTHER 10 MINUTES.

Serve with stuffed potatoes (see recipe page 427)

GREEK SHRIMP
with Tomato and Feta

1 TABLESPOON OLIVE OIL	**4 OUNCES** FETA CHEESE, CRUMBLED
1 CUP ONIONS, CHOPPED	**1/2 CUP** BLACK OLIVES, PITTED
2 CLOVES GARLIC, FINELY CHOPPED	**2 TABLESPOONS** FRESH PARSLEY, CHOPPED
1/2 CUP WHITE WINE, CHICKEN STOCK OR WATER	**2 TABLESPOONS** DRY OREGANO
32 OUNCES FRESH PLUM TOMATOES, PEELED & CHOPPED	SEA SALT & PEPPER TO TASTE
32 OUNCES LARGE SHRIMPS, BUTTERFLIED BUT NOT SPLIT	

READY TO COOK

1. **HEAT** OIL IN A LARGE DEEP SKILLET.
2. **ADD** ONIONS AND COOK ON **MEDIUM** HEAT UNTIL TENDER.
3. **ADD** GARLIC AND COOK A MINUTE LONGER.
4. **ADD** WINE AND COOK UNTIL IT IS ALMOST EVAPORATED.
5. **ADD** TOMATOES, SEA SALT AND PEPPER AND BRING TO A BOIL.
6. **BREAK** TOMATOES UP WITH A SPOON AND COOK, ON **MEDIUM** HEAT, STIRRING OFTEN, FOR ABOUT 10 TO 15 MINUTES OR UNTIL THICK.
7. **ADD** SHRIMPS AND BLEND WELL WITH TOMATOES.
8. **TRANSFER** TO A BAKING DISH.
9. **SPRINKLE** SHRIMPS WITH FETA AND OLIVES.
10. **BAKE** IN A PREHEATED **375⁰ F** OVEN FOR 10 TO 15 MINUTES OR UNTIL SHRIMPS ARE COOKED.

Serve with a sprinkle of parsley and dry oregano.

VERATI *Twist*

IF YOU ARE IN A HURRY, YOU CAN USE A 28 OUNCE CAN OF PLUM TOMATOES WITH JUICE.

Bacon and Cheese Potato Skins

4 LARGE POTATOES, WASHED AND PICKED WITH A FORK

2 SLICES PANCETTA, 1 CM THICK, DICED

9 OUNCES MOZZARELLA

¹ CUP SOUR CREAM

1/4 CUP BUTTER

1/4 CUP FRESH CHIVES, CHOPPED

SEA SALT & PEPPER TO TASTE

READY TO COOK

1. COOK THE POTATOES IN THE MICROWAVE OVEN SET AT MAXIMUM FOR ABOUT 7 MINUTES.

2. TURN AND COOK UNTIL TENDER, ABOUT 8 MORE MINUTES DEPENDING ON THEIR SIZE. LET COOL.

3. PREHEAT THE GRILL, SETTING THE BURNERS TO HIGH.

4. FRY THE PANCETTA IN A SKILLET UNTIL CRISP. SET ASIDE.

5. LAY THE POTATOES ON A CLEAN SURFACE AND CUT A HORIZONTAL SLICE OFF THE TOP OF EACH POTATO.

6. SCOOP OUT THE FLESH, LEAVING ABOUT (1 CM) ALL AROUND.

7. SET THE FLESH AND SKINS ASIDE.

8. IN A BOWL, MASH THE POTATO FLESH WITH THE SOUR CREAM, BUTTER, CHIVES AND PANCETTA.

9. SEASON WITH SEA SALT AND PEPPER.

10. STUFF THE HOLLOWED SKINS GENEROUSLY.

11. SPRINKLE WITH THE MOZARELLA CHEESE.

12. SET THE GRILL TO MEDIUM.

13. PLACE THE POTATOES UNDER THE GRILL AND COOK UNTIL THE CHEESE IS GOLDEN.

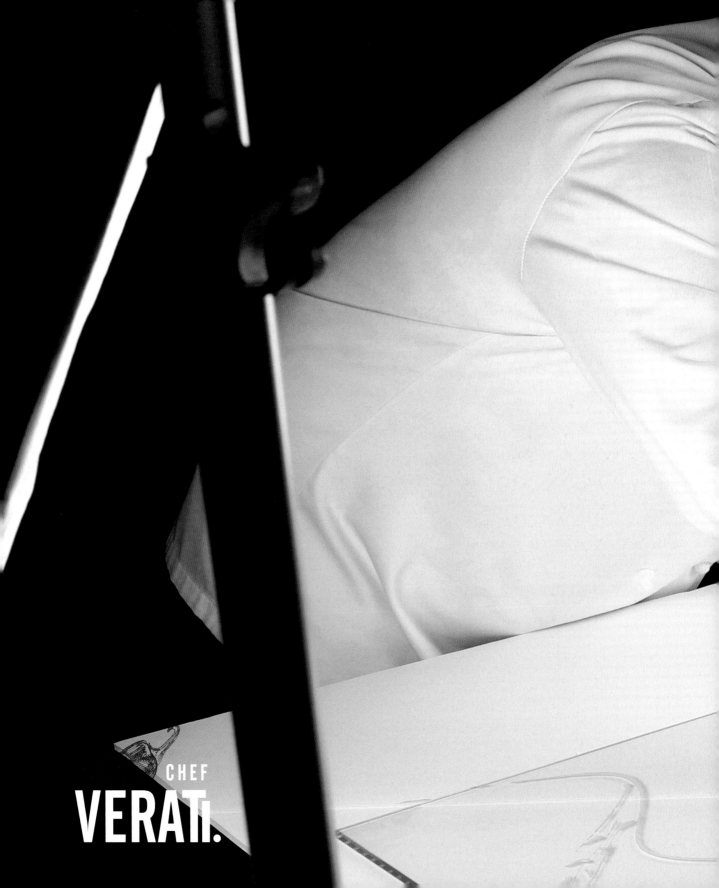

CHEF
VERATI.

SHRIMP
& MANGO
Avocado Salsa

32 OUNCES	SHRIMPS, PEELED & DEVEINED (*SEE PAGE 353*)
1 CLOVE	GARLIC, CHOPPED
4 TABLESPOONS	OLIVE OIL
1 TABLESPOON	APPLE CIDER VINEGAR
1	SHALLOT, CHOPPED
4 CUPS	BOSTON LETTUCE
4	AVOCADOS, DICED
12	CHERRY TOMATOES, HALVES
2	MANGOS, PEELED & DICED
1/4 CUP	RED ONIONS, CHOPPED
1	LIME, JUICED
1 BUNCH	FRESH CILANTRO, CHOPPED
	SEA SALT & PEPPER TO TASTE

READY TO COOK ⬇⬇⬇

1. MIX 3 TABLESPOONS OF OLIVE OIL WITH 1 TABLESPOON OF APPLE CIDER VINEGAR **2. COMBINE** THE AVOCADOS, TOMATOES, MANGOS, RED ONIONS, LIME JUICE AND CILANTRO IN A BOWL. **3. MIX** AND SET ASIDE. **4. HEAT** REMAINING TABLESPOON OF OIL IN PAN AND ADD THE GARLIC AND SHALLOTS. **5. WHEN** BOTH ARE COOKED AND LIGHT BROWN, ADD SHRIMP AND SAUTÉ FOR ABOUT 3 MINUTES, UNTIL JUST COOKED. **6. COMBINE** BOSTON LETTUCE WITH SOME SALSA. **7. ADD** SHRIMP TO THE LETTUCE. **8. TOP** WITH LEFT OVER MANGO AVOCADO SALSA.

Serve shrimps hot or cold however you prefer.

CHEF
VERATi.

You don't often have that much place in your plate to have fun! The glass we used gave us that freedom!
—Chef Verati

HALIBUT AVOCADO
Peach Strawberry Blueberry Salsa

24 TO 32 OUNCES HALIBUT, SKIN REMOVED (4 FILLETS)

1 CUP AVOCADOS, CUBED

2 CUPS TOMATOES, CUBED

1 CUP FRESH PEACHES, CUBED

1 CUP STRAWBERRIES, CUBED

1 CUP BLUEBERRIES

1 1/2 LIME, JUICED

1 TABLESPOON GROUND CUMIN

1 TABLESPOON SMOKED PAPRIKA

1 TABLESPOON CORIANDER SEEDS

1 TABLESPOON FENNEL SEEDS

6 TABLESPOONS OLIVE OIL

SEA SALT & PEPPER TO TASTE

READY TO COOK

1. **PREHEAT** OVEN TO 375°F.

2. **SPRINKLE** SEA SALT AND PEPPER ON BOTH SIDES OF THE FISH.

3. **HEAT** A CAST IRON PAN OVER **MEDIUM-HIGH** HEAT. WHEN HOT, POUR 2 TABLESPOONS OF OLIVE OIL AND ADD THE FISH TO THE PAN.

4. **ALLOW** FISH TO BROWN IN THE PAN FOR 2-3 MINUTES WITHOUT MOVING.

5. **TRANSFER** THE PAN TO THE OVEN.

6. **IN** A BOWL, MIX TOGETHER THE AVOCADOS, TOMATOES, PEACHES, STRAWBERRIES, BLUEBERRIES, LIME JUICE, CUMIN, PAPRIKA, CORIANDER SEEDS, FENNEL SEEDS AND LEFTOVER OLIVE OIL. SET ASIDE.

7. **ONCE** FISH HAS COOKED FOR 10 TO 15 MINUTES, REMOVE THE PAN FROM THE OVEN AND DRESS.

Serve with left over salsa on the side and enjoy on your patio this summer.

VERATITRICK

A GREAT WAY TO KNOW WHEN A PAN IS HOT ENOUGH, IS TO SPRINKLE A FEW DROPS OF WATER IN IT. IF IT IMMEDIATELY BOILS VIOLENTLY AND EVAPORATES AFTER ONLY A COUPLE OF SECONDS, YOU ARE READY TO COOK YOUR FISH.

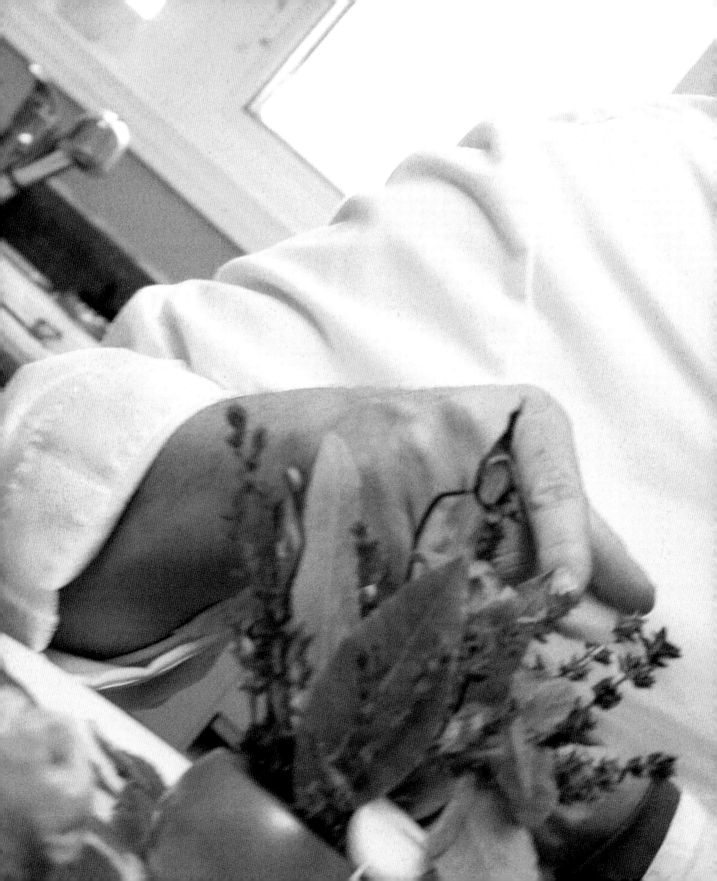

CHEF
VERATi.

THE FUN DAY CAN ALSO BE FUN FOR THE KIDS.
MY GIRLS COOK WITH ME AND THEY
SURPRISE ME WITH LOTS OF QUESTIONS!
-CHEF VERATI

SPICE-CRUSTED PORK
with Peach Salsa

2 PORK TENDERLOINS	**1 CUP** PEARS, DICED
2 TEASPOONS GROUND CUMIN	**1/2 CUP** RED BELL PEPPERS, DICED
1 TEASPOON BROWN SUGAR	**1/4 CUP** SCALLIONS, CHOPPED
1 TEASPOON SMOKED PAPRIKA	**2 TABLESPOONS** JALAPENO CHILI PEPPERS, SEEDED & MINCED
1/2 TEASPOON GROUND GINGER	**1/2** RED ONION, DICED
1 TEASPOON CURRY	**2 TABLESPOONS** LIME JUICE
1 TEASPOON CORIANDER SEEDS	**1 TABLESPOON** FRESH CILANTRO, CHOPPED
1 TEASPOON DILL SEEDS	**8 CUPS** MIXED SALAD
1 TEASPOON GRAPE SEED OIL	**4 OUNCES** LOW CARBOHYDRATE HOUSE DRESSING (*SEE PAGE 95*)
1 CUP PEACHES, PEELED & DICED	SEA SALT & PEPPER TO TASTE

READY TO COOK

1. **PREHEAT** THE GRILL TO **HIGH.**
2. **IN** A MEDIUM SIZE BOWL, COMBINE THE PEACHES, PEARS, BELL PEPPERS, SCALLIONS, JALAPENO PEPPERS, ONIONS, LIME JUICE, CILANTRO, SEA SALT AND PEPPER AND TOSS TO MIX WELL THEN SET ASIDE.
3. **IN** A SMALL BOWL, COMBINE THE CUMIN, BROWN SUGAR, PAPRIKA, GINGER, CURRY, CORIANDER, DILL SEEDS, AND SEA SALT AND PEPPER.
4. **ADD** THE OIL AND MIX WELL.
5. **RUB** THE SPICE PASTE OVER THE PORK.
6. **GRILL** THE PORK COVERED, OVER **MEDIUM HEAT**, TURNING OCCASIONALLY 20 TO 25 MINUTES OR UNTIL COOKED.
7. **TRANSFER** TO A CUTTING BOARD AND LET STAND FOR 5 MINUTES.
8. **CUT** INTO 1 INCH THICK SLICES AND PUT SOME SALSA ON EACH PIECE.

Serve 1 inch thick slice of pork tenderloin with some salsa on each piece and a mixed green salad on the side.

VERATI *Twist*

CHANGE IT UP AND GRILL YOUR FAVOURITE VEGETABLES TO REPLACE THE MIXED SALAD.

VEGETABLE & DILL RICE
with Shrimps

2 **CUPS** BASMATI RICE, COOKED

32 **OUNCES** RAW TIGER SHRIMPS PEELED & DEVEINED (*SEE PAGE 353*)

2 LIME JUICES

4 **TABLESPOONS** GRAPE SEED OIL

2 **TEASPOONS** SESAME OIL

1 **TABLESPOON** SOY SAUCE

2 **CUPS** BROCCOLI, SMALL FLORETS & BLANCHED (*SEE PAGE 129*)

2 SNOW PEAS, HALVED LENGTHWISE

1 **CUP** YELLOW PEPPERS, THINLY SLICED

1 **CUP** GREEN ONIONS, SLICED

4 **TABLESPOONS** FRESH DILL CHOPPED

SEA SALT & PEPPER TO TASTE

READY TO COOK

1. **COOK** THE RICE WITH THE LIME RIND IN A SAUCEPAN OF BOILING WATER FOR 20 MINUTES OR ACCORDING TO THE PACKAGE INSTRUCTIONS, UNTIL TENDER.

2. **DRAIN** THE RICE AND PUT IT INTO A WIDE SALAD BOWL. DISCARD THE LIME RIND.

3. **WHISK** TOGETHER 1 TABLESPOON OF THE LIME JUICE, 2 TABLESPOONS OF THE SUNFLOWER OIL, THE SESAME OIL, SOY SAUCE AND SEA SALT PEPPER IN A SMALL BOWL.

4. **DRIZZLE** THIS DRESSING OVER THE RICE AND STIR TO MIX.

5. **SPREAD** OUT THE RICE IN THE BOWL AND LEAVE TO COOL.

6. **BLANCH** THE BROCCOLI AND SNOW PEAS.

7. **HEAT** THE REMAINING SUNFLOWER OIL IN A LARGE FRYING PAN.

8. **ADD** THE SHRIMP AND COOK OVER **HIGH** HEAT FOR 1-2 MINUTES.

9. **REMOVE** FROM THE HEAT AND SPRINKLE WITH THE REMAINING LIME JUICE.

10. **ADD** THE BROCCOLI, SNOW PEAS, YELLOW PEPPERS, ONIONS AND 4 TABLESPOONS OF THE DILL TO THE RICE AND STIR GENTLY TO MIX.

Serve shrimp on a bed of rice and add a sprinkle of dill.

VERATI **TIPS**
ONCE YOUR SHRIMP ARE PINK THEY ARE COOKED!

ORANGE GLAZED BEEF
with Snow Peas

24 TO 32 OUNCES COLD LEFTOVER ROAST BEEF, SLICED

1 CUP ALL-PURPOSE FLOUR

3/4 CUP + 2 TEASPOONS CORN STARCH

1 TABLESPOON SUGAR

3/4 CUP BEER

1/2 CUP WATER

1/4 CUP SOY SAUCE

4 TABLESPOONS SUGAR

2 TABLESPOONS RICE VINEGAR

3 CLOVES GARLIC, MINCED

2 ORANGES, ZESTED

1 CUP ORANGE, JUICED

2" PIECE FRESH GINGER, PEELED & CHOPPED

1/4 TEASPOON HOT PEPPER FLAKES OR CAYENNE

8 CUPS SNOW PEAS, BLANCHED (*SEE PAGE 129*)

SEA SALT & PEPPER TO TASTE

READY TO COOK

1. **HEAT** THE OIL, SETTING THE DEEP FRYER TO **HIGH** AND PREHEAT THE OVEN TO **300°F**.

2. **BLANCH** THE SNOW PEAS.

3. **IN** A BOWL, COMBINE THE FLOUR, 1/2 CUP OF CORN STARCH AND SUGAR. MIX WELL AND ADD THE BEER AND THE WATER AND SET ASIDE.

4. **IN** ANOTHER BOWL, COMBINE THE BEEF AND 1/4 CUP OF CORN STARCH. COAT WITH BATTER.

5. **DROP** THE BATTERED STRIPS 1 BY 1 INTO THE FRYER TO PREVENT THEM FROM STICKING TOGETHER AND FRY FOR 2 TO 3 MINUTES.

6. **DRAIN,** TRANSFER TO THE BAKING SHEET AND KEEP WARM IN THE OVEN.

7. **IN** A BOWL, COMBINE THE SOY SAUCE AND 2 TABLESPOONS OF CORN STARCH AND SET ASIDE.

8. **IN** A LARGE SKILLET BRING THE SUGAR, VINEGAR, GARLIC, ORANGE ZEST, GINGER AND HOT PEPPER FLAKES TO A BOIL.

9. **SIMMER** UNTIL THE SUGAR STARTS TURNING GOLD.

10. **ADD** THE ORANGE JUICE AND SIMMER FOR 1 MINUTE.

11. **ADD** THE SOY SAUCE MIXTURE, WHISK TOGETHER AND BRING TO A BOIL.

12. **TURN** OFF THE HEAT, ADD THE BEEF AND TURN IT GENTLY WITH A SPATULA UNTIL WELL COATED.

Serve immediately with snow peas.

VERATI *Twist*

USE THE LEFTOVER ROAST BEEF OF THE PAGE 272 RECIPE
OR SIMPLY USE BEEF STRIPS AND COOK THEM AS YOUR STEP 1.

A WELL STACKED LASAGNA
with Veal and Tomato Sauce and Béchamel

6 TABLESPOONS GRAPE SEED OIL	**48 OUNCES** CANNED WHOLE ITALIAN PLUM TOMATOES
32 OUNCES GROUND VEAL	**1 TABLESPOON** TOMATO PASTE
1 WHITE ONION, CHOPPED FINELY	**4** SUN-DRIED TOMATOES, DICED
6 CLOVES GARLIC, CHOPPED	**1** BAY LEAF
2 CUPS CELERY STALKS, COARSELY CHOPPED	**2 TABLESPOONS** DRIED OREGANO
1 CUP GREEN PEPPERS, DICED	**1 BUNCH** BASIL LEAVES, CHOPPED
1 CUP CARROTS, DICED	**1 STEM** FRESH ROSEMARY

READY TO COOK

1. **HEAT** THE OIL IN A SKILLET AND BROWN VEAL FOR 5 MINUTES AND ADD SEA SALT AND PEPPER.
2. **ADD** THE ONIONS, GARLIC, CELERY, PEPPERS AND CARROTS AND COOK FOR 10 MINUTES.
3. **ADD** THE CANNED TOMATOES, DRIED TOMATOES, TOMATO PASTE AND SEASONINGS, REDUCE HEAT.
4. **COOK** FOR 15 MINUTES STIRRING SAUCE OCCASIONALLY.
5. **ADD** THE GRATED ORANGE ZESTS AND COOK FOR ANOTHER 10 MINUTES, SET ASIDE.
6. **IN** A BOWL, MIX THE RICOTTA, MOZZARELLA AND PARMESAN CHEESE.
7. **IN** A SAUCEPAN MELT THE BUTTER AND ADD THE FLOUR AND COOK FOR 2 MINUTES OVER **LOW HEAT**, STIRRING CONSTANTLY.
8. **ADD** THE MILK WHILE STIRRING AND COOK FOR 5 MINUTES OVER **MEDIUM HEAT**, STIRRING CONSTANTLY. SEASON WITH SEA SALT, PEPPER AND NUTMEG.
9. **ADD** THE CHEDDAR CHEESE STIRRING WELL AND SET THE BÉCHAMEL ASIDE TO COOL.
10. **PREHEAT** OVEN TO **400ºF.**

4 STEMS FRESH THYME	**8 OUNCES** PARMESAN CHEESE
1/2 TEASPOON CHILI PEPPER FLAKES	**1/3 CUP** BUTTER
1 TEASPOON FENNEL SEEDS	**1/3 CUP** FLOUR
1 ORANGE, ZEST	**2 CUPS** MILK
1 BOX OF LASAGNA NOODLES, COOKED	**1 TEASPOON** NUTMEG,
16 OUNCES RICOTTA CHEESE	**1 CUP** OLD CHEDDAR CHEESE, GRATED
16 OUNCES MOZZARELLA CHEESE,	SEA SALT & PEPPER TO TASTE

11. **POUR** A LAYER OF MEAT SAUCE IN THE BOTTOM OF A LASAGNA PAN.

12. **COVER** WITH A LAYER OF NOODLES, THEN HALF OF THE COMBINED CHEESES AND HALF OF THE BÉCHAMEL SAUCE.

13. **CONTINUE** WITH ANOTHER LAYER OF THE NOODLES AND THE REST OF THE MEAT SAUCE.

14. **COVER** WITH ONE MORE LAYER OF NOODLES AND THE REMAINING BÉCHAMEL SAUCE.

15. **FINISH** WITH THE REMAINING CHEESE MIXTURE.

16. **GARNISH** WITH FRESH BASIL LEAVES.

17. **BAKE** IN CENTRE OF OVEN FOR 40 MINUTES.

Serve with garlic bread (no butter) or ceasar salad .

VERATI**TIPS**

LASAGNA IS MOST COMMONLY MADE IN A DEEP 13" BY 9" BAKING DISH, BUT LASAGNA CAN BE MADE IN MANY SHAPES AND SIZES. KEEP IN MIND THAT THIS CAN AFFECT YOUR COOKING TIME.

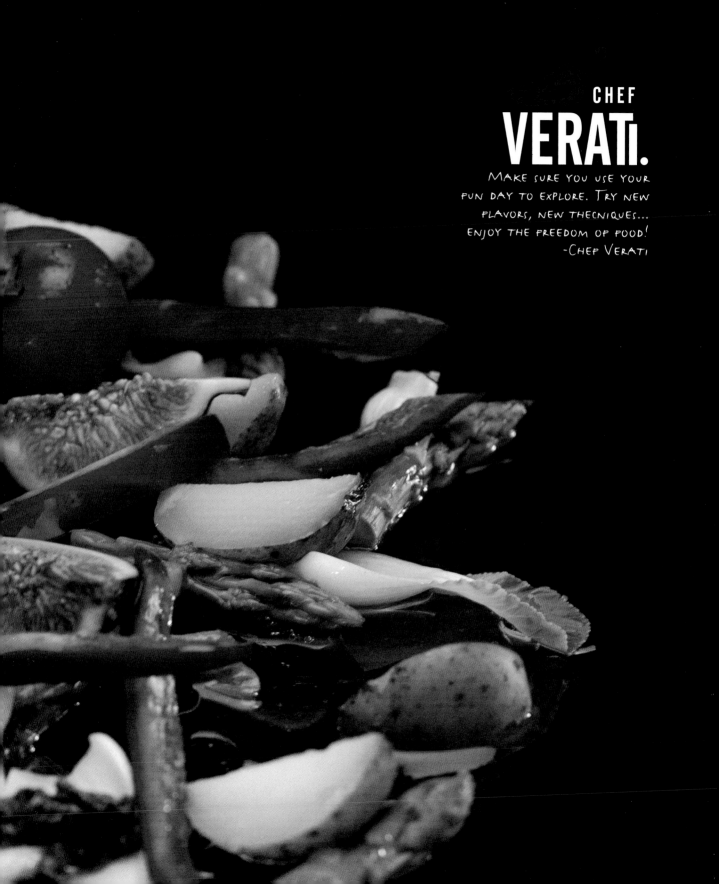

CHEF
VERATi.

MAKE SURE YOU USE YOUR
FUN DAY TO EXPLORE. TRY NEW
FLAVORS, NEW THECNIQUES...
ENJOY THE FREEDOM OF FOOD!
-CHEF VERATI

CHEF
VERATi.

What a great job!
For us, it is the end of a great
adventure, for you it's only the beginning of freedom cooking...
—Chef Verati